1976

W9-CZM-967

This book may be kept

NTEEN DAYS

TEXTBOOK OF LIMNOLOGY

Textbook of limnology

GERALD A. COLE

Department of Zoology, Arizona State University,
Tempe, Arizona

with 146 illustrations

Saint Louis

The C. V. Mosby Company

1975

Library of Congress Cataloging in Publication Data

Cole, Gerald A   1917-
    Textbook of limnology.

    Bibliography: p.
    Includes index.
    1. Limnology.   2. Fresh-water ecology.   I. Title.
[DNLM: 1. Ecology.   2. Fresh water. QH541.5.F7
C689L]
QH96.C63   574.5′2632   75-4850
ISBN 0-8016-1015-X

TS/CB/B   9   8   7   6   5   4   3   2   1

To those closest to me—
JEAN, WENDY, SALLY, TOM,
STEVE, and JEFF.

And to the memory of
SAMUEL EDDY,
who helped me get my feet wet.

Preface

Recently, a fellow limnologist said something to me that I found heartening. His words were, "The test of a good textbook is that it is written for the student and not to impress the author's peers." The major goal in writing this book was to explain to beginning students of limnology what I think the subject is all about and to help them understand certain areas of the discipline that many of us find difficult. Limnology professors may discover sections in this text that need further explanation or elaboration in classroom sessions, but it is more important to me that students find the book interesting and worthwhile.

In the process of writing I learned much about my own feelings toward limnology. I recalled many published reports of research efforts that had made impressions on me—papers that I have remembered through the years. These have been cited in the text in an effort to stimulate and arouse students, even though some instructors might consider them less important than I do. Perhaps they have other papers—favorites of their own—to use as examples in place of mine. I learned that certain lakes one studies tend to become old friends, and some have become a part of me; as a result, some of their names appear often in the following pages. Everyone who studies Lake Itasca seems to fall in love with it, and I was no exception. Although Tom Wallace Lake is almost unknown, this little body of water stratifies sharply and outdoes itself to follow the rules of classical limnology, and I gained much from research there. The bleak, beautiful Montezuma Well taught me a great deal, and that giant limnocrene (never viewed by the Aztec emperor for whom it was named) is mentioned often.

Certain people helped me especially, and I acknowledge their support with gratitude. The manuscript was typed by Mary Frances Knox. Roger Heath fashioned the line diagrams from rough sketches I supplied. The plates of lake profiles (Figs. 2-1 and 2-3) and of aquatic biota (Figs. 2-2 and 3-1 to 3-8) were drawn by my colleague David I. Rasmussen, whose talent and style cannot be matched.

GERALD A. COLE

Contents

1
Introduction

DEFINITIONS OF LIMNOLOGY

The most frequent question asked the student of limnology is, "What is limnology?" With time he learns an acceptable answer that sounds something like, "It can be described as inland oceanography." This satisfies the questioner; he nods, quite content, even though he might find difficulty in defining oceanography, if required to do so. The response that appeased the inquirer is similar to the first definition of limnology, one we owe to F. A. Forel (1892), a Swiss professor, who has been called the Father of limnology. Translated, Forel's definition was "the oceanography of lakes."

Other terse definitions—aquatic ecology or hydrobiology—could be set forth, but a simple phrase, sentence, or paragraph is hardly enough to explain the topics encompassed by modern limnology. The subject is not a single discipline. It is a synthesis, drawing upon many disciplines and owing its substance to the contributions of workers from diverse scientific fields. In this respect limnology resembles geography, and indeed you will find some valuable references catalogued in your library as a segment of geography rather than biology.

The late Edgardo Baldi, a prominent Italian limnologist, set limnology apart from other disciplines by defining it as the science dealing with interrelations of processes and methods whereby matter and energy are transformed within a lake. He stated further that it should not be confused with the zoology, botany, or ecology of aquatic organisms.

The Russian Winberg (1963), who delivered the Baldi Memorial Lecture at the Eighteenth Congress of the International Society of Limnology held in the USSR in 1971, implied that the most important goal of limnology is to study the circulation of materials—especially organic substances—in a body of water. Biotic and abiotic phenomena are, of course, interrelated, and the concept of balance is a major part of this interrelationship. All primary organic material produced each year is accounted for, in terms of energy flow. Thus, the aim of limnology is to comprehend and calculate the whole of productive and destructive processes that are involved in this energy flow.

One cannot deny that Winberg and Baldi put forth a commendable goal and format for aquatic study, but their criteria should not preclude other research. There are numerous facets of limnology, and many different kinds of research contribute to the mosaic. Moreover, research scientists are inclined to follow paths they find engaging and to pursue work that is fun; this is the way it should be.

A historical thread runs throughout the subject, because the data and concepts derived from the research of many men and women in the past are now part of modern limnologic theory. I find it impossible to deal with limnology without thinking of the people who, with their individual aesthetic tastes and inclinations, have contributed to the synthesis.

The term limnology is derived from the Greek word *limne* meaning pool, marsh, or lake. The science arose from lake investigation, however. It was born on the shores of Lake Geneva (Le Léman), its original description in French (Forel 1892); or according to Deevey (1942a), it was described earlier, when Henry David Thoreau recorded mid–nineteenth century observations from Walden Pond, a respectable lake despite its name. As time passed, limnology became the science of inland waters, concerned with all the factors that influence living populations within those waters. It now includes study of running water (*lotic* habitats) as well as of standing water (*lentic* habitats), although the former has been set off specifically by some as potamology. It embodies the largest of lakes to the smallest of ponds and embraces ephemeral waters as well as permanent lakes that have existed for millions of years. It is incorrect to designate it the study of fresh waters; for in arid regions extremely saline pools and lakes are found, and these fall within the realm of limnology.

FACETS OF LIMNOLOGY
Geology

The origin of lake basins, their resultant morphology, and subsequent modification of shape are the results of geologic processes. Because erosion and sedimentation are within the scope of geology, it is apparent that the birth, life, and death of a lake, as its basin fills, are geologic functions.

The substrate in which a water-filled depression lies or from which it receives its soluble salts and other nutrients is dependent on its geologic legacy. This heritage of nutrients available to the aquatic habitat via the weathering of soils within its drainage area is the *edaphic* factor.* *Allochthonous* materials are

---

*The adjective edaphic (Gr. *edaphos*, ground or soil), pertaining to the soil and particularly with respect to its influence on organisms, was first used by plant ecologists.

derived from without the lake basin, and *autochthonous* from within.*

The so-called trophic nature of a body of water (referring basically to its soluble nutrients and resultant biotic productivity) is the result of interaction of at least three important factors. First is the edaphic factor, which determines whether a lake is rich and productive or comparatively sterile. Second are the morphologic features, best defined as dimensions of the basin. These first two factors are of a geologic nature. The third is the climatic element, a meteorologic-geographic matter. There is a range of climates from severe to favorable for growth and productivity, with many meteorologic ramifications. These are fairly obvious, including extreme temperature differences, duration of growing season, solar radiation, precipitation, evaporation rates, and wind.

Aquatic systems in which these three main factors are working in harmony may exhibit the extremes of a trophic scale. Thus, a remarkably poor lake, exhibiting what will be defined later as *oligotrophy*, has soil, basin shape, and climate working in concert. Many lakes fit on the scale somewhere between oligotrophy and marked *eutrophy*, characterized by water rich in nutrients and high biotic productivity, and are a result of edaphic, morphologic, and climatic features working in unison.

Also within the province of geology is *paleolimnology*, the study of lacustrine (L. *lacus*, lake) sediments and the relics preserved in them. The nature of the sediments implies something of past condi-

tions in the lake and involves chemistry as well as structure. In some instances, contrasting seasonal layers, called *varves*, can be discerned and counted. The chitinous remains of aquatic arthropods, calcareous molluscan shells, siliceous structures from diatoms and sponges, and other resistant structures tell something about the communities that occupied the basin in the past and what changes have occurred in the biota. The study of these microfossils was reviewed admirably by Frey (1964).

Closely related to paleolimonology is *palynology*, the study of spores and pollen grains. These plant structures remain preserved in lake and bog deposits, where they imply much about neighboring plant communities and climates of the past. Sometimes fossilized pollen from aquatic plants are present, and from them information about conditions in the lake itself can be inferred.

Physics and mathematics

The first concern of physical limnology is the very nature of the water molecule. Water is of course a mixture of hydrogen, deuterium, and tritium isotopes combined with isotopes of oxygen, rather than a single type of molecule. Water's high specific heat and the nonlinear relation of density and viscosity to temperature are unique properties. They play important roles in the penetration, absorption, and distribution of light and heat and in the resultant density stratification in lakes.

In addition, the various movements of water—eddies, currents, and waves— come under the heading of physical limnology, and we are indebted to those limnologists well grounded in mathematics for our knowledge of these topics. Here we discover meteorologic overtones in the synthesis called limnology. Meteorologists have applied techniques proved useful in investigating aerial conditions to the study of lacustrine currents.

Physicists' special contribution to lim-

---

*Toward the end of the nineteenth century a German geologist coined the words "allochthonous" and "autochthonous" to apply to rock formation. Unwieldy and forbidding though they seem, they are nevertheless useful in limnologic descriptions. Autochthonous sediment, for example, forms in situ from sources produced within the lake; allochthonous sediments are composed of materials that were transported from elsewhere.

nology has been the development of electronic apparatus to facilitate rapid, accurate measurements. In the United States the late L. V. Whitney's efforts were especially valuable; his electric subsurface thermometers, conductivity meters, and photometers represented milestones in the journey of North American limnology.

Chemistry

Analysis and study of the chemical constituents in natural waters is a big part of limnology. Much of chemical limnology has been inorganic, but more is being learned continuously about the importance of complex organic compounds in the dynamics of fresh water. It is apparent that water chemistry is closely allied to geology and to the biology of aquatic habitats. The relationship of physical limnology to the distribution of chemical compounds within inland waters is discussed subsequently.

Biology

The organisms of inland waters range from bacteria to mammals. Bacteriologists, botanists, and zoologists are, therefore, members of the limnologic fraternity. Their discipline is aquatic biology, the study of aquatic species and populations. This definition rests on shaky grounds, for when the biologist concerns himself with environmental factors that affect the species or population, he has ventured into limnology.

Investigations of population dynamics and life histories of aquatic plants and animals are still needed, despite the research that has been carried out in biologic limnology. The first would fall under the heading of *synecology*, the latter *autecology*. These are older terms that may have limited value now. Autecology, the study of an individual species' ecologic and physiologic life history, and synecology, the study of groups of species, overlap as disciplines.

Historically, the ecosystem concept had important limnologic beginnings. This concept is especially important in the aquatic habitat where clear-cut distinctions between the nonliving and living segments of the community are not easily denoted. Discussion and good examples of biogeography, speciation, interspecific competition, and succession of communities can be found in limnologic literature. Behavioral ecology inquiries and sophisticated physiologic investigations also appear in modern limnologic publications.

The concept of biologic productivity, as well as the search for factors that make one lake more productive than its neighbors or than a distant counterpart, is a major and unifying theme of limnology. The basis for biologic productivity is photosynthesis or primary production. The plant physiologist who is interested in photosynthetic mechanisms and rates, and the phycologist, who concerns himself with algal nutrients and growth, have become major contributors to the science of inland waters.

Historical and personal facets

Forel's first volume on Lake Geneva (1892) dealt with environmental factors rather than with the lacustrine biota. Since then geographic-physical-chemical studies have been termed forelian limnology. The work performed during the first four decades of this century by E. A. Birge, C. Juday, and their students at the University of Wisconsin marked the onset of modern American limnology and made conditions in Wisconsin lakes a touchstone for later studies in other regions. Birge, who was one of the first Americans to work seriously with the microcrustaceans known as Cladocera, was led from a biologic study of their spatial and seasonal distribution in Lake Mendota to a study of the physical and chemical reasons accounting for puzzling fluctuations of cladoceran populations—in other words, to forelian limnology.

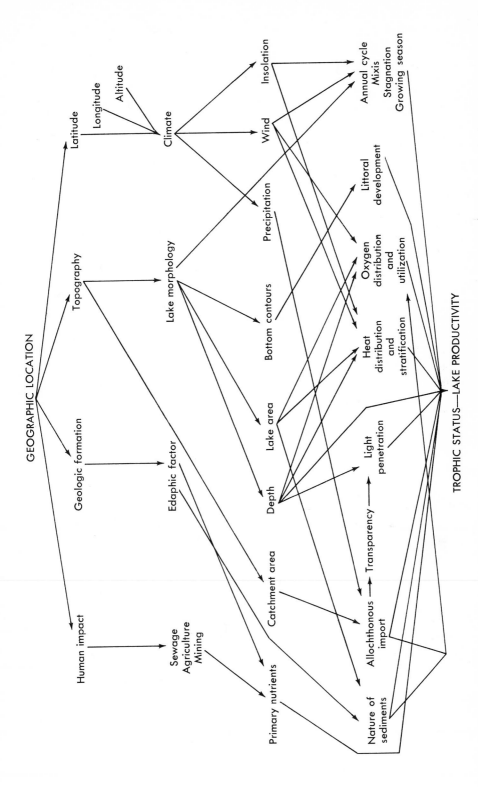

Fig. 1-1. Interaction of factors that ultimately determine the composition, distribution, and amount of biota, the rates at which nutrients are recycled, and the general productivity of the lake. (Modified from Rawson 1939.)

Although the Wisconsin workers touched on many elements of limnology, their interests were focused on the smaller bodies of water, the so-called inland lakes of Wisconsin. Wisconsin shores are washed by enormous bodies of water, Lake Superior and Lake Michigan, but Birge and Juday apparently did not find them appealing.

Similarly, in the first two volumes of *A Treatise on Limnology* Hutchinson (1957, 1967) revealed a preference for standing water. In these extremely valuable books, the reader's attention is directed almost entirely toward lakes, with few references to lotic environments. On the other hand, Hynes (1970) has shown his long-term interest in running waters by recently publishing a comprehensive book on rivers and streams.

Despite the fact that various limnologic researchers and authors have revealed their preferences and tastes for certain fractions of limnology, contributions to the science have come from many nations. The International Association of Limnology was formed in 1922 by Thienemann, a German, and Naumann, a Swedish scientist. Some important textbooks appear in many languages: in German by an Austrian (Ruttner, 1952) and later translated cooperatively by an American (Frey) and a Canadian (Fry); in Portuguese by a man from the Netherlands living in Brazil, who resided in Canada for years before moving to Texas (Kleerekoper 1944); in English by the Americans Welch (1935) and Reid (1962) and by the Englishmen Macan and Worthington (1951); and in French by Dussart (1966). The latest limnologic text is based on the collaboration of two Australian zoologists, colleagues at Monash University (Bayly and Williams 1973). Bayly came to Australia via New Zealand, and Williams is a native of Liverpool, England.

AN OVERVIEW: RAWSON'S DIAGRAM

The late D. S. Rawson, a Canadian limnologist whose contributions were numerous, varied, and of consequence, constructed a diagram that displays the multitide of factors that interact to give a lake a certain character and to determine its productivity and its inhabitants. Although the diagram was published many years ago (Rawson 1939), it retains its usefulness and impact. Perhaps the factor "human impact" should be set in bold type today; otherwise the chart remains instructive. Much of any limnology course could be developed from this diagram.

2
A limnologic perspective

Many terms and concepts important to limnology are defined in detail in later pages. However, limnologic jargon, in the best sense of the word, needs introduction at this point. In addition, a generalized look at the lentic and lotic habitats, with which ensuing chapters are concerned, seems in order here. The inland lake, the regions within it, its life history, and the classification that limnologists have constructed to define its types are merely scanned. However, the sediments that accumulate in the deeps are examined in more detail, for they imply much of the past and present, both in the lake itself and in its catchment basin. The part that human activity has played in modifying lakes is saved for emphasis in future pages and is only touched upon here. Finally, some physical features of streams—the lotic environment being unique to the inland scene and different in most respects from the standing waters of limnology—are presented.

BIRTH AND DEATH OF LAKES

Lakes arise from phenomena that are almost entirely geologic in nature. Once formed, they are doomed. Because of the concave nature of basins, there is a compulsory trend toward obliteration as they fill with sediments. Thus, a lake lives through youthful stages to maturity, senescence, and death when the basin is finally full. The procedure does not necessarily follow such a smooth sequence, and periods of rejuvenation are known to have occurred in some lakes. Eventually, marshes, swampy meadows, and forests occur where water-filled depressions once existed. In such instances, there appear to have been successional stages preceding the terrestrial one. Enormous and deep lakes may be far from death as a result of shoaling, but climatic changes or geologic events leading to desiccation or drainage eventually mark their ends.

LAKE REGIONS
Benthic zones and benthos

The adjective *benthic* applies to bottom regions. The word *benthos* designates the community of bottom-dwelling organisms.

Littoral zone. The peripheral shallows are subject to fluctuating temperatures and erosion of shore materials through wave action and the grinding of ice. The result is a bottom region of relatively coarse sediment, especially evident near unprotected shores. These shallows are usually well lighted and inhabited by rooted aquatic plants extending to some lakeward depth and contributing fragments to the littoral sediments as well as providing support and sustenance for other organisms. This is the littoral zone, the shore region (Fig. 2-1).

The band from shoreline to the depth where "weeds" disappear is often defined as the littoral region. Sometimes wave action is so extreme that large aquatic angiosperms are absent and only algae, attached and streaming in the currents or growing as benthic mats, are present, their outer margin fixing the lakeward limits of the littoral area.

The littoral benthos is composed of many species and taxonomic groups. Great diversity and high annual production set this community apart from the benthos in deeper areas. This is a result of the abundance and variety of habitats and ecologic niches in near-shore regions as compared with the deeps.

Sublittoral zone. The sublittoral region extends lakeward from the littoral. Its sediments are finer grained. Although dimly lighted and lacking a benthic macroflora, it is usually well oxygenated. The sublittoral fauna contains fewer species than the littoral assemblage; this is a result of the reduced number of habitats.

In some lakes the old shells of gastropods and pelecypods that inhabited the littoral zone are found accumulated at sublittoral depths. These shell zones are thought to mark the place where interactions of wind, wave, shoreline configuration, currents, and countercurrents have carried and dropped the calcareous remains of the littoral molluscan fauna. There is some evidence that clams retreating to deep water for the winter season die in the sublittoral region and contribute to the shell zone. Whatever the case, parts of the sublittoral zone serve as the cemetery of some littoral species.

Profundal zone. The profundal zone can be defined in lakes deep enough to exhibit summer temperature stratification. Under such conditions a deep, cold region is formed where currents are at a minimum and where light is much reduced. The temperature is nearly uniform throughout this region, and under some conditions oxygen is scanty or depleted, while gases such as methane and CO_2 are abundant. The hydrogen ion concentration is high because of the presence of carbonic acid, and this stratum of water is characterized by decay rather than by production of organic matter. This is the hypolimnion, the "below lake" stratum that overlies the profundal zone.

Profundal sediments are fine particles

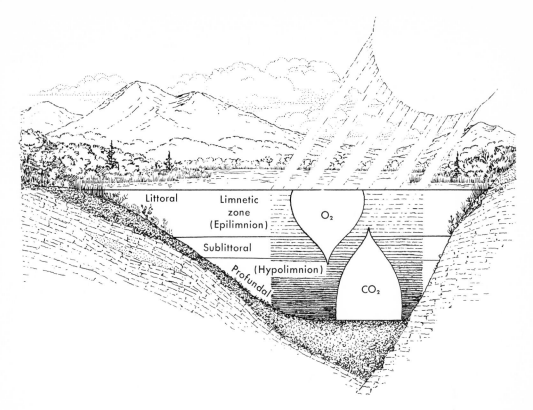

Fig. 2-1. Lake zones: benthic regions, littoral, sublittoral, profundal; open-water or limnetic zone, including well-lighted epilimnion. O_2 profile represents trophogenic zone; CO_2 profile represents tropholytic zone.

largely made up of material produced within the lake and whatever matter from outside is small enough to be blown in or carried by currents to the deeps before settling. The profundal benthos has attracted the lion's share of attention from limnologists. Commonly, lake researchers move directly to the deeper parts, passing over the rich littoral biota to dredge up the impoverished profundal fauna. The benthos of the profundal zone tells something of conditions in the hypolimnetic water and, ultimately, a great deal about the nature of the lake. Moreover, dredge samples of profundal ooze are easily washed through sieves, leaving the animals exposed.

Open-water zones

Beyond the pond weeds (a common term for the marginal vegetation) is the open water. This is the limnetic or pela-gic zone, a region in the lake where shore and bottom have lessened influence. It is the habitat of the plankton, an assemblage of tiny free-floating, drifting, or swimming plants and animals representing many taxa. In the upper wind-swept and well-illuminated layers photosynthesis prevails in daylight hours as phototrophic algae, the primary producers, fix inorganic carbon to manufacture organic compounds. It is called the *trophogenic* zone, where synthesis of organic carbon compounds occurs. Farther shoreward the littoral macrophytes and benthic algae, bathed by the same upper stratum, are part of the trophogenic layer. They are of less relative importance in primary productivity except in shallow lakes.

The limnetic trophogenic zone is largely defined by the *epilimnion*—the "above" or upper lake. The sunny epilimnion is mixed throughout by the wind, many of its algal producers being moved throughout it as a result. The limnetic or plankton community includes the plant members (phytoplankton) and the animal species (zooplankton).

Below the trophogenic layer is a darker *tropholytic* region, the hypolimnion, where respiration and decomposition predominate. Ideally, between the two regions a compensation depth marks a place where photosynthetic processes are matched by respiratory events.

LAKE TYPOLOGY
Oligotrophy and eutrophy

From a simplistic viewpoint, there are two fundamental types of lakes to consider. Many lakes cannot be fitted to either of the two categories, but this is a starting point.

Thoreau (1854) perceived the different types. In the *Walden* chapter "The Ponds" he described White and Walden Ponds as "great crystals on the surface of the earth . . . ," with "their remarkable transparencies, their hues of blue and green, their lack of muck," but "not very fertile in fish." These characteristics contrast with Flint's Pond, "more fertile in fish . . . ," but "comparatively shallow," "not remarkably pure," and having a "sedgy shore." His words about the farmer who "ruthlessly laid bare" the shores of this lake are especially significant. Thoreau had recognized, in the first examples, *oligotrophic* lakes, and in the second, a *eutrophic* lake.

These adjectives and the nouns oligotrophy and eutrophy have come to us by a devious route. Both Hutchinson (1969) and Rodhe (1969) reminded us of origins largely overlooked during the past 6 decades. Weber (1907) wrote of the vegetation and development of north German peat bogs that gradually built up to become *hochmoore,* bogs raised above the lips of the despressions that contain them. Nutrients that were present in the water bathing the bog plants became

readily leached out as the hochmoore built up. The nutrients decreased from a rich eutrophic state to a poor oligotrophic state, Weber coining these words.

Naumann (1919), a student of Swedish phytoplankton, applied Weber's words to the nutrients available for the algae in natural waters. This left us with names that might be used properly to designate a glass of water; it could be rich in a plant essential, phosphorus for example, and be called eutrophic; similarly, it could be extremely poor and be termed oligotrophic; mesotrophic water would fall somewhere in between.

Further lake studies in Europe showed there were contrasting phytoplankton types that could be related to water chemistry. Blue-green algae, for example, were characteristic of eutrophic waters in the lowlands. Oligotrophic waters from mountainous regions produced a different limnetic flora. The concept of richly or poorly endowed water, described in Weber's words, had not been lost.

Thienemann (1925), summarizing much of his earlier study on a lake district in Germany's Eifel highlands, proposed broader interpretations of eutrophy and oligotrophy. He found that conditions in the deep lakes differed from those of the shallow lakes, even though they lay in the same climatic and edaphic region. The summer oxygen supply in the hypolimnion of a deep basin was always abundant, and the bottom fauna was diverse, including many species incapable of withstanding low oxygen tensions. By contrast, the dissolved oxygen became critical in the shallower Eifel lakes, often disappearing completely as a result of decay. Only hardy species were found in the profundal benthos in such lakes.

The mention of the gas oxygen prompts discussion of an important limnologic concept. Gas exchanges accompany the metabolic processes of organisms when organic substances are built up or broken down. The rate at which oxygen is consumed, for example, or the total amount that disappears is a measure of the organic matter mineralized through bacterial action or dissipated by respiration of aquatic organisms. Increases in carbon dioxide follow oxygen's decrease, so that, typically, there is an inverse relationship between these gases. The production of oxygen as a by-product of photosynthesis, quantitatively assayed in the epilimnion, is marked by a concurrent decrease in CO_2. The rate of either process is a measure of the remarkable phenomenon photosynthesis, whereby new organic matter is formed from mineral substances. All subsequent echelons of production in a body of water stem from this new material and from other organic matter that may have been blown or washed into the lake. Herbivores and carnivores—heterotrophic rather than autotrophic organisms—build their bodies and live their lives at the expense of this primary organic material. They consume and destroy it, spending a part of the chemical energy stock available to them. Their corpses, dead algal cells, and the organic juices leaking from both are eventually mineralized by bacteria, with attendant consumption of oxygen and elaboration of CO_2. This disappearance of oxygen in the tropholytic zone, then, mirrors the basic production in upper strata.

Thienemann was an outstanding student of the Chironomidae; the profundal representatives of this fly family were especially engaging to him. The adult chironomids or midges superficially re-

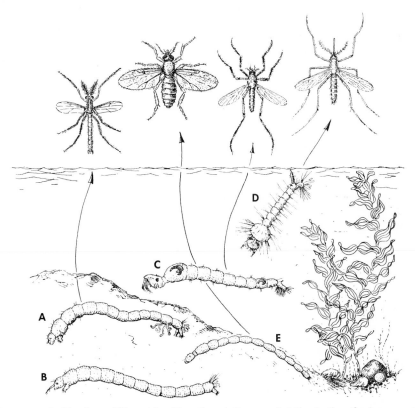

Fig. 2-2. Some aquatic flies from different families: the adults superficially similar; the larvae quite different. **A,** *Chironomus,* Chironomidae; **B,** *Tanytarsus,* Chironomidae; **C,** *Chaoborus,* Chaoboridae; **D,** *Culex,* Culicidae; **E,** *Culicoides,* Heleidae. The pondweed is *Potamogeton richardsonii.*

semble mosquitoes but do not sting. Their larvae are quite different, however. The species of limnologic interest are worm-like and live in the sediments. One group, bright red and commonly called "blood worms," belongs to the genus *Chironomus* and tolerate low oxygen tensions. These were the characteristic midge larvae of Thienemann's shallow lakes, much as they had been found to typify eutrophic waters elsewhere. Other species, including those of the genus *Tanytarsus,* are intolerant of low oxygen levels. They occur in profundal deposits of the deeper Eifel lakes, along with a varied collection of other types of animals, in contrast to the taxonomically meager benthos of the shallow lakes.

The oxygen supply and the nature of the benthos became important indicators to Thienemann as he categorized the two kinds of lakes: shallow, *Chironomus* eutrophic lakes and deeper, well-oxygenated, *Tanytarsus* oligotrophic lakes. The former includes the bizarre phantom larva, *Chaoborus,* a member of another fly family, although often called a midge.

It is present in lakes where oxygen's lack is too severe even for *Chironomus* but is rarely found in the bottom fauna of oligotrophic lakes (Fig. 2-2).

The nutrient content of the water was glossed over to a great extent in the years following Thienemann's work as eutrophy and oligotrophy came to pertain to types of biota, oxygen distribution, lake dimensions, water transparency, and sediments. These features, by which a generation of limnologists distinguished an oligotrophic from a eutrophic system, are contrasted in Table 2-1.

Morphologic or secondary effects. With Weber's original meaning for eutrophic and oligotrophic waters kept in mind, a question arises concerning Thienemann's classification. The Eifel lakes were found in a uniform climatic region and, more important, shared an edaphic heritage. Theoretically, they should have had similar concentrations of nutrients and minerals. Had they been of identical dimensions, their trophic states would have been much alike, governed by the nutrient supply. If low in nutrients, they would have been primari-

Table 2-1. Features contrasting oligotrophic and eutrophic lakes—factors contributing to or resulting from the two types

Oligotrophy	*Eutrophy*
Deep and steep-banked	Shallow, broad littoral zone
Epilimnion volume relatively small compared with hypolimnion	Epilimnion/hypolimnion ratio greater
Blue or green water; marked transparency	Green to yellow or brownish green; limited transparency
Water poor in plant nutrients and Ca^{++}	Plant nutrients and Ca^{++} abundant
Sediments low in organic matter	Sediments an organic copropel
Oxygen abundant at all levels at all times	Oxygen depleted in summer hypolimnion
Littoral plants limited, often rosette type	Littoral plants abundant
Phytoplankton quantitatively poor	Abundant phytoplankton, mass great
Water blooms of bluegreens lacking	Water blooms common
Profundal bottom fauna diverse; intolerant of low oxygen tensions	Profundal benthos poor in species; survive low oxygen
Profundal benthos quantitatively poor	Profundal benthic biomass great
Tanytarsus-type midge larvae in profundal benthos; *Chaoborus* usually lacking	*Chironomus,* the profundal midge larva; *Chaoborus* present
Deep-water salmonid and coregonids	No stenothermal fish in hypolimnion

Modified from Thienemann 1925.

ly oligotrophic; if richly endowed, they would have exhibited primary eutrophy. Thienemann had hit upon modifications that Lundbeck (1934) referred to as secondary: the morphology of the basin overrides the edaphic effect. A deep basin with a relatively voluminous hypolimnion contains enough deep-water oxygen to support a benthic fauna typical of oligotrophic lakes despite eutrophic or mesotrophic water in the sense of Weber, as well as a high production of organic material in the epilimnion. Conversely, a shallow basin with a small hypolimnion may run out of oxygen above the profundal sediments even though it contains oligotrophic water and epilimnetic production is not especially great. Its zoobenthos includes *Chironomus* as in lakes that are primarily eutrophic. Thus, an important ratio is to be taken into account: the epilimnion's volume (E) in relation to the hypolimnion's (H). If E/H is great, the oxygen in the tropholytic hypolimnion may be depleted rapidly; whereas if E/H is small, there may be large stores of deep-water oxygen, hardly diminished by respiration and decay. This leads to secondary oligotrophy even if in a favorable edaphic setting (Fig. 2-3).

Primary and secondary eutrophy are not entirely independent, however. In a small hypolimnion a comparatively great area of sediment is in contact with the water; the effects of nutrients diffusing out from the profundal ooze are more pronounced than in a large hypolimnion. Similarly, the contribution of dissolved and particulate substances via runoff from the drainage area could have greater impact in a small body of water than in a large, deep lake. Thus, in theoretic considerations, we are left with the concept that shallowness, a secondary factor, can contribute to primary eutrophy and all that attends it.

Bog lakes and dystrophy

Northern waters, protected from wind and poorly drained, may become bog lakes. They are fringed by floating mats of vegetation growing inward to encroach upon the open water. Cedar Bog Lake, Minnesota, famous because of Lindeman's (1942b) influential paper, is a senescent lake, nearly obliterated by the marginal mat. It occupies a depression in soils moderately supplied with calcium, and its waters are circumneutral in pH and fairly clear. Farther to the northeast in Minnesota, in northern Wisconsin, and in the Upper Peninsula of Michigan

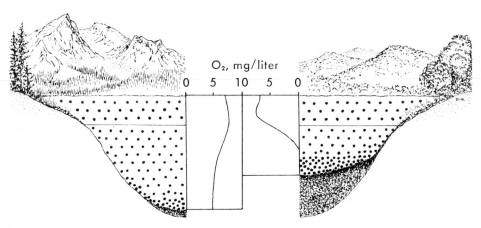

O₂, mg/liter

Fig. 2-3. Two morphologically different types of lakes: oligotrophic lake at left; eutrophic lake at right. Epilimnion volumes and sestonic particles (dark circles) same in both lakes; hypolimnion volumes differ and oxygen profiles differ. Oligotrophic E/H volume ratio small; eutrophic E/H volume ratio larger.

are some glacial soils derived from Precambrian rocks.

The Canadian Shield is deficient in calcium, and bog lakes there show features defined as *dystrophy.* The earliest examples studied were Scandinavian lakes. The stained waters are acid and brown, low in electrolytes, with reduced transparency caused by colloidal and dissolved humus material.

The importance of calcium shortage in bringing about dystrophy was demonstrated by Hasler and co-workers (1951) in a brown-stained lake of the Wisconsin Highlands. Adding commercial hydrated lime, mostly $Ca(OH)_2$, raised the pH from 5.4 to 7.1 and resulted in clearing the water and increasing vertical light penetration. Dystrophy seems to be linked to the blocking of bacterial action by calcium's scarcity; organic matter, then, does not decay rapidly and is not recycled in a normal fashion. Stained, murky waters, characterizing dystrophy, are not restricted to northern bogs; many southern waters in North America and elsewhere fit this category.

Dystrophic lakes probably belong to the oligotrophic series even though, except for some in deep basins, the oxygen in lower strata is much reduced or lacking. Furthermore, the benthos is taxonomically poor, consisting of a *Chironomus* fauna reminiscent of eutrophy. Despite this, the scantiness of the plankton and benthic crops, the lack of dissolved nutrients, and the nature of the algal flora in part suggest oligotrophy.

Primary productivity and lake classification

It is not always easy to place a lake into a definite class. Some seem to be mosaics of what we assume to be eutrophic as well as oligotrophic characteristics. Rodhe (1969) approached the problem directly. In an *autotrophic* lake—one in which the organic compounds produced are from photosynthesis rather than imported from the outside—the trophic status can be related to the primary productivity. Going directly to the source of biologic productivity, we can ask how much inorganic carbon is fixed, and at what rate, by the phototrophic producers. Rodhe suggests rates of: 7 to 25 g of carbon per year for every square meter of lake surface in examples of oligotrophy; 75 to 250 g C per m^2 per year in natural eutrophic lakes; and 350 to 700 g C per m^2 per year in polluted lakes. This leaves us with mesotrophy lying somewhere between annual primary production of 25 to 75 g carbon fixed and converted to organic molecules by the lacustrine green plants under an average square meter of lake surface. Rodhe's definition of ranges and limits are not applicable everywhere, but his approach frees us from some of the difficulties in pigeonholing certain perplexing aquatic ecosystems.

Desert waters, where solar radiation is intense, growing seasons are long, and nutrients are condensed, often surpass the limits of Rodhe's polluted waters in carbon fixation per year. Carpelan (1957) discussed primary productivity amounting to 1.42 kg C per m^2 per year in some California brine pools. The productivity of Arizona's Montezuma Well is about 798 g C per m^2 per year, although no pollution is involved. Similarly, enriched waste lagoons may annually fix about 3.0 kg C for every square meter of surface. A record high for annual production may have been found by Talling and associates (1973) in two Ethiopian lakes, rich in sodium carbonate—perhaps near 5.0 kg C per m^2.

Extremely low rates of carbon fixation are also known to fall below Rodhe's oligotrophic boundary. Goldman and others (1967) reported about 0.014 g C per m^2 for an average summer day (February) in an Antarctic lake. Likewise, the pristine mountain lake, Waldo, in Oregon, fixes about 0.03 g C per m^2 during an average summer day (Malueg and others 1972).

LAKE SEDIMENTS AND PALEOLIMNOLOGY
Gyttja (copropel)

The profundal sediments of any lake are fine grained because of the size sorting that has gone on during transport from littoral regions and because of the significant portion derived from settled plankton. These sediments contain organic material and mineral matter of two types, allochthonous and autochthonous. The autochthonous inorganic component is made up, to a great extent, of siliceous diatom frustules and perhaps sponge spicules, along with calcium carbonate precipitated by biologic events. In oligotrophic lakes, the deposits are scanty and mineralized. Their organic content is low because the abundant oxygen in waters overlying them has favored bacterial decay.

The common lacustrine sediment of eutrophy was named and described more than 110 years ago by a Swedish scientist, von Post; this is *gyttja,* pronounced something like yū-tcha by Anglo-Saxons. Regrettably, much confusion and muddling of the original definition has come about since then. Gyttja consists of a mixture of humus material, fine plant fragments, algal remains, grains of quartz and mica, diatom frustules, exoskeleton fragments from aquatic arthropods, and spore and pollen relics. Derived to a great extent from the plankton, but not entirely so, it has been mixed and modified by the bottom fauna that both consume it and contribute their feces to it. Coprogenesis, referring to origin via feces, is a major aspect of its formation. Its color ranges from gray to dark brown, and it is near neutral on the pH scale. In deeper layers it is compact and gelatinous. A gentle stream of water played on gyttja breaks it up into fluffy fecal pellets.

In a paper on the sediments of Cedar Bog Lake, Swain and Prokopovich (1954) coined the term *copropel* to replace gyttja. The word comes from the Greek *kopros* and *pelos* (dung and mud, respectively) and accents the coprogenic nature of gyttja. Because of the vague way in which gyttja has been applied by authors during the past century, use of copropel is to be recommended.

Iovino and Bradley (1969) found that *Chironomus* larvae grazing on bluegreens produced coherent and durable pellets. Two species of green algae served as a more valuable food source for the insects, but the resultant fecal ejecta disintegrated rapidly, returning to the water whatever undigested cells were present. Such cells were ingested again, but contributed little to the accumulation of lacustrine sediment. Perhaps this shows that, with eutrophic conditions and a relatively greater abundance of blue-green algae, there is a faster sedimentation rate and an increase in the coprogenic proportion of the bottom deposits.

These two authors were especially concerned with conditions in Mud Lake, Florida, where a rich organic sediment is composed almost entirely of fecal pellets from chironomids with diets nearly restricted to blue-green algae. Because of the current interest in fossil fuels, it is noteworthy that the Mud Lake ooze seems to be the kind that was laid down 50 million years ago by some Eocene lakes and represented now by oil-rich shale beds in Wyoming, Utah, and Colorado.

Nutrients such as nitrogen and phosphorus are abundant in copropel; the phosphorus is commonly united with iron, aluminum, and to a lesser extent calcium. Plant pigments can be extracted from the copropel, and there is a growing literature on the organic chemistry of this material; carbohydrates, bitumens, amino acids, and various hydrocarbons are but a few of the substances within this profundal ooze.

Profundal deposits beneath oligotrophic and eutrophic hypolimnia differ mainly in their abundance, their rate of deposition, and their relative organic contents. "Lake mud" is often used to describe them, even though lake soils differ from soggy terrestrial dirt.

Sapropel

If bottom deposits are subjected to extraordinarily long periods of anoxia when reducing conditions prevail, another organic sediment forms. This is *sapropel,* a glossy black material, rather watery and lacking the structure of copropel. It gives off the rotten-egg odor of H_2S, contains the marsh gas methane, CH_4, and owes its shiny black color to ferrous sulfide.

In many lakes sapropel overlies copropel, reflecting a long-term change in the annual oxygen regime, in most instances effected by organic pollution. Thus, Crystal Lake in Minnesota now shows effects of organic pollution from surrounding homes; 6 to 7 cm of watery black sapropel overlies compacted brown copropel. Farther north in eutrophic but unpolluted Lake Itasca, the surficial sediments are copropelic, much like the deeper layers in Crystal Lake.

Sapropel mixed with oxygenated lake water turns brown, but no coprogenic structure is revealed. Usually the stress of environmental conditions that promote sapropel precludes development of a macrobenthic fauna, and coprogenesis is not part of the picture. In Tom Wallace Lake, Kentucky, the uppermost film of sediment is brown during winter when oxygenated water exists throughout the lake but turns to black from early May to late October when anaerobic water overlies the profundal ooze.

Dystrophic sediments

The sediments of dystrophy are called *dy* (pronounced *dü*), and were originally described as being much like the copropel of eutrophic waters but with acid humus abundantly present. According to Hansen (1959) the brown humus of dy has a carbon/nitrogen ratio greater than 10, while the C/N proportion is less in copropel. The organic percentage is higher in dy, if we rely on the loss of weight following ignition as an index.

The meaning of dy has changed through the years, and it is usually referred to yellow-brown, flocculent, fibrous plant material derived to a great extent from peat of the bog sedge mat or from allochthonous sources. These watery, undecomposed plant fragments frequently create a false bottom, seemingly firm but almost without substance. Sometimes the brown, humic acids combine with calcium or magnesium, precipitate, and form an amorphous organic component of dy.

Thus it is evident that sediments from deeper regions yield a great deal of information about the nature of a lake.

Varves

Varves are especially instructive because they make possible direct estimates of age and sedimentation rates. Varves are sedimentary layers laid down at regular intervals, usually two per year, although massive seasonal blooms of plankton sometimes account for annual laminae of more than two members. In some northern lakes, snow melts and spring freshets introduce large amounts of inorganic material that is spread out over their bottoms. This stratum is laid down on the principally organic substances that settled in quiet water beneath winter ice and in the still hypolimnion of summer. Varved sediments of alternating allochthonous and autochthonous materials result.

According to Dussart (1966) the conspicuous varves in Lake Geneva are largely allochthonous in origin. They are owed to the Rhone introducing a mixture of mica, siliceous particles, and calcareous bits. These arrivals separate according to size and precipitate at different seasons, bringing about laminated sediments alternating between dark gray bands, predominantly calcareous, and lighter layers composed mostly of silica and mica. Two contrasting bands represent a year's deposit. In other lakes calcareous material is deposited annually as a result of biologic activity within the lake (Megard 1968).

Sediments and paleolimnologic implications

Cores of profundal sediment taken from a lake bottom can reveal much of the lake's history. Deevey's (1942b) study of Linsley Pond deposits serves as a good example of what happened to lakes formed roughly 12,000 years ago in glaciated North America. The core extended to the original lake floor, composed of glacial debris. Above this floor early sediments were inorganic and mineralized, compared with overlying deposits. Organic material had been oxidized to a great extent by the aerobic bacteria of decay. (Combustion of a gram of such sediment at about 550° C results in a loss in weight amounting to less than 10%.)

The Linsley Pond sediments above the first meter increased rapidly in organic content, showing a mounting loss on ignition, which stabilized at about 60%. They represented material laid down when hypolimnetic waters were low in oxygen much of the time—nature had not oxidized them. They were the typical deposits of eutrophy.

It appears, then, that Linsley Pond, formed when Pleistocene ice retreated from New England, was oligotrophic for a relatively short period before becoming enriched enough to make the transition to eutrophy. This stage persisted in a state of dynamic equilibrium for millennia.

A somewhat different situation, based on Whiteside's (1965) work at Potato Lake, Arizona, is portrayed in Fig. 2-4. The lake basin was formed thousands of

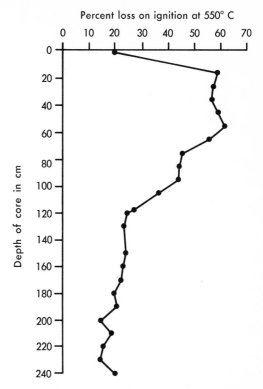

Fig. 2-4. Results of combustion of sediments from a core from Potato Lake, Arizona, showing percentages lost on ignition. Lower part of curve represents inorganic sediments; upper part of curve represents organic sediments. (Modified from Whiteside 1965.)

years before Linsley Pond and laid down inorganic sediments until the end of the last ice age—about the time the Linsley basin was created. Then, perhaps in response to ameliorating climate, Potato Lake began to deposit organic oozes typical of eutrophy. The pollen relics in the sediments showed that such northern trees as spruce and fir disappeared at this level, as some oak and especially pine came into prominence. There seems to have been an increase up to the level of about 60% loss on ignition, but near the sediment-water boundary a sudden decline in organic percentage occurred. This represented accelerated erosion of inorganic matter from the drainage basin, the result of logging and possibly limited agriculture. (The lake is said to have gained its name from an early settler's potato field near its shores.)

The natural eutrophication of Potato Lake might have been brought about by factors other than the lessening of climatic severity. Obviously the basin was shoaling. Its morphology was changing; its hypolimnetic volume was diminishing markedly. Secondary factors may have begun to assume an important role in the interplay of climatic, edaphic, and morphologic factors that determine a lake's trophic status. Moreover, at the elevation of almost 2,300 m, a winter ice cover is a regular feature of Potato Lake. Perhaps, with a decreased volume of water beneath blankets of snow-covered ice, respiration and decay placed so great a demand on the limited oxygen supply that the lake became anaerobic during winter at least, mimicking the conditions of a eutrophic hypolimnion. Schindler and Comita (1972) were on hand to witness the first instance of winter anaerobiosis in a small, aging Minnesota lake. This momentous event in the lake's life was marked by abrupt changes, drastically affecting the biota.

There is infinitely more to the sediments than their relative and changing organic content, for they contain plant and animal relics that have much to say about a lake's history (Frey 1964). Chlorophyll does not preserve well, but its degradation products remain, implying much about past algal productivities. The presence of blue-green algae long ago can be inferred from the myxoxanthophyll contents of buried ooze. The chitinized head capsules of midge larvae resist decay to a remarkable degree and remain to be identified and related to conditions of oligotrophy or eutrophy. These are just tiny samples of the array of lake microfossils that can be studied. As knowledge grows about the biology of their living representatives, the remnants in the bottom deposits will serve increasingly in interpretations of the lacustrine past.

MAN'S EFFECT

One thing implied by the stratigraphy of Linsley Pond's sediment was that after eutrophy was reached, there was a long period of equilibrium, and in the case of Potato Lake, there was a prolonged oligotrophic state before eutrophy was triggered in some way (Fig. 2-4). The amount of nutrients that an undisturbed lake receives via runoff each year results in a steady state of annual production, reflected in part by the bottom deposits accumulating in a regular fashion. "Trophic equilibrium," as it was termed by Hutchinson (1969), reflects the status of the entire edaphic-climatic-morphologic system.

When European men came to North America, most lakes were probably in trophic equilibrium. With forest-cutting and farming, man upset the dynamic balance. Bormann and associates (1969) quantified this disturbance when they measured the effects of deforestation on the runoff to a small New Hampshire lake. The rate of nutrient input to the lake was accelerated greatly. Longstreth (1972) showed that, even in arid Arizona, removal of the natural shrubby cover, called chaparral, and its replacement by grass resulted in a marked erosion of edaphic nutrients, especially nitrate, from the watershed.

Recently, Whitehead and co-workers (1973) described oscillations in the past productivity of a New England pond that seemed to be related to natural forest changes. Core samples implied increasing productivity as nutrients leached from the new glacial substrate and as a spruce-pine forest developed, the sequence also shown in Linsley Pond. A decline in productivity followed the replacement of these early conifers by a northern hardwood forest, including a coniferous component, hemlock. A second eutrophication cycle accompanied an abrupt decline in hemlock and an increase in deciduous trees, which contributed significant amounts of leaf litter to the lake. The implications are that trophic equilibria are influenced and upset by various factors, natural and man-induced, that bring about changes in nutrient retention in the lacustrine watershed. At this time, eutrophication connotes the effects brought about by increased input of plant nutrients to a lake, the increase being a function of human activity in the catchment basin.

Anthrogenic or cultural eutrophication commenced, then, with the early European settlers of North America and has been greatly augmented by introduction of sewage into streams and lakes. It started earlier in the Old World. A reference is made in later pages to effects Neolithic man may have had on at least one Austrian lake (Frey 1955), and several workers, including Cowgill and Hutchinson (1970), have documented the rapid eutrophication brought about by lakeside construction of the Via Cassia by the Romans a few centuries B.C.

Examples of man's accelerating the eutrophication process, assembled by Hasler (1947) served as a warning in an important paper somewhat ahead of its time. Since then, the "smirchment lake" appears as a new term (Veatch and Humphrys 1966), referring to a grossly polluted, or otherwise modified, body of water and reminding us of the narrow boundary between enrichment and destruction. There is hope, however, for just as past natural reversals are known in lacustrine trophic trends, there are examples of modern lakes recovering from effects of man's mistreatment. Diverting sewage from Lake Washington, near Seattle, Washington, has resulted in heartening responses and dwindling of some undesirable consequences of cultural eutrophication (Edmondson 1972ab). A Swedish program is under way to rejuvenate lakes by dredging and deepening, as well as by diverting sewage; it seems to be achieving some success (Bjork and others 1972).

RUNNING WATERS—LOTIC ENVIRONMENT

Much of what pertains to the lake basin is also relevant to oceanography, and vice versa. The river and its environmental features do not have close marine counterparts. Contrasts between lotic and lentic habitats are briefly pointed out below.

Hynes (1970) assembled most of what is known about running waters and their biota in a book, *The Ecology of Running Waters.* That book and an earlier review paper by Leopold (1962) are invaluable as sources of information on the unique physical dynamics of rivers.

Rivers, in general, represent the excess of precipitation over evaporation. According to Leopold (1962) the annual precipitation falling on the United States is about 76 cm; of this about 53 cm is returned to the atmosphere, and 23 cm is "runoff"—the excess, flowing via river routes to the sea. Many stream channels are ancient compared with most lakes. Leopold draws an analogy between a river and a biologic species: the existing river was inherited from a preexisting river which, in turn, came from an earlier stream; it evolved during geologic time. Most lakes come into being in quite different manners (see Chapter 5).

The linear morphology of streams and rivers is uniquely different from lakes. Moreover, even the largest rivers are usually shallow compared with lakes. As a result, a pronounced longitudinal zonation of the biota is characteristic of stream ecosystems compared with depth distribution, seen strikingly in lakes.

The unidirectional flow of streams sets their waters off from lentic habitats. This current is a salient stream feature, but it varies seasonally, with depth, and throughout the longitudinal profile of the watercourse. Some small streams are intermittent; this is especially true in arid regions, but even in humid climates there are temporary streams. They are the lotic equivalent of the temporary pond and have biota equipped to deal with the seasonal contrasts. Although differing seasonal flow rates are particularly pronounced in impermanent streams, probably the phenomenon of erratic discharge throughout the year characterizes most rivers.

An ideal longitudinal profile of a stream would show two main regions grading into each other. In the upper reaches, *erosional* effects are predominant; more material is being washed away than is being deposited. As sea level is approached in the lower courses the *deposition* of materials assumes greater importance. As a result, the bottom substrates are coarser in the upper parts of the stream than at lower altitudes, where silty deposits prevail.

Discharge is augmented as the river flows on, receiving contributions from its tributaries. Discharge is the product of width, depth, and velocity, any one of which can vary. Generally then, it can be stated that the volume of water passing a given point during a period of time increases downstream.

Stream flow rates range from near zero to more than 8 m/sec, although velocities surpassing 6 m/sec are unusual; and generally currents do not exceed 3 m/sec (Hynes 1970). The generally accepted idea that the stream far from its source flows at a markedly reduced rate is disputed by Leopold (1962). Velocity is relatively constant or may even increase downstream in spite of a decrease in riverbed slope. If depth increases faster than the river gradient decreases, velocity may increase somewhat. Narrowing of the channel suddenly lowers the flow rate, but the usual tendency is for width to increase with discharge. Furthermore, as shown in a table presented by Hynes (1970), a river 200 m wide and 4 m deep with a slope of only 0.5 m/km would have a velocity almost 1.2 times that of a small stream, 20 m wide and 0.5 m deep, flowing down a gradient ten times steeper.

At any given spot along the course of a stream, water velocities differ. The current, ideally, is swiftest at the center and near the surface. Frictional forces at the banks and at the bottom decrease the flow. One method of timing the rate is to introduce fluorescein dye and to observe its progress. This should reveal turbulent eddies and zones of circulating water that are not part of the main water mass. At irregularities along the edge, regions of nearly "dead water," where flow is almost nonexistent come to light. A diversity of habitats is thus shown in one segment of the stream.

Coarse bottom rubble offers habitats for organisms and impedes flow. The localized currents at the downstream, upstream, and top surfaces of a small rock are quite different, and measuring their flow rates calls for special techniques. Most mechanical velocity or current meters are too bulky to detect microcurrents over the surfaces of submerged objects. McConnell and Sigler (1959) described an ingenious method for estimating small currents and turbulence at rock surfaces. This was based on establishing the rates at which standard sodium chloride tablets lose weight while immersed 1 minute in various flows.

Annual temperature variations in streams can be marked, following the seasonal trends of the region. Vertical temperature extremes, however, are much reduced, there being little stratification except in quiet marginal pools. A lake 12 m deep may have a summertime range of 15° or 20° C, whereas a nearby big river of the same depth may roll along with a bottom temperature not much different from that of the surface. Thus, current velocity and substrate, more than temperature, bring about the major diversity of habitat and, hence, diversity of life in streams.

There are no hypersaline flowing waters that can compare with lakes and ponds of arid regions. These lentic habitats are characterized by no outlets and a concentration of ions and compounds via high rates of evaporation. There is little or no opportunity for retention of dissolved substances in a stream.

Usually the total salinity of a stream increases downstream, a function of ever-increasing drainage area marked by entrance of tributaries. An exception to this general rule is seen in some spring brooks, fed from underground sources. In these there may be a lowering of dissolved solids within the first few kilometers because certain saturation equilibria are upset after the water emerges. Calcium carbonate and sometimes iron are precipitated, lowering the total dissolved material carried by the stream.

3

The freshwater biota and aquatic habitats

Students of the inland aquatic biota see evidence that some major taxonomic groups invaded from the sea, others from land, and a minority seem to have arisen in fresh water itself. Formidable barriers must be surmounted in moving from a life adapted to marine or terrestrial environments to the habitats afforded by lakes, ponds, and streams. For this reason entire groups of animals on the class level, or even ranked as phyla, have no representatives in fresh water. Other marine and terrestrial groups have contributed disproportionately to the limnologic biota. Although the array of tiny plants and animals to be found floating, swimming, and gliding about in collections taken from freshwater habitats may seem staggering at first, the inland waters are taxonomically impoverished compared with the sea. Groups such as the Cephalopoda, Ctenophora, Kinorhyncha, Priapulida, and Amphineura, for example, have no freshwater representatives, and from a total of about 4,500 species of the Porifera, only about 150 are found in fresh waters (Pennak 1963).

PHYSICAL FACTORS

Water levels in freshwater environments range from stable conditions throughout the year to an astatic series terminating in such extremes as Australia's tremendous Lake Eyre, often dry for decades between its irregular fillings. Some temporary ponds have a regular seasonal rhythm, a dry phase alternating with a wet phase. The liquid phase appearing each spring is a certainty in most northern depressions that hold snow melt. The basins of temporary waters vary from those whose sediments are moist even during the empty phase to those that are powdery dry between fillings.

Oceans and inland waters differ in behavior and temperature range. Even the largest lakes, characterized by stable water levels, show no significant response to the moon. The tidal regime set up by the earth's satellite has resulted in marine communities adapted to conditions alien to inland lakes: within the shallows alternately bared and covered by tides, complex zonation of plants and animals occurs, and their biologic clocks operate on a twice-a-day schedule.

The crashing of ocean surf against the shore can be matched, to some extent, in windswept lakes that are subject to a long fetch, but the continuous unidirectional flow of rivers and brooks is not seen in marine habitats. Moreover, the annual variation in surface waters of the ocean is usually less than 10° C, with the exception of the North Atlantic and North Pacific, where cold continental air masses may depress temperatures as much as 18° from the warmest time of year. This range is small compared with the annual variation of temperature in inland waters, where 25° C would not represent an unusual range for lake surfaces in temperate regions.

CHEMICAL FACTORS

The pH of the well-buffered seas ranges but little, from 8.1 to 8.3. However, all extremes are known in inland waters: alkaline lakes may go above pH 10 or 11, and the acid waters of some northern bogs often fall below pH 3.0.

Marine life is adapted to waters with a salinity scarcely varying from 3.5% and composed largely of NaCl. Freshwater life has involved survival in and adaptation to dilute water, best described as a calcium bicarbonate type subject to much variation. Even when inland waters approach or surpass the sea in salt content, the proportion of major ions may be much different from, and bear little resemblance to, sea brine.

ADAPTATIONS TO
FRESH WATER

Probably the major adaptation to be made in the journey from sea to fresh water is of an osmoregulatory nature. Marine forms are characterized by blood and other body fluids that are isotonic to seawater; moving to hypotonic waters brings up problems of maintaining a stable internal environment against the constant threat of osmotic water diluting the fluids and leaching out the salts. Few marine plants or animals can survive dilute water. At the opposite extreme are the hypersaline waters found in some desert regions. Here the salinity may be seven times greater than the sea's brine, and only a few forms can colonize such habitats. Most of these have freshwater ancestors rather than immediate marine antecedents. The freshwater plants and animals show greater general adaptability and ecologic versatility than their marine relatives.

A further factor in an organism's successful freshwater existence is its adaptation to prolonged desiccation. As a result, resistant stages and mechanisms for enduring dry or other unfavorable periods are common in inland water forms but are lacking in their close marine relatives. The gemmules of freshwater sponges and the statoblasts of inland bryozoans are well-known examples of such mechanisms for endurance.

The immigrants from land that are found in fresh water have overcome osmotic problems, but the switch from aerial to aquatic respiration may have been more of a hurdle. In many instances the structures that were used to guard against desiccation in terrestrial existence serve as barriers in the water, thereby reducing the area of unprotected membranes through which environmental water enters the rather concentrated body fluids. The abundance of oxygen mixed with other gases of the air, however, is far greater than the oxygen in water; and except for some ingenious arthropods that carry bubbles of atmospheric gas underwater with them, most aquatic animals of terrestrial origin have devised new respiratory structures that function in an aqueous environment.

Many freshwater animals lack a larval stage, thus differing from their close relatives in the sea. It has been theorized that such stages are weak links in the life cycle, especially in lotic environments, or that nutrients in dilute inland waters are so scarce that diminutive larvae could not fend for themselves. Nature's answer has been to pack salts and yolk into the egg where embryologic development includes larval stages, and to set free the young, which resemble miniature adults, when ready to cope with conditions in the freshwater habitat. Similarly, the motile medusa stage of the hydrozoans was eliminated in the highly evolved freshwater *Hydra*. The unusual and sporadic occurrence of one of the freshwater jellyfish, the medusa of *Craspedacusta,* is always exciting to zoologists, although medusae are common in the sea.

Doing away with delicate motile stages, whether adult or larval, may be of adaptive significance for many species, but there are many freshwater larvae that seem to be faring well. For example, the nauplius of copepod and some branchiopod crustaceans is well developed in inland waters. The recent spectacular spread of the Asiatic clam *Corbicula* in North America and *Dreissena* in the Old World implies that there has been no disadvantage in retaining the *veliger,* a typical marine-mollusc larva (Sinclair 1964).

The presence or absence of the nauplius larva (see Figs. 3-4, *F* and 3-8, *F*) is especially interesting. In the marine world many diverse groups of the Crustacea produce this larva, which links such unlikely forms as the barnacles with other, more conventional Crustacea. It is the simplest larva that hatches from a crustacean egg, bearing three pairs of jointed swimming appendages that are destined to become the first and second antennae and the mandibles. The first pair of appendages is unbranched, but the following are characteristically Y-shaped or biramous (two branched) and appear one pair per segment. With subsequent molts, additional segments bearing appendages appear. These stages are the metanaupliar instars, although often simply designated as later nauplius instars. Many freshwater crustaceans have relegated the nauplius-metanauplius stages to their embryology.

THE MONERA—PROKARYOTA

Bacteria and blue-green algae have a structural organization that sets them off from all other organisms. They are simple cells (or groups of cells) lacking nuclear membranes, the endoplasmic reticulum, chloroplasts, and mitochondria. Cell division occurs with little change in gross appearance and, therefore, without apparent mitosis. In the bacteria that possess flagella (bluegreens have none), these locomotor organelles are distinct from the complex flagella and cilia of the plant and animal eukaryotes. However, the flagella and cilia of the higher organisms have a similar basic structure.

The close relationship that exists between bacteria and bluegreens has been stressed only in recent years. (The name

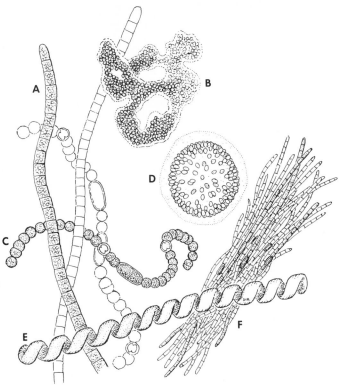

Fig. 3-1. Some blue-green algae (Cyanophyta) from inland waters. **A,** *Oscillatoria;* **B,** *Microcystis aeruginosa;* **C,** *Anabaena;* **D,** *Coelosphaerium;* **E,** *Spirulina;* **F,** *Aphanizomenon flos-aquae.*

blue-green algae recalls the days when they were classified with the eukaryotic plants termed algae. Perhaps today they should be called bluegreens without reference to algae.) The algae are not really a natural taxonomic group, and the higher plants within the province of the phycologist are a heterogeneous mixture of various divisions and phyla. From a phylogenetic standpoint the bluegreens belong to the bacteriologist, but the overwhelming bulk of research being done on them is by phycologists.

Bacteria and bluegreens are remarkably adaptable and exist in a wide variety of habitats, being abundant in the soil, sea, and fresh water. Bacteria are gaining prevalence in lake studies. Much attention has been focused on them as mediators in cycles of such elements as hydrogen, sulfur, carbon, iron, nitrogen, and phosphorus. Thus they serve as decomposers and recyclers in food chains and agents in biogeochemical cycles. Only recently has discussion been directed toward the bacteria as a major food item in trophic dynamics and energy transfers (Sorokin 1965).

THE CYANOPHYTA

The bluegreens (Fig. 3-1) referred to variously as the Cyanophyta or Myxophyceae derive their name from the pigment phycocyanin. Another pigment, phycoerythrin, is red and, mixed with the former and two or three other pigments, gives masses of bluegreens colors ranging from red through violet to black. They are photosynthetic, as are many bacteria, but use chlorophyll *a,* not seen in the bacteria. Apparently the invention of chlorophyll *a* was a major evolutionary step, and it appears as the paramount photosynthetic pigment in all higher plants.

Some bluegreens can carry out what we tend to think are bacterial reactions—fixing nitrogen, for example. According to Stanier (1973), all the blue-green algae that have been studied use light as an energy source and CO_2 as a carbon source. Thus they are primarily photoautotrophs. Some can assimilate organic substances such as acetate and amino acids, and some are chemoautotrophs, being able to grow on a few sugars in the dark.

Blue-green algae are the objects of intensive research now because of the unpleasant growths they form in lakes where eutrophication has been brought about by domestic, agricultural, and industrial pollution. In such cases, accelerated growth of bluegreens results in noxious "water blooms" of such forms as *Microcystis* and *Anabaena.* Often their respiratory demands surpass their daylight oxygen production, and upon death their decay promotes further deoxygenation.

A few lakes have been plagued by races or strains of bluegreens that produce dangerous toxins. Six genera have been implicated in fish kills and in the deaths of horses, cattle, swine, dogs, chickens, squirrels, and other animals: *Microcystis, Nodularia, Coelosphaerium, Gloeotrichia, Anabaena,* and *Aphanizomenon.* Putrid masses of these bluegreens accumulate in the shallows or at the strand line, where they are often unsightly and possibly dangerous. Papers by Gorham (1964) and Whitton (1973b) review much of what we know about algal toxins.

Many experiments have been performed over the years to elucidate the value of bluegreens to grazing zooplankters. Arnold (1971) reviews the literature and reports on the effects of seven species of blue-green algae as a diet for *Daphnia pulex.* (He also compares the bluegreens with green algae as food sources.) Arnold concludes that cladocerans would survive only at low levels

of abundance if their food mixture were dominated by bluegreens. This has been the opinion for many years—the bluegreens have been considered weed species. But we must not forget that the cyanophytes of some African soda lakes are noted for the abundant animal life they support: the beak of the lesser flamingo *(Phoeniconaias minor)* is marvelously adapted for straining out strands of bluegreen filaments, and the important fish *Tilapia nilotica* in Lake Rudolph consumes and digests *Spirulina* and *Anabaenopsis,* two genera typical of concentrated sodium-carbonate water. Furthermore, in the deeps of freshwater lakes elements of the bottom fauna, such as *Chironomus plumosus,* feed on bluegreens that reach the profundal ooze (Iovino and Bradly 1969; Jónasson and Kristiansen 1967).

In European lakes, and to a lesser extent in North America, the reddish filamentous *Oscillatoria rubescens* has gained a reputation as an indicator organism. Its initial appearance in lakes seems to announce the approach of cultural eutrophication (Hasler 1947; Whitton 1973a).

THE EUKARYOTA
The plants

All organisms above the bluegreens have eukaryotic mitotic cells characterized by true nuclei and other intracellular organelles, such as mitochondria and chloroplasts. The eukaryote choroloplast seems to be homologous to an entire bluegreen cell.

Some large marine groups of plants are scarcely represented in limnologic habitats. However, other algae are important freshwater groups, although they are far more abundant in the seas.

Perhaps typical of the terrestrial environment and the inland waters are those forms that possess the blue-green invention chlorophyll a and an accessory pigment, chlorophyll b. These are the vascular plants, the abundant green algae

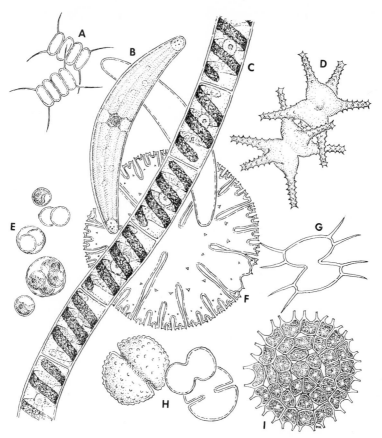

Fig. 3-2. Some green algae (Chlorophyta) from inland waters. **A,** *Scenedesmus;* **B,** *Closterium;* **C,** *Spirogyra;* **D,** *Staurastrum;* **E,** *Chlorella;* **F,** *Micrasterias;* **G,** *Xanthidium;* **H,** *Cosmarium;* **I,** *Pediastrum.* **B, D, F, G,** and **H** belong to the Desmidaceae.

(Chlorophyta), and the euglenoids, assigned to another large taxon, the Euglenophyta. The green algae embrace such familiar genera as *Spirogyra, Volvox, Chlorella,* and *Ulothrix,* each belonging to a different order of the chlorophycean algae, made up of more than 8,000 freshwater species. The Desmidaceae (a family of green algae) are especially interesting because typically they are found in acid bogs, very dilute water low in electrolytes, and in oligotrophic lakes (Fig. 3-2, *B, D, F, G,* and *H*).

The search for indicator organisms is especially rewarding where algae are concerned, although complicated by the occurrence of physiologic races and taxonomic problems. Brook (1965) classified

desmids on the basis of their occurrence in oligotrophic, mesotrophic, or eutrophic waters. In Brook's opinion, 27 of 46 species were oligotrophic indicators; one genus, *Cosmarium* (Fig. 3-2, *H*), had more eutrophic species than oligotrophic, while the beautiful *Micrasterias* (Fig. 3-2, *F*) and *Xanthidium* (Fig. 3-2, *G*) typified oligotrophic waters.

Another category of freshwater plants includes the various groups with both chlorophyll *a* and chlorophyll *c;* these are the golden brown phyla (Fig. 3-3). The Pyrrophyta, peridinians or dinoflagellates, are extremely abundant in the sea; fresh water has fewer than 200 species. The armored *Ceratium hirundinella* (Fig. 3-3, *E*) is a spectacular and easily identi-

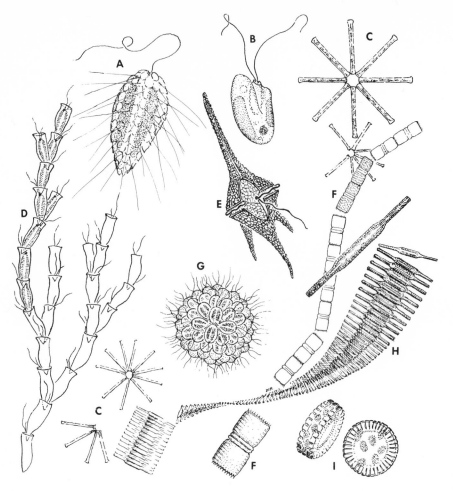

Fig. 3-3. Representatives of the golden brown phyla in inland waters. **A,** *Mallomonas*, Chrysophyceae; **B,** *Cryptomonas*, Cryptophyta; **C,** *Asterionella*, Bacillariophyceae; **D,** *Dinobryon*, Chrysophyceae, **E,** *Ceratium hirundinella*, Pyrrophyta; **F,** *Melosira*, Bacillariophyceae; **G,** *Synura*, Chrysophyceae; **H,** *Fragilaria*, Bacillariophyceae; **I,** *Cyclotella*, Bacillariophyceae.

fied form that is very common in plankton collections.

Two groups of golden brown algae containing flagellated forms are the Cryptophyta, or cryptomonads, and the Chrysophyceae, a family of the Chrysophyta (Fig. 3-3). The cryptomonads include many small, colorless, as well as pigmented, species. The Chrysophyceae is a family containing interesting colonial flagellates such as *Dinobryon* (Fig. 3-3, *D*), *Synura* (Fig. 3-3, *G*), and *Uroglenopsis,* and scaled and spiked unicellular forms typified by *Mallomonas* (Fig. 3-3, *A*). Both

groups are well represented in the ELA lakes* of the Precambrian Shield in Canada (Schindler and Holmgren 1971).

The most important group of the Chrysophyta are the diatoms (Fig. 3-3, *C, F, H,* and *I*), the Bacillariophyceae of many authors. The diatoms compose the great

---

*The ELA, or Experimental Lakes Area, is a region covering about 30,000 km² of the Precambrian Shield in Ontario. Hundreds of small lakes are present in the area, and 46 of them were set aside in the 1960's for experimental research on eutrophication by the Freshwater Institute of the Fisheries Research Board of Canada.

"pastures" of the sea, carrying on most of the world's photosynthesis. There are perhaps 2,000 freshwater species of these golden algae. Because they utilize silica to build their frustules (glassy shells), this compound is an essential nutrient to them. The diatom relics in lake sediments serve the paleolimnologist in interpreting past conditions of the body of water. Some diatoms seem to be good indicators of the fertility elements within the water.

The animals

There are probably several zoologists specializing in any given group of animals in inland waters. Despite this, only a small number of phyla or classes are of limnologic importance. The rotifers, crustaceans, insects, and fishes are the major taxa in the eyes of many limnologists. The reasons for the interest in fish is obvious. Rotifers and crustaceans are well represented in the lake plankton, and insects make up a great part of the lake-bottom and the lotic fauna. There is hardly a body of fresh water that lacks a rotifer fauna; this group is poorly represented in the seas by comparison. Insects belong to the terrestrial scene, but there are many in all sorts of freshwater habitats, while almost none exist in the oceans. The thirty species or so of *Halobates,* a hemipteran genus, found skimming about on the water surface far at sea are exceptions. The crustaceans include a class or subclass, the Branchiopoda, that is almost entirely restricted to fresh water, where one important group of them, the Cladocera, doubtless arose.

The rotifers (see Fig. 3-6) have been classified variously as a class of the Aschelminthes or as a separate phylum, the Rotatoria. They are minute, pseudocoelomate animals, characterized by a ciliated "corona" at the anterior end. The cilia serve for locomotion and for spinning food into the mouth, below which an internal mastax apparatus, consisting of trophi or jaws, is located. There are about 1,800 species of rotifers known, of which 94% are restricted to fresh water and only about 2.5% are normally found only in salt water (Pennak 1963). There are a bewildering array of shapes and modifications in the group. An excellent reference for North America is the account by Edmondson (1959). The latest description of the planktonic rotifers is by Ruttner-Kolisko (1972). There are so many cosmopolitan species that both references—the first in English, the second in German—are valuable.

With great injustice to many elements of the freshwater fauna and to those specialists who have given us so much information about them, the discussion here is limited to certain species and larger taxonomic groups that are typically freshwater forms and to their places in the various communities of inland waters. For details not presented here, Volume 2 of Hutchinson's *Treatise on Limnology* (1967) is recommended. Other easily acquired books that teach the natural history, taxonomy, and some physiology of the freshwater biota are Pennak's *Fresh-water Invertebrates of the United States* (1953) and the "new" Ward and Whipple's *Fresh-water Biology* edited by Edmondson (1959).

IMPERMANENT HABITATS AND SOME INHABITANTS

The temporary pond could be considered the aquatic habitat most unlike the oceans. At least the dry phase of an ephemeral pool is a phenomenon unmatched in the sea.

Most temporary waters are likely to be found in arid and semiarid regions, where evaporative loss exceeds the water income. This does not mean that humid regions lack them. A great number of vernal ponds fill with snow melt in the temperate regions, and in polar climates there is a physiologic "arid" period in winter when the water is present only as ice.

Hartland-Rowe (1972) has elaborated

on some older classifications of temporary waters, pointing out that they are markedly *astatic* (their surface levels fluctuate). He defines two categories: *seasonally astatic* waters, which dry up annually, and *perennially astatic* pools, whose levels rise and fall but do not dry up every year. The first category includes the cold, clear spring ponds of the North and the transitory waters of the desert, including those that fill with warm summer rains, those that fill with winter precipitation, and those that fill during both seasons. The perennially astatic waters range from depressions that always contain some water, but whose marginal flats are both exposed and inundated with some periodicity during the year, to such temporary waters as Australia's great Lake Eyre, which has no regularity to its cycle of wet and dry phases, and is often empty for decades.

Temporary ponds reflect the immediate climate and meteorologic regime far more than do ponds deep enough to be permanent. The biota of transitory waters are adjusted to a set of unusual environmental factors of which the dry phase commands the most attention. Mechanisms to survive the dry phase include: resistant cysts or diapausing eggs (usually shelled embryos), resistant diapausing immature or adult stages, or escape by flight or burrowing.

When in the watery phase, the biota is subjected to widely varying physico-chemical characteristics. The oxygen tension often falls to low levels; salinity varies and becomes unusually high in some pools toward the end of the wet phase; and temperatures are extremely variable even during short periods.

The temporary pond can be likened to a refugium for some species because there are few predators present, although some African depressions that are dry for 8 months each year support cyprinodont fishes of the genus *Nothobranchius*. Usually the predators in impermanent

water are hemipterans and coleopterans that fly in to feed on the abundant resources offered by the ponds.

Restriction to temporary waters for some groups can be a matter of need for drying of the fertilized egg at some stage. This is controversial; it is true for certain species, but evidence is conflicting for others.

Adaptation to ephemeral waters may be a kind of retreat to a haven where competitors are excluded. Proctor (1957) showed that *Haematococcus,* a small green flagellate characteristically found in bird baths and funeral urns, readily survives drying in temporary waters but is inhibited by the presence of substances produced by less talented algae in permanent, larger ponds.

Temporary pond faunas often include species that develop more rapidly than relatives in permanent waters. There is a race for life in many ephemeral pools. Rzoska (1961), who studied the short-lived temporary pools in the Sudan, described life in such habitats as a race against time, often culminating in death for thousands of animals in the last few hours.

The Branchiopoda

Some "typical" freshwater crustaceans are the branchiopods, or phyllopods (Fig. 3-4, *B, C, D,* and *E*). Views on the taxonomic status of the Crustacea have undergone some recent changes. There has been a tendency of late to recognize these animals as more than a class of the Arthropoda, perhaps as a subphylum or a separate phylum. In either case, the Branchiopoda can be treated simply as a class of the Crustacea.

The Branchiopoda, except for the Cladocera, are presently confined to inland waters. They are found especially in temporary pools, but may occur in permanent habitats where fishes and other large predators are absent. Their permanent habitats include the hypersaline lakes and

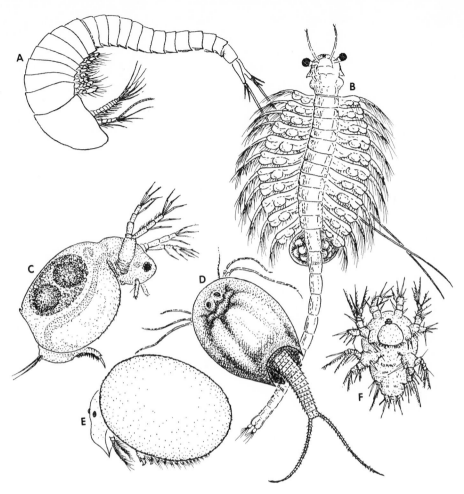

Fig. 3-4. Some crustaceans, including inhabitants of temporary ponds. **A,** *Hutchinsoniella,* Cephalocarida, marine; **B,** female *Artemia salina,* Anostraca from hypersaline waters; **C,** *Moina wierzejskii,* Cladocera; **D,** *Triops,* Notostraca; **E,** *Lynceus,* Conchostraca; **F,** crustacean metanauplius larva.

shallow northern lakes where prolonged ice and snow covers lead to anoxic conditions. Some Alaskan lakes are this shallow type, where the summer swimmer finds himself among a rich "temporary pond" fauna but in what appears to be a respectable body of water. The occurrence of these branchiopods is understandable since fish are wanting. However, the presence of *Lepidurus arcticus* (Notostraca) in permanent Norwegian lakes, where it serves as an item in trout diet, and of the conchostracan *Cyclestheria hislopi* in Lake Victoria (Hartland-Rowe 1972) is baffling when one believes

the branchiopods cannot tolerate predation.

The branchiopods were long considered the most primitive of the Crustacea, an assumption that was not entirely acceptable to many zoologists in light of the evidence supporting a marine origin of crustaceans. Howard L. Sanders' 1955 report of a small arthropod found in the bottom sediments of Long Island Sound eased the discomfort of those who felt that the most primitive living crustacean should be found somewhere in the sea rather than in vernal pools of snow melt or in desert rainwater depressions.

Sanders was a graduate student at Yale when he found puzzling specimens of a tiny crustacean in the marine sediments south of New Haven. His discovery represented far more than a new species or genus; it could only be reconciled with a new subclass the Cephalocarida. Perhaps now, with the elevation of the Crustacea to phylum or subphylum level, the Cephalocarida is better termed a class. Sanders assigned the animal to a new genus, *Hutchinsoniella* (Fig. 3-4, *A*), in honor of Professor G. E. Hutchinson. Since then at least three other members of the Cephalocarida have been discovered. The remarkable feature of *Hutchinsoniella* is that it seems to link the long-extinct trilobites and some puzzling fossil crustaceans with the modern living Crustacea. Furthermore, from some such *Hutchinsoniella*-like ancestor, it would be easy to derive at least the modern Malacostraca and Branchiopoda.

At present there are three orders of Branchiopoda; others are extinct. Some authors would raise the modern orders to four or lower them to two. In Paleozoic sediments assigned to the Devonian, fossils of Conchostraca and Anostraca have been found. The Anostraca are represented by the soft-bodied fairy shrimps and the brine shrimp, *Artemia,* of today (Fig. 3-4, *B*). Members of the Conchostraca superficially resemble shelled fairy shrimps; Pennak (1953) coined the name clam shrimp to emphasize their dorsally hinged valves (Fig. 3-4, *E*). Early fossils include marine, estuarine, and freshwater forms. Their resting eggs hatch to a metanauplius.

The third order of branchiopods, the Notostraca, now represented by *Triops* (Fig. 3-4, *D*) and *Lepidurus* and termed the tadpole shrimps by Pennak (1953), are known as fossils ranging from the Upper Carboniferous to Recent. They are now restricted, or nearly so, to temporary ponds.

A fourth order of the branchiopods could be the Cladocera (Figs. 3-4, *C,* and 3-7). An alternate scheme, adopted by Brooks (1959), is to join the Cladocera and the closely related conchostracans as the order Diplostraca composed of two suborders, or as a superorder embracing two orders.

It may be best to speak of the branchiopods other than the cladocerans as phyllopods—the branchiopods of temporary ponds, the stay-at-homes. The youngest group, the cladocerans, are everywhere but are a product of fresh water.

The Cladocera. The typical cladoceran is 1.5 mm long and has a distinct head and a body covered by an unhinged bivalved carapace. It has a single compound eye and a smaller eyespot, or ocellus. The first antennae, or antennules, are small, although larger in some males. The second antennae are large, branched swimming structures, the typical biramous crustacean appendage. Most species have five or six pairs of legs beneath the carapace. There is a posterior extension of the abdomen to form the postabdomen or abreptor, presumably formed from fusion because it terminates in a pair of claws; features of the postabdomen are very important in taxonomic determinations. There is a dorsal heart and a more posterior dorsal brood chamber beneath the carapace roof and over the upper part of the body. Here the eggs are held during development.

Typically the life cycle includes many generations of females parthenogenetically producing more females from diploid "eggs." There comes a time when some eggs develop into males, and meanwhile other females are producing haploid sexual eggs that require fertilization. The diploid males produce haploid gametes. The carapace surrounding the sexual eggs secretes a dark, sometimes sculptured case, the *ephippium,* which is shed at a subsequent molt. The ephippial eggs are the resistant, diapausing stage so characteristic of freshwater animals. They will hatch later as parthenogenic females. There are no larval stages.

It is significant that Cladocera of temporary ponds, such as certain species of the Daphniidae and Moinidae, produce better-developed and faster-developing ephippia than do the species from other families found in stable bodies of water.

Keys prepared for identification of Cladocera (Brooks 1959) usually feature female structures, because males appear so seldom. An exception is made in the genus *Moina* (Fig. 3-4, *C*), commonly found in temporary puddles and in short-lived sewage beds subjected to frequent drying. Here the male first antennae and ephippial structures are used to distinguish species (Goulden 1968).

The Cladocera arose relatively late, the first known fossil being from Oligocene strata. They are the most characteristic of freshwater animals and presumably were offshoots from the freshwater Conchostraca. Cladocerans are much like immature conchostracans—neoteny was probably involved in their evolution. A living conchostracan, *Cyclestheria hislopi,* is very similar to a cladoceran, having no larval stages and giving birth to "miniature adults." Also this conchostracan's eyes are united into a single cyclopean structure, recalling an early name for a cladoceran—*Monoculus.* The females of another conchostracan, the Panamanian *Gatuna spinifera* (perhaps conspecific with *C. hyslopi*), carry their young in a dorsal brood chamber well past the naupliar stages and may liberate them in the adult form, a most cladoceran-like feature.

Clams and others

The Sphaeriidae, or fingernail clams, are a group of little bivalved freshwater organisms with a long history of marine ancestry. They are hermaphroditic, and there are no larval stages. The fingernail clams are the only clams in temporary ponds of North America, although the exotic *Corbicula* is capable of surviving

drought in drained canals and ditches. One species of fingernail clam, *Sphaerium occidentale,* occurs in transitory forest pools and may require such habitats. As the water subsides, the clam moves down into the leafy sediments and diapauses in the adult form until the following spring when the pool fills again. Another sphaeriid genus, *Pisidium,* the tiny pea clam (Fig. 3-9), contains temporary pond species and others that are capable of some sort of dormancy in anaerobic lake waters.

The larger freshwater mussels (Unionaceae), now split into several families, are still loosely called the unionids. They are dioecious, and the females release a unique larva, the *glochidium,* that must either find a proper fish host to parasitize or die. This accounts for the lack of freshwater mussels in temporary ponds.

This discussion hardly touches on the fauna of impermanent waters: protozoans, flatworms, nematodes, rotifers, other crustaceans, snails, and insects are well represented in some pools, especially in humid areas.

THE PLANKTON

The plankton community is a mixed group of tiny plants and animals floating, drifting, or feebly swimming in the water mass. The name is owed to Hensen (1887), who applied it to what we would now call *seston.* Seston includes the living plankton and the nonliving particulate matter, termed *tripton.* The freshwater plankton lacks many elements that are abundant in the sea, where nearly every phylum is represented.

The individual plant, animal, or bacterium in the plankton community is called a *plankter.* The plant plankters compose the *phytoplankton,* and the animal plankters are the *zooplankton.* There are all sorts of schemes for classifying the plankton further; a division based on size is dealt with later.

The phytoplankton

Plankters have been the subject of many studies on adaptations for flotation. Oil droplets, gas bubbles, gelatinous envelopes, and water-filled and saccoid bodies are adaptations for reducing weight or specific gravity. Horns, spines, setae, and elongate stick-like bodies are some of the structures that increase total surface area and resistance to sinking. The weight-reducing factors and the increases in specific surface area are thought to function in response to viscosity of the medium, which is usually dependent on temperature. On this basis, flotation devices should be needed most in warm and least in cold water. There have been many studies on the effectiveness of these devices; just recently Conway and Trainor (1972) showed that *Scenedesmus* with bristles and spines has greater buoyancy than spineless types of this green alga. But observations of natural habitats at low and high temperatures often reveal some inadequacy in the scheme. Sometimes the structures needed for buoyancy are absent in habitats where we believe they would be necessary.

One theoretical consideration of cell shape in phytoplankters has been largely overlooked. It may be difficult for us to comprehend the watery world of the planker, since we exist at an interface where there is an abrupt density difference of 27,000 times (earth and atmosphere). Hutchinson (1970a) tells us that cellular properties interacting with water turbulence to determine sinking rates may be as important as the familiar skeletal and muscular structures interacting with gravity. The structure of an organism depends on where it lives. Adaptations for sinking have been almost completely ignored. Munk and Riley (1952) theorized that a phytoplankton cell will absorb nutrients by diffusion and forced convection, the current relative to the cell as it sinks. A plankton cell such as a diatom absorbs nutrients as it sinks, which is the only way it can move from the impover-

ished envelope of water immediately surrounding it. We can appreciate the security enjoyed by plants rooted in lotic environments constantly washed by water containing fresh nutrients, in contrast to the nourishment of phytoplankters.

Size, shape, and density determine the rate of sinking for algal cells. As they sink, the cells divide, some of the lighter daughter cells standing a good chance of being swept to upper layers again by turbulence. Munk and Riley's work shows that phytoplankton adaptations include response to three problems: flotation, absorption, and herbivory. In large diatoms the first two are the most important; in smaller forms the grazers present the greatest threat. On the basis of Munk and Riley's computations and conclusions, it is evident that marine phytoplankters are not just a bunch of cells floating in a willy-nilly manner.

Although the lacustrine phytoplankton is taxonomically diverse, it can be divided into two main groups on the basis of size. The *net plankters* are retained by the silk of a plankton net; the *nannoplankton* includes the tiny algae not captured by the net. The gauge of the bolting silk used in constructing the net is relevant here. The no. 20 mesh net, a very popular size, has interstices of about 63 μm; no. 25 silk, usually the finest employed, has mesh openings of 50 μm. A rather coarse no. 12 silk has mesh openings of 106 μm.

Various limits have been put on the size of the nannoplankton. Dussart (1966) presented a scheme in which nannoplankters are from 2 to 20 μm, those smaller than 2 μm being the ultranannoplankton. Hutchinson (1967) lists the nannoplankton (-seston, -tripton) with linear dimensions from 5 to 60 μm, and the ultra classification from 0.5 to 5 μm. There are further subdivisions for the seston particles larger than 60 μm. The 60 μm limit is close to what the no. 20 silk would separate into net plankton and nannoplankton.

The nannoplankton can be estimated in

at least three ways. First, an adequate sample of water that has passed through the silk of a plankton net is saved. Some can be preserved in a small glass cylinder and the cells allowed to settle over a period of time. An inverted microscope, with which one examines the settled cells from the bottom of the cylinder, is handy in counting them. An early method of separating the nannoplankton cells was based on using a centrifuge that spun the water out and concentrated the cells, just as cream is separated from the heavier milk. With the invention of membrane filters, water that has been strained through the plankton net can be subsequently filtered by using membranes or fiberglass filters that stop all algal cells.

Former generalizations held that the nannoplankton was composed of minute chlorophyllous algae. Now it is obvious that bacterial cells are very much a part of the plankton assemblage. Usually investigations show that nannoplankton biomass, chlorophyll, and production surpass those of the algae retained by the net. The report of Kalff (1972) following a 2-year study of Lac Hertel, a small eutrophic lake in Quebec, is typical. Seventy-seven percent of the mean annual production was owed to the nannoplankton. Kalff defined the nannoplankton algae as those smaller than 64 μm. The very obvious bluegreen and diatom complex was photosynthetically inefficient by comparison.

Within the net phytoplankton or the nannoplankton, individual species may be doing far more than their share of the autotrophic work. Stull (1971) found that the uptake of ^{14}C by phytoplankton was often out of proportion to numerical dominance in Castle Lake, California. Using autoradiography, she showed that species that took up most of the carbon were sometimes greatly outnumbered by inactive species.

According to Findenegg (1971), the differences in photosynthetic activity of phytoplankton in 30 alpine lakes were due largely to the varied composition of the algal communities from lake to lake. Using an *activity coefficient,* the ratio of carbon assimilated in photosynthesis to carbon content in the algae, he found that chlorophyceans were above the mean and that the diatom populations were somewhat below average. The activity coefficient of the small flagellate *Cryptomonas* (Fig. 3-3, *B*) was ten times higher than that of *Oscillatoria rubescens,* the bluegreen that made up the least active community.

In North temperate regions a common annual cycle of the phytoplankters is a spring bloom of diatoms, followed by a summertime bluegreen predominance, and a second diatom bloom in late fall and early winter before the ice cover. Such a succession would be revealed by a summer peak in the chlorophyll *a*/chlorophyll *c* ratio.

On the basis of existing reports in the literature, Williams (1969) generalized that the phytoplankton of oligotrophic lakes includes such members as the desmid *Staurastrum* (Fig. 3-2, *D*), the chrysophyte *Dinobryon* (Fig. 3-3, *D*), noted for its intolerance of anything but low phosphate concentrations, and the diatoms *Tabellaria* and *Cyclotella* (Fig. 3-3, *I*). The eutrophic lake, however, has a different group of diatoms and a mixed crop of bluegreens that may eventually replace them. The filamentous diatom *Melosira* (Fig. 3-3, *F*) and *Stephanodiscus,* a form similar to *Cyclotella,* appear first. Then with agricultural runoff or increased erosion due to stripping forest cover, the beautiful *Asterionella* (Fig. 3-3, *C*) appears, perhaps in response to a need for soil substances. Later another diatom, *Fragilaria* (Fig. 3-3, *H*), shows up, if sewage enters the lake. Various paleolimnologic studies have shown that this may be a good generalization about the sequence of organisms. Recently, Moss (1972a) discussed eutrophication in Gull Lake, Michigan, the site of Michigan State University's Biology Station, and cited evidence for a diatom sequence very similar to that outlined above.

The zooplankton

The zooplankton of inland waters derives its members mainly from the Protozoa, the Rotatoria, the Cladocera, and the Copepoda. In addition, there are occasional minor elements contributed by ostracod crustaceans, water mites (arachnids), larval molluscs such as *Dreissena* in Europe, mysid crustaceans (Fig. 3-9, *B*), and the larva of the insect *Chaoborus* (Fig. 2-2, *C*).

The Protozoa. The protozoans (Fig. 3-5) are mostly nannoplankters about which little is known. A few larger species are trapped by the net, but often these should be classified with the phytoplankton (for example, *Volvox, Dinobryon, Ceratium*). The Rhizopoda, or Sarcodina, include some shelled forms, which occur abundantly at times in limnetic waters and are retained by plankton nets. These are the members of the Testacea, such as *Difflugia* (Fig. 3-5, *C*), and of the Heliozoa, such as *Actinophrys.*

The *Difflugia* species build tests (hard shells around themselves) of tiny sand grains and are able to float with the aid of gas vacuoles. We owe much of our knowledge of these shelled amoeboid forms to Schönborn (1962), who studied the biology of *Difflugia limnetica.* In early summer this testacean rises from littoral sediments to become limnetic (pelagic); in October it sinks to the sediments and forms a winter cyst. During the spring months it is a member of the littoral microbenthos. (This cycle is rather typical of plankton organisms, both plant and animal.) The distinction between benthos

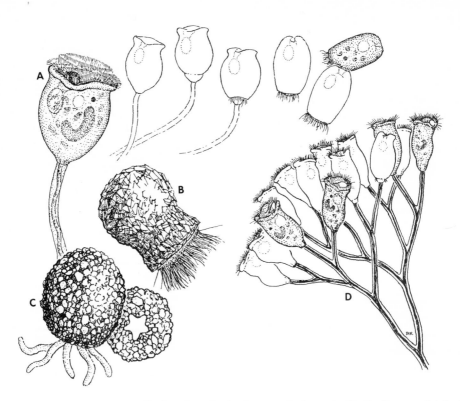

Fig. 3-5. Some protozoans occasionally found in the freshwater plankton. **A,** *Vorticella,* a peritrich ciliate, its free-swimming telotroch stage shown at right; **B,** *Codonella cratera,* a tintinnid ciliate; **C,** *Difflugia lobostoma,* Testacea, Rhizopoda; **D,** *Zoothamnium,* a peritrich ciliate.

and plankton communities is hazy because of the movements between the two. Quite often plankters cannot be found in collections from the open water, because they are resting in some sort of cyst or diapausing form in the bottom deposits.

The tintinnid ciliates are much like *Difflugia* in that they build tests of foreign particles. Indeed, *Codonella cratera* (Fig. 3-5, *B*), a common limnoplankter, was originally described as a species of *Difflugia* on the basis of its test. There are about 1,000 tintinnids, but most are marine. These ciliates are true plankters, grazing on small diatoms and chrysomonads. Another genus, *Tintinnidium*, is probably less abundant than *Codonella* in inland plankton communities.

The peritrich ciliates include several genera, most of which are epizoic or *aufwuchs* forms. The telotroch stage of *Vorticella* (Fig. 3-5, *A*) occasionally swarms throughout the lake and shows up in plankton collections. A colonial, branched peritrich, *Zoothamnium limneticum* (Fig. 3-5, *D*), is said to be a euplankter (true plankton form), feeding on bacteria and nannoplankton algae. In general, there are many ciliates in the plankton habitat about which we know little, because they become distorted and unrecognizable when preserved and because they are not easily retained in plankton nets.

The Rotatoria. Relatively few genera of the rotifers have planktonic forms, yet certain species are to be found in most collections of lake plankton. A typical plankton form is *Asplanchna* (Fig. 3-6, *A*); it is the largest of the rotifers (0.5 to 1.2 mm) and is predaceous. Its transparent body is sac-like and filled with watery fluids that reduce its specific gravity. It is a "plankton predator," a secondary consumer, or first-level carnivore in planktonic ecosystems. It is a viviparous species, the parthenogenic young developing within the mother's body.

Synchaeta (Fig. 3-6, *G*) is another transparent and predaceous rotifer. There are thirty or more species, of which a few appear in the lake plankton assemblage. Its adaptations to planktonic life, reduction of specific gravity by inflating the body as a water-filled sac, are the same as those of *Asplanchna*. Its dimensions are at the most 0.6 mm, and it is far less saccoid than *Asplanchna*.

The colonial *Conochilus* forms spherical colonies, the individual rotifers extending from a central gelatinous matrix that is said to reduce specific gravity.

Most planktonic rotifers have done away with the "foot and toes," attachment organs common to many other species. This is true of such organisms as *Synchaeta*, *Asplanchna*, and *Polyarthra* (Fig. 3-6, *B*). The last is characterized by six paddle-shaped or feather-like swimming devices; it is one of the commonest planktonic genera. *Hexarthra* (Fig. 3-6, *F*) has also done away with the foot and has muscular swimming or leaping devices bearing feathery setae. *Filinia* (Fig. 3-6, *C*) trails long bristles that can be flicked instantaneously to make the animal "jump."

The other common planktonic rotifers are loricate, possessing a shell. The loricas of *Kellicottia* (Fig. 3-6, *E*) and *Keratella* (Fig. 3-6, *D*) have projecting, elongate, and immovable spines. The species of *Brachionus* (Fig. 3-6, *H*) have openings in their loricas through which they project their "feet." Certain species, such as *Brachionus rubens*, use this foot as an attachment organ, holding on to cladocerans in a manner recalling the peritrich ciliate *Epistylis*. These loricate species are particulate feeders probably belonging to the herbivorous or primary-consumer trophic level that graze on plant cells, bacteria, and detritus.

Hardly a collection of plankton can be examined without finding a species of *Keratella*. In North America *Keratella cochlearis* is the most frequently encountered planktonic rotifer.

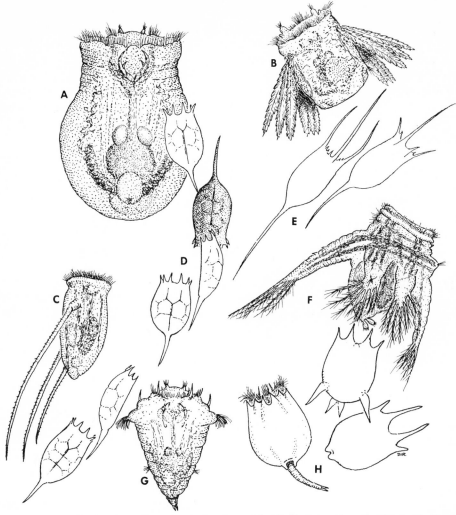

Fig. 3-6. Some common planktonic rotifers. **A,** *Asplanchna sieboldi;* **B,** *Polyarthra;* **C,** *Filinia;* **D,** *Keratella cochlearis;* **E,** *Kellicottia;* **F,** *Hexarthra;* **G,** *Synchaeta;* **H,** *Brachionus plicatilis, B. calyciflorus* (two at right).

The Cladocera. Among the common North American cladoceran plankters (Fig. 3-7) are the species of *Daphnia* (Fig. 3-7, *B*), *Diaphanosoma* (Fig. 3-7, *F*), and *Bosmina* (Fig. 3-7, *C*). *Ceriodaphnia lacustris* (Fig. 3-7, *D*) occurs in limnetic communities of some lakes, and *Chydorus sphaericus* (Fig. 3-9, *D*) often clambers about on planktonic blue-green algae. In small ponds, *Simocephalus* may be found, but it is usually close to the bottom in the shallows of larger lakes. These species are filter feeders, serving as prey for the so-called plankton predators.

In northern lakes, the Holarctic *Leptodora* occurs (Fig. 3-7, *A*). This is a transparent crustacean, the largest of the cladocerans, and is noteworthy on several accounts. It rises at night to prey on the other zooplankton. At this time it is easily collected, but during the day it is not readily found. It has a greatly reduced carapace, consisting of no more than a bubble-like dorsal brood pouch. It is parthenogenic during the summer, but males appear in late fall, and fertilized eggs serve as the overwintering stage. At the vernal overturn, these sexual eggs

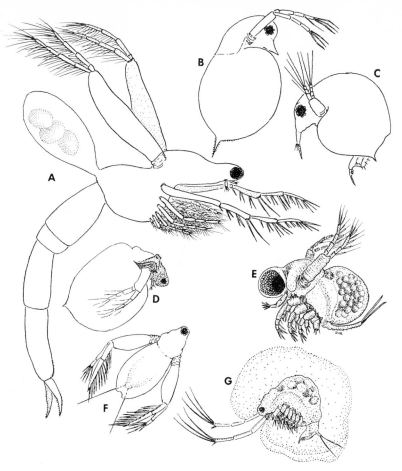

Fig. 3-7. Some planktonic cladocerans. **A,** *Leptodora kindtii;* **B,** *Daphnia rosea;* **C,** *Bosmina longirostris;* **D,** *Ceriodaphnia lacustris;* **E,** *Polyphemus pediculus;* **F,** *Diaphanosoma;* **G,** *Holopedium gibberum.*

hatch to release a naupliar stage, quite unlike the other Cladocera. Holarctic *Leptodora* remains have been found in the postglacial deposits, and it is theorized to have evolved sometime in the Pleistocene. It is an aberrant form, and some authors have questioned whether it is a true cladoceran; others say that its naupliar stage simply relates back to its ancestral condition: it retains the old conchostracan metanauplius.

In the shallows of northern lakes there is another curious cladoceran, *Polyphemus* (Fig. 3-7, *E*). This is an active form, darting about in a jerky fashion, and it is also a predator. It lacks a well-developed carapace, simply retaining the brood pouch, as does *Leptodora*. *Polyphemus* belongs to the group Polyphemoidea, with many more representatives in the Old World. In the Caspian Sea complex a host of endemic species have arisen. The marine cladocerans belonging to the genera *Evadne* and *Podon* are probably derived from freshwater polyphemoids.

A form said to be limited to waters low in calcium is *Holopedium* (Fig. 3-7, *G*), often presented as the typical planktonic cladoceran. It has unusual second antennae that lack the biramous condition; they are flexible, unbranched structures. Most peculiar, however, is the gelatinous coat it secretes as an encasement. This is thought to be an elaboration for better flotation.

Cyclomorphosis in rotifers, limnetic dinoflagellates, and cladocerans has engaged some limnologists for years. This is a form of polymorphism where all members of a species vary seasonally in their body form. The environmental cues that trigger the changes and the possible adaptive significance of these changes have been sought by limnologists. Brooks and Dodson (1965) showed that the composition of the zooplankton changes when planktivorous fish, such as *Alosa,* enter a lake. As predators appear, large plankters disappear and are replaced by smaller species, which are not preferred food items. Zaret (1972) discusses this and another type of polymorphism, where two morphs co-occur temporally but are separated spatially. Thus *Ceriodaphnia cornuta* has a small-eyed, reproductively inferior morph that survives in the presence of planktivorous fish. The other morph can be found elsewhere in the lake where predaceous fish are scarce. In these areas where predation is lessened, the vulnerable morph is not endangered by the visual cue afforded by its larger, black eye. According to Zaret, seasonal predation pressure can account for much of the cyclomorphosis seen in zooplankton.

The Copepoda. The copepods are a tremendous group of 10,000 or more species. Most are in the sea, but a handful have come to fresh water, where there are three main groups, the Harpacticoida, the Cyclopoida, and the Calanoida (Fig. 3-8). The harpacticoids (Fig. 3-8, *D*) are mostly litoral microbenthic forms or members of the *psammon.* The cyclopoids (Fig. 3-8, *B*) are found in a variety of habitats, from caves, wells, and small puddles to the open waters of the largest lakes. Most of them are littoral, and only a few are typically limnetic. The calanoids, however, are all open-water plankters, if we overlook some deep sea species said to be benthic.

The Copepoda brought the typical nauplius larva of the marine crustacean to fresh waters. In cyclopoids there are usually five naupliar stages followed by six *copepodid* stages, which give the distinct appearance of a copepod. The sixth copepodid stage is the adult. The calanoids differ by having six distinct nauplii before the first copepodid form.

The common calanoid in North America, *Diaptomus* (Fig. 3-8, *E*), is divided into subgenera. The Europeans have raised these to generic rank, and it is hoped that eventually this will be done in North America, since studies of the zoogeography of the diaptomids would profit from this splitting. The genus *Diaptomus,* being widespread, tells us little; but when the subgenera are raised to generic level, we see interesting patterns of distribution from continent to continent.

Diaptomus is found in temporary waters, small ponds, and large lakes. In most instances temporary pond forms differ specifically from small pond species or big lake inhabitants. They have an interesting geographic distribution and provide a fascinating ecologic picture. Unlike the cyclopoids, there are no cosmopolitan diaptomids.

Diaptomus is essentially a filter feeder straining out phytoplankton cells. In large lakes members of this genus are usually transparent and often rather small. There are exceptions to this in some large northern lakes. In temporary ponds large red species are common, and in small alpine lakes (high-altitude lakes) and northern ponds some large species have become predaceous (Anderson 1967).

Diaptomus and the filter-feeding Cladocera convert the proteins, fats, and carbohydrates produced by the phytoplankton into animal tissue. In the seas the calanoids are relatively more important for this conversion, because the oceans do not have a comparable cladoceran fauna.

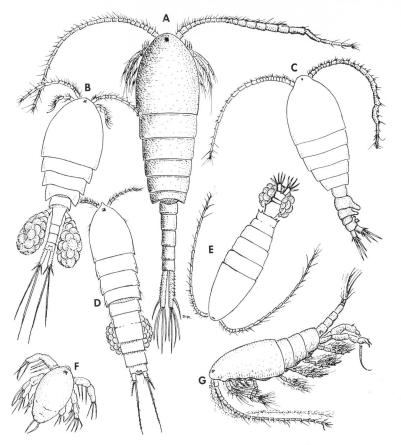

Fig. 3-8. Some copepods of inland waters. **A,** *Limnocalanus macrurus,* Centropagidae, Calanoida, male; **B,** *Eucyclops serrulatus,* Cyclopoida, female; **C,** *Epischura lacustris,* Temoridae, Calanoida, male; **D,** *Cantho-camptus,* Harpacticoida, female; **E,** *Diaptomus siciloides,* Diaptomidae, Calanoida, female; **F,** nauplius larva of *Diaptomus;* **G,** *Senecella calanoides,* Pseudocalanidae, Calanoida, male.

The Diaptomidae include only fresh-water species. Some other calanoids found in inland bodies of water are from marine families. The Centropagidae is a marine group, but two species of *Limno-calanus* (Fig. 3-8, *A*) occur in North America, and there are continental species of *Calamoecia* in Australia. The Te-moridae have given us *Heterocope, Epis-chura* (Fig. 3-8, *C*), and *Eurytemora; Sen-ecella* (Fig. 3-8 *G*) represents the Pseudo-calanidae.

In North American lakes the cyclopoids *Tropocyclops prasinus, Meso-cyclops edax,* and *Cyclops bicuspidatus (C. thomasi)* are common in the zoo-plankton. The last two are probably pre-

daceous forms. The cyclopoids in general have biting mouth parts and chew on ei-ther plant material or animals. In Europe-an waters and elsewhere *Mesocyclops leuckarti* takes the place of *M. edax,* and it would be possible to list many shared and replacement species in the plankton of different parts of the world. In general, there are just a few truly open-water cyclopoids, and they are probably plank-ton predators in most instances. The cyclopoids have probably been in fresh water for a long time; many species are nearly cosmopolitan.

Cyclops bicuspidatus was the first known of many cyclopoids that have the trick of escaping from the plankton and becoming microbenthic. This mechanism occurs at the fourth copepodid stage in *C. bicuspidatus,* when the entire population moves to the deep and burrows into anaerobic sediments, diapausing for months before returning to the upper waters to mature and mate.

The insect *Chaoborus.* The flies assigned to the genus *Chaoborus* (see Fig. 2-2, *C*) are closely related to the mosquitoes (Culicidae). Some authorities consider *Chaoborus* to belong to a subfamily of the Culicidae; others have placed them in their own family, the Chaoboridae.

The lake-dwelling larvae of *Chaoborus* are most abundant in dystrophic and eutrophic waters; they do occur in oligotrophic lakes, although this is unusual. The larvae are very transparent, bear prehensile antennae at the apex of a rostral extension of the head, and have four conspicuous, pigmented air sacs.

The larvae have been the object of many experiments that test their hardiness and general resistance to anoxia and starvation. They have been known to survive 2 or 3 weeks in anaerobic water, which in nature would be an unusual stress, except in populations trapped beneath an ice cover in rich, shallow ponds where deoxygenation has come about.

Typically, the larvae spend the day in the hypolimnion, either in the profundal sediments or immediately above. Toward sunset they, like another transparent predator, *Leptodora,* start their ascent to the upper waters where they feed on microcrustaceans and rotifers. They are plankton predators and secondary consumers, except when they prey on such forms as *Leptodora* and *Asplanchna,* thereby functioning as tertiary consumers.

The pigmented gas bladders of the larvae serve to move them from the deeps to the upper layers. The mechanism is apparently an expansion of the pigment cells that make up the wall of the sacs. It enlarges the sacs and thus decreases the density, and the larva is then able to balloon up from the anaerobic water that it sometimes must endure to the aerobic hunting grounds. These bladders also serve as targets for echo sounders; the daily migrations of *Chaoborus* have been studied by echo location (Malueg and Hasler 1966).

Chaoborus belongs to three worlds. It is found in dredge samples from profundal sediments, where it is a part of the benthos; it is captured by net near the lake surface at night; and after four larval instars have passed, it forms a bizarre motile pupa that rises to the surface to metamorphose and take wing as a little mosquito-like fly which, happily, has nonbiting mouth parts.

Glaciomarine relicts and other plankters. A cluster of animals with their closest relatives in ocean habitats are lumped as glaciomarine relict species (Fig. 3-9). They occur in deep, cold oligotrophic lakes distributed in a rough circle from northern Germany and the Scandinavian countries to Siberia, Canada, and the northern United States. The Baltic Sea Basin may have been a center in the transition of these animals from salt to fresh water. One theory states that, where heavy Pleistocene glaciation depressed land that was inundated by the sea and subject to later upwarping, some species were stranded in "relict" lakes. Other notions are that some of these species were living in dilute waters during preglacial times and that proglacial lakes, in contact with ice and marginal to it, provided a migratory path. As a result, there are many species with marine affinities living in the deeps of northern lakes. Holmquist (1962) rejects the word "relict" for these organisms because most are not detached remnants of existing marine populations past or present. A marine relict, she points out, is exemplified nicely by *Zostera* (eelgrass), a widespread littoral marine angiosperm that exists in the Caspian Sea. The Caspian was formerly

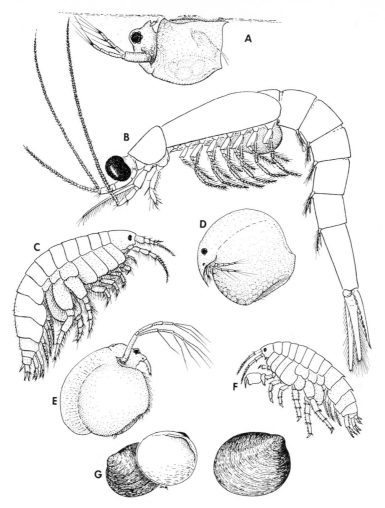

Fig. 3-9. Miscellaneous lacustrine species of special interest. **A,** *Scapholeberis kingi,* female; a hyponeustonic cladoceran. **B,** *Mysis relicta,* female, a nektonic glaciomarine relict from northern lakes. **C,** *Pontoporeia affinis,* female; a benthic glaciomarine relict amphipod. **D,** *Chydorus sphaericus;* a common chydorid cladoceran. **E,** *Bunops* sp.; a macrothricid cladoceran. **F,** *Hyalella azteca,* male; a North American amphipod. **G,** *Pisidium conventus;* a cold-water sphaeriid clam.

part of the oceans, but was isolated through uplifting.

The relict concept probably is overstressed with regard to such copepods as *Limnocalanus macrurus* and *Senecella calanoides,* although they represent marine families. Their present distribution, nearly circumpolar, and their restriction to northern oligotrophic lakes implies, however, spreading via proglacial lakes. *Eurytemora* is different. It seems to be actively invading fresh water

even today and has recently appeared in Lake Erie (Engel 1962).

Mysis relicta (Fig. 3-9, *B*) belongs to a large marine order, the Mysidacea. Although not a copepod, *Mysis* must be discussed with the glaciomarine species. It is believed to have spread from the Baltic region via proglacial lakes. Today it is considered both a deep-water plankton species and a member of the profundal benthos in northern oligotrophic lakes.

Because *Mysis* is a strong swimmer,

moving independently of turbulence, it is classified as *nekton* by some authors. Fishes are more typical of this category, but there is a hazy distinction between plankton and nekton.

The amphipods belong to the peracaridian crustaceans along with the mysids and the isopods (better known because of the familiar terrestrial "sow bugs"). Most of the amphipods are marine; those in fresh water are mostly stream dwellers or benthic forms in the shallow weed beds of lakes. One third of the freshwater amphipod crustaceans, comprising a "species flock" of endemic forms, occur in Lake Baikal. Some are planktonic, especially *Macrohectopus,* a substantial forage item for the fish of that ancient lake.

Other planktonic amphipods in fresh water are scarce. Interestingly, in Montezuma Well, Arizona, where no fish are found, the common *Hyalella azteca* (Fig. 3-9, *F*) is planktonic. It makes daily migrations, rising nocturnally to the surface. These vertical migrations are minor compared with those of *Macrohectopus. Hyalella* thrives in the littoral vegetation of North American lakes, but rarely ventures into open water where fish are found.

THE BENTHOS

The benthos is composed of bottom-dwelling organisms and has the obvious phylogenetic divisions of phytobenthos and zoobenthos. Further categories are based on the lake region—littoral, sublittoral, and profundal—and size of the organisms. The study of benthic forms has generally involved the use of sieves in separating organisms from the sediments. The sieves usually have mesh openings from 0.833 mm to 0.417 mm, ranging from the U. S. Sieve Series no. 20 to the finer no. 40 screen. The *macrobenthic* forms are retained by the meshes of a sieve, while the *microbenthic* species pass through the interstices of a no. 40 screening device. The category *meiobenthos* for intermediate organisms is useful to marine biologists but has little value in freshwater studies.

The phytobenthos

The phytobenthos includes the aquatic macrophytes and the bottom-dwelling algae. The former are the larger "pondweeds," including forms with terrestrial pasts, their ancestors having moved from land to the water. There are other important large plants that are considered to be algae and closely related to the chlorophyceans. These are the Charophyta, including *Chara* and *Nitella.* Some species of *Chara* owe their name "stonewort" to the encrusting calcareous coverings they form on their "stems" in hard-water lakes. *Nitella* is a delicate plant found in acidic and dilute waters; it is not calcified.

Generally speaking, the spermatophytes have contributed most to the littoral flora, the largest family being the Potamogetonaceae, the pondweeds. In North America roughly 20 families of the monocotyledons and 30 of the dicotyledons have aquatic representatives.

The mosses (Bryophyta) and ferns (Pteridophyta) have contributed relatively few species to aquatic environments; the latter especially are poorly represented and are considered curiosities. Several species of moss and the pteridophyte *Isöetes* extend into deep water of transparent lakes.

The zonation seen in aquatic plants of the littoral zone is due to more than one factor. Wave action and the physical and chemical nature of the substrate are obviously important. Spence and Chrystal (1970ab) found a nice correlation between depth distribution and the inherent photosynthetic ability of some species of *Potamogeton*. Deep-water species, such as *P. praelongus* and *P. obtusifolius,* are more shade tolerant and carry on photosynthesis at light intensities too dim for the maximum efficiency of a shallow-water form, such as *P. polygonifolius.*

The littoral macrophytes support epiphytic algae and attached animals such as bryozoans. Snails and other organisms crawl over the weeds, consuming the epiphytic plants. Berg (1950) and McGaha (1952) showed that the pondweeds are extremely important to immature insects from various orders. Leaf miners and channelers devour the plant tissue, while other insects are adapted for living in rolled-up leaves, where they trap planktonic forms. These authors showed that the weeds are far more than clinging, hiding, and nesting places for animals, an idea that had been put forth more than 30 years earlier.

In recent years it has been found that the macrophytes not only take up inorganic nutrients from the water and sediments but also release quantities of dissolved and organic compounds that play a part in the lake's economy (Wetzel 1969; Allen 1971).

The spongy tissues of many aquatic plants store metabolic gases (Hartman and Brown 1967), letting them out at times that only serve to confuse the student of photosynthesis. Sometimes oxygen released to surrounding lake water at night was produced hours earlier in the daylight; the diel oxygen curve in the adjacent lake water is anomalous as a result of this delay.

Most submersed aquatic plants are extremely susceptible to desiccation soon after being hauled from the water. On the other hand, the floating leaves of water lilies are waxy coated and have unusual resistance to desiccation.

The highest known rates of primary production in natural communities come from beds of emergent reeds and rushes. Such plants stand rooted in fertile soils with available water resources unknown to terrestrial plants and are exposed to solar radiation far in excess of that energy available to the submersed phototrophs deeper in the lake.

The zoobenthos

The littoral zoobenthos is extremely varied when compared with that of deeper regions, obviously a reflection of the abundant microhabitats. Protozoans, sponges, coelenterates, rotifers, nematodes, bryozoans, decapods, ostracods, cladocerans, copepods, pelecypods, gastropods, insects, and predaceous leeches are abundant in the shallows.

A unique feature of the littoral benthos is its nearness to the plankton. Littoral bottom samples often include planktonic forms, which serve as a source of nourishment for littoral animals. However, these plankton organisms are available to the benthos of deeper regions only after they have died, settled, and undergone some mineralization.

The microbenthic fauna may be more important in lake production than generally realized. Kajak and Rybak (1966) found that the microbenthic fauna contributed up to 50% of the benthic production in rich Polish lakes. The microbenthic fauna in eutrophic lakes of the United States has been investigated by Moore (1939) and Cole (1955). Their research involved some interesting burrowing and creeping entomostracans.* One group of these littoral microcrustaceans, the chydorid cladocerans, is especially noteworthy.

Most arthropods of an aquatic habitat leave scanty remains after death, but certain cladocerans are exceptions. The head shields and carapaces of *Bosmina* are especially resistant, while *Daphnia, Diaphanosoma,* and the copepods that are part of the limnoplankton leave little

---

*The small crustaceans have been called entomostracans since the time when they were lumped as Entomostraca, a name no longer valid. The term is useful, however, to designate cladocerans, ostracods, and copepods, which are related mainly by being small.

in the way of chitinous relics.* The most remarkable example of resistance comes from a family of Cladocera, the Chydoridae. They are typical of the littoral region, but following death parts of their bodies are swept lakeward. The result is that a sample of surficial sediment taken offshore, perhaps near the center of a small lake, contains the head shields, carapaces, and perhaps postabdomens of all the chydorid species living in the lake.

Today the chydorid crustaceans are the most-studied family of Cladocera. We are indebted to David G. Frey for giving impetus to this branch of research by pointing out methods by which sedimentary chydorid relics can be identified as to specific rank (Frey 1959). Since the late 1950's he and his students have shed light on some taxonomic and ecologic riddles in the group. Fryer (1968), supplementing the work performed by the Frey school, related the chydorid's anatomy to its ecologic role. It is now possible to gain more paleolimnologic insight from core samples than ever before, although knowledge of the biology of the chydorid Cladocera has just started to be gathered.

When we move to the sublittoral region, we find that species diversity drops sharply. Some unionid clams, ostracod crustaceans, copepods, and cladocerans from the littoral region are there, but very few are typically sublittoral dwellers.

In the eutrophic profundal zone the macrobenthic list is more impoverished. Interestingly, a species or two of the sphaeriid genus *Pisidium* may be in pro-

fundal ooze; they become dormant during anaerobic periods. This recalls the hardy species of *Sphaerium* and *Pisidium* in temporary ponds, burrowing and diapausing during the dry phase.

The profundal zone is most interesting from an overall limnologic point of view. Beneath hypolimnetic waters the dark environment can impose stress to which organisms in shallower depths are not subjected. The profundal sediments in a eutrophic lake lie below water that is quite different from the water overlying sublittoral and littoral deposits. Generally, the water is colder, lower in dissolved oxygen and pH, and higher in carbon dioxide, methane, bicarbonate, organic compounds, phosphorus, and nitrogen compounds, including ammonia. The environment is apt to be a chemically reducing one, the redox potential being low; this means there is an excess of reducing substances over oxidizing ones. The reducing substances in hypolimnetic waters and in the organic ooze compete with the animals for oxygen.

In some respects the eutrophic profundal benthos resembles the fauna of grossly polluted waters or of hypersaline desert lakes. Comparatively few species can survive such conditions, and there is little diversity. Low diversities mean "monotony"—a great number of individuals, but only one or two species represented. This is what would characterize a polluted environment. Below the sewage outfall in a stream, diversity is much lower than farther downstream where unfavorable conditions have ameliorated somewhat and more species have colonized.

The oligotrophic profundal benthos is more diverse than the bottom fauna of eutrophic lakes. A varied group of animals live in the firm, oxygenated sediment-water interface at the bottom of oligotrophic lakes. Most of these animals are intolerant of low oxygen tensions, such as found in eutrophic lakes. Midge

---

*Chitin, known especially from the exoskeletons of arthropods, occurs also in the jaws and gut lining of annelids, in the radulae of gastropods, and in nematode egg cases. Chemically, it is very similar to cellulose. Chitin is linked to protein, but boiling in strong alkali removes the protein, leaving almost pure chitin. There are many chitin-destroying fungi and bacteria and some soil protozoans, nematodes, and earthworms that show chitinase activity.

larvae belonging to the genera *Orthocladius, Tanytarsus, Calopsectra,* and *Sergentia* are forerunners of a monotonous *Chironomus plumosus* type of fauna, which prevails if eutrophy occurs and oxygen is at a premium in the summer hypolimnion. Tubificid worms of the Oligochaeta are represented by several species in aerated, unpolluted sediments. According to Brinkhurst (1966), the occurrence of *Limnodrilus hoffmeisteri* nearly alone and in great abundance would indicate pollution. A prime example of the loss of diversity with pollution and oxygen reduction comes from the western basin of Lake Erie. Once the sensitive mayfly *Hexagenia,* along with many other high-oxygen-requiring forms, occurred in numbers. Then it reached such nuisance proportions that the swarming adults were known as either Yankee soldiers or Canadian soldiers, depending on which side of the border you made your home. The mayflies have been gone for about 20 years now, and a chironomid-tubificid fauna has replaced them (Carr and Hiltunen 1965).

The cold oligotrophic lakes to the north have a special fauna consisting of at least four widely separated taxa. There is a little assemblage of bottom forms that have a similar Holarctic geographic distribution and may have migrated via proglacial lakes, marginal to Pleistocene ice. These species are found today in northern oligotrophic lakes. Henson (1966) reviews them in a paper on the benthos of the Laurentian Great Lakes. One of these, *Mysis relicta,* has already been mentioned. Another, the amphipod crustacean *Pontoporeia affinis* (Fig. 3-9, *C*), is a member of the marine Haustoriidae and occurs in brackish water of the Baltic Sea and many Eurasian freshwater lakes. It has been collected from about 50 oligotrophic lakes in glaciated North America.

A cold-stenothermal sphaeriid, *Pisidium conventus* (Fig. 3-9, *G*), has a geographic distribution much like that of *Pontoporeia,* although probably restricted to freshwater lakes. A comparison of the rich North American *Pisidium* fauna with that of Europe suggests that it moved in the opposite direction from *Pontoporeia.* The occurrence of *Mysis, Pontoporeia,* and *Pisidium conventus* in oligotrophic Green Lake, the deepest of Wisconsin's inland lakes, is typical today.

A fourth species, the chironomid *Heterotrissocladius subpilosus,* is an example of an oligostenothermal (restricted narrowly to cold temperatures) fly found in the Laurentian Great Lakes but never found at depths less than 20 m. There has been taxonomic confusion, and this species went unrecognized in North America until rather recently. According to Henson (1966), it is a deep-water larva, and the mating adults swarm over the water far from shore. The Swedish specialist Brundin considers this midge to be the best indicator of ultraoligotrophic lakes in Europe (Brundin 1958).

The profundal benthos of eutrophic lakes is distinguished by a few hardy forms that can tolerate low levels of oxygen. A typical macroscopic assemblage would include: bright red midge larvae of the genus *Chironomus;* a few species of oligochaete worms, *Limnodrilus* being a common genus; tiny sphaeriid clams belonging to the genus *Pisidium;* and the phantom larva of the dipteran *Chaoborus.* There are a few microscopic forms present, although they are often overlooked. If conditions are not too severe, some ciliates *(Loxodes, Coleps, Rhagadostoma,* and *Metopus)* and other protozoans (the rhizopod *Pelomyxa* and flagellates such as *Bodo, Chilomonas, Monas,* and *Phacotus)* may be found in or near the sediments. The rotifer *Rotaria rotatoria* and nematodes belonging to the genus *Trilobus* are especially hardy in low oxygen conditions.

Some of these forms occur in polluted

habitats, where oxygen is also in short supply. If anaerobic spells are lengthy, however, even the hardy species show signs of stress. Chironomid larvae reduce the time spent in feeding and increase the respiratory undulations, finally ceasing even that and becoming anoxybiont when the oxygen falls to 0.5 mg/liter. *Pisidium* closes its valves tightly and becomes dormant during prolonged anaerobic periods. *Chaoborus* is not so hard pressed, since it is able to move up to the aerated epilimnion each night. In meromictic lakes the inability of the average benthic animal to survive anaerobiosis and the reduced substances associated with the lack of oxygen is evident. In Fayetteville Green Lake, New York, no macroscopic animals were collected below 20 m, although nearly 300 dredge samples were raised from that isobath to the maximum depth of 59 m (Eggleton 1956). Twenty meters was the level where oxygen disappeared and H_2S became evident.

Animals in the profundal benthos differ in their feeding behavior, but much of their food comes from the phytoplankton; spurts of growth often follow the arrival of planktonic algae at the bottom. Jónasson and Kristiansen (1967) show how feeding behavior varies with the season and with the taxonomy of phytoplankton in Denmark's eutrophic Lake Esrom. Diatoms are distributed to the bottom in spring and autumn when the lake circulates completely. Most green algae are rapidly circulated to the deeps, but blue-green algae sink slowly, reaching the bottom after having undergone some decay. The ooze-dwelling animals of the profundal zone rely heavily on the phytoplankton and are essentially primary consumers. Some, especially the tubificid worms, feed on bacteria. In Lake Esrom there are three primary consumers, the tubificid worm *Ilyodrilus, Chironomus anthracinus,* and *Pisidium.* Two other forms are carnivores: *Procla-*

dius (a chironomid) and the planktonic larvae of *Chaoborus.*

Procladius is not a permanent member of the Esrom profundal benthos, because it is absent during the summer anaerobic period. Even *Chaoborus* is not especially tolerant, but it can escape anoxia by nocturnal vertical migration. The diel migrations, however, vary seasonally and with respect to the four larval instars within a single species (Goldspink and Scott 1971). Moreover, five species of *Chaoborus* show distinct preferences for different types of Ontario lakes (Hamilton 1971), and diel migrations occur even in shallow, well-oxygenated lakes.

Hemoglobin is common in benthic animals. The bright red species of *Chironomus* are especially characteristic; even the tiny burrowing cladoceran *Ilyocryptus* of the littoral and sublittoral microbenthos is red. Hemoglobin permits the animals to quickly gain trace amounts of oxygen from the environment; this helps, but only for a matter of minutes. The resistant species of *Chironomus, C. plumosus* and *C. anthracinus,* may be able to excrete some end products of anaerobic respiration into the water (Walshe 1947, 1950).

A great many studies of bottom fauna have quantified profundal benthos on the basis of standing crop in weights, numbers, or volumes. Production is different and must be expressed in terms of rate. To illustrate some of the problems that can be encountered, Anderson and Hooper (1956) estimated that the annual production of a species of *Tanytarsus* in the littoral zone of Sugarloaf Lake, Michigan, was about 74 kg/ha, while the mean standing crop was about 22 kg/ha. This midge was univoltine (one generation a year) in that lake. Had it produced two generations per year, as is often the case with chironomids, the average standing crop might have been roughly the same, but the yearly production would have doubled.

Some generalizations can be made about the concentrations of benthos in lakes. The bottom fauna is probably 85% to 90% water, and a profundal standing crop averaging a dry weight of 4 g/m² is considered unusually high. Most lakes would perhaps have only one tenth this value. In North America, Last Mountain Lake in Saskatchewan may hold the record: Rawson and Moore (1944) reported 8.6 g/m² for the mean dry weight of their samples.

Estimation of standing crop on the basis of a few samples can be biased, for it depends on when and where the collections were made. Commonly there is an upward migration of midge larvae to form a summer concentration zone at the boundary of the sublittoral and profundal zone (Eggleton 1931; Deevey 1941). Also, it is not unusual for predation and general mortality to take a toll of 1% each day, so that June collections gather more animals than August samples. Brooks and Deevey (1963) presented some estimated annual benthic production rates ranging from 0.6 g/m² for Lake Nipigon, Ontario, to 14.8 for Beloje, USSR. Two of the highest rates in North America, from Linsley Pond and Lake Mendota, were 7.2 and 5.5 g/m² per year, respectively.

THE PERIPHYTON

The microbenthic flora blends with another community, the *periphyton,* a word used originally to describe the organisms attached to artifically submerged objects. It has been broadened to include the entire sessile community of organisms. If used strictly, it would refer to organisms on plant stems, leaves, and perhaps submersed sticks. The German term *aufwuchs* enjoyed popularity for years following the Frey and Fry translation of Ruttner's work (1953), but "periphyton" seems to have come back and is widely used.

The periphyton includes both flora and fauna. Most people have experienced the treacherous slipperiness of stones in streams. A film of diatoms attached by gelatinous stalks accounts for this. Living with these algae are other encrusting types and also such animals as the stalked peritrichous ciliates *Vorticella* and the branched *Carchesium.* (*Vorticella* often abounds in the open-water plankton of lakes while in its telotroch stage, a motile wandering phase in the life of this protozoan. Similarly, the typical attached form of *Vorticella* is gathered in plankton collections because it rides about on strands of blue-green algae.)

Periphyton assemblages on stones (*epilithic* organisms) can hardly be distinguished from microbenthic assemblages unless the strict sessile nature of the organisms is observed. *Epipelic* algae are those on sediment surfaces and come closer to being defined as microphytobenthos. *Epiphytic* organisms are the aufwuchs of plant leaves and stems, hardly different, if at all, from the narrow definition of periphyton. *Epizoic* periphyton communities dwell on animals and are spectacularly demonstrated by the "mossy" backs of some freshwater turtles. A unique community of such epizoic periphyton as the green alga *Basicladia* and a group of suctorean ciliates make up the major part of this movable aufwuchs.

Studying the role of attached algae in lacustrine productivity, Wetzel (1964) discussed the confusing history of the terminology referring to these forms. Probably one can now speak of epizoic, epiphytic, epilithic, and epipelic periphyton as four kinds of aufwuchs. Care should be used to designate periphyton algae as opposed to periphyton animals.

The early techniques for studying the periphyton were reviewed in a valuable paper by Sládečková (1962). The production of both primary (algal) and secondary (animal) periphyton has been estimated in various ways. A common technique is based on submerging racks of glass plates (microscope slides are often used) for a period of time and measuring the organic matter that accrues. Castenholz (1960) measured the increment of organic material in Washington's Grand Coulee chain of lakes in this manner. The maximum daily rate, amounting to a dry weight of 1,043 mg/m², was in saline Soap Lake.

Wetzel (1964) used carbon 14 methodology to determine annual primary production in Borax Lake, California. He found that 731.5 mg C per m² were fixed on an average day by the periphyton algae, dominated by the rare chlorophycean *Ctenocladus,* a saline-water form. This represented 69% of the carbon fixed by the autotrophs in the entire lake. The planktonic algae took second place (23.6%) in production rate, and the macrophytes fixed 7% of the annual carbon. Such relatively high littoral production by periphyton algae is probably found only in shallow lakes. The mean depth of astatic Borax Lake is usually less than 1 m, despite its area of 40 ha. Naiman (1974) reported some remarkable periphyton production from a shallow thermal stream in the Mojave Desert of California. An unshaded benthic mat of blue-green algae was responsible for the mean fixation of 3.3 g C per m² each day.

THE NEUSTON

The *neuston* is the community of flora and fauna associated with surface tension. The difference in density between the water and the air above is on the order of 1,000 times. This great density difference produces a film with which small organisms are associated.

Another thin organic film on the upper surface of the water is said to contain lipoproteins. This layer and the material collecting in it support the animals of the *epineuston.* Two very abundant taxa in this assemblage are small arachnids, the Acari, and the insect order Collembola.

The collembolans or springtails have a markedly hydrophobic cuticle fitting them for such a habitat. The water striders, consisting of two hemipteran families, the Beliidae and Gerridae, are among the most conspicuous of the epineuston. These are all essentially terrestrial organisms, or at least aerial rather than aquatic.

The conspicuous green covering on some ponds is made up of the duckweeds, members of the Lemnaceae. These tiny angiosperms float with rootlets hanging in the water below the surface.

The dusty or oily appearance of some pond surfaces is due to an epineustic microflora. Floating chrysophyceans, euglenophytes, and chlorophyceans contribute to this appearance.

The *hyponeuston* is the community living at and under the surface film. A host of algae and protozoans can be found here. They provide food for other organisms, such as mosquitoes, which in turn are preyed upon by cyprinodont topminnows, such as *Gambusia.*

Two crustaceans are of special interest here. One is the ostracod *Notodromas;* the other is *Scapholeberis,* a cladoceran (Fig. 3-9, *A*). They both are remarkably adapted for moving smoothly upside down along the underside of the film.

THE PSAMMON

A group of plants and animals living in the interstitial water among sand grains makes up the community called *psammon.* In general usage, the term applies to the communities living in the beach sands above the water of the lake, and the term hydropsammon has been coined for the sand dwellers beneath the water. Suitable habitats may extend back from the beach for 1 to 4 m, depending on the slope of the beach. There is some vertical zonation, the upper lighted areas being occupied by a special diatom flora and the lower levels containing only animals and bacteria. Often the sand is blackened and anaerobic not far below the surface, and aerobic organisms are restricted to a thin upper stratum. Interstitial water makes up more than 40% of the volume in many samples of moist beach sand.

A host of tiny animals in the psammon may be entirely absent from the microbenthos of the littoral region only a few meters away. This community has been neglected in North America, although a few workers have published on the psammon. The first detailed study was that of Pennak (1940), writing about the sandy beaches of Wisconsin lakes. His description of the biota to be found there is enlightening. He wrote that if a sample of 10 cm^3 containing 2 or 3 ml of water is collected about 1.5 m from the water's edge, it will contain 4 million bacteria, 8,000 protozoans, 400 rotifers, 40 copepods, and 20 tardigrads, along with a few other species. The copepods will be largely harpacticoids. Neel (1948) listed 248 species of animals and plants from the psammon community of Douglas Lake, Michigan.

The biota of the interstitial water often contains species previously unknown, and some remarkable discoveries have been made in this area. For example, Pennak and Zinn (1943) found a small, elongate crustacean in the marine psammon at a beach at Woods Hole, Massachusetts. These shores had been trodden for 70 years or so by countless zoologists, including students, researchers, and all-around collectors. At first glance, the animal living in the interstitial water seemed to be a copepod. However, further study showed that it represented a new, previously unknown, primitive order of the Crustacea. It could not be assigned to any known group. Since then, other Mystacocarida, as Pennak and Zinn named the group (now raised to class), have been found along the Mediterranean and other coasts of Europe, Africa, and western South America.

One of the most noteworthy finds was that of an archiannelid worm from the interstitial habitat in gravels along a Colorado mountain stream (Pennak 1971). At the time Pennak collected this worm, the species *Troglochaetus beranecki* was known only from central Europe (Tilzer 1973). *Troglochaetus* is either a member of a primitive, archaic class of the Annelida, restricted to the sea with this exception, or else it belongs to a very specialized order of the Class Polychaeta. Whatever the case, this rare find shows how little we have studied the psammon. Pennak's article (1968) on the history of interstitial investigations listed many striking phylogenetic discoveries from this habitat even before he had found the Colorado specimens of *Troglochaetus.*

LOTIC COMMUNITIES

Some physicochemical features of flowing waters were touched on briefly in Chapter 2. The study of lotic habitats and their inhabitants comes under the heading of *potamology,* a division of limnology. The prefix *potamo-* designates lotic, as opposed to lentic, phenomena and biota. Furthermore, the adjective *rheophilous* is commonly used to describe "current-loving" forms as opposed to standing-water species.

The potamoplankton is poorly developed except in large streams far from their sources or in relatively quiet side pools where conditions are much like a lentic environment. Microorganisms are found in the water of small, fast-flowing streams, but they are usually plants and animals torn loose from the substrate and swept downstream. The outflow from lakes usually introduces plankton organisms into streams, but they are destined to disappear rather rapidly. Chandler (1937) and Reif (1939) studied the fate of lake plankters in effluent streams in Michigan and in Minnesota, respectively, documenting rapid reductions of the limnoplankton as it drifts. Much is filtered out by vegetation; another fraction falls prey to the rheophilous benthic animals adapted for capturing particulate matter brought to them by currents.

In larger streams the bulk of the phytoplankton is composed of diatoms, and the zooplankton is marked by more rotifers, relative to microcrustacea, than are typical of lake plankton communities (Hynes 1970). The reasons for these phenomena are not obvious, although survival rate varies for different lake plankters swept into streams: the crustaceans do not persist as long as the rotifers, and diatoms outlast other algae.

Most primary productivity in small streams comes from the periphyton algae rather than the phytoplankton, although running-water communities seem to derive most of their energy from allochthonous (outside) sources, such as leaves from adjacent terrestrial communities (Minshall 1967, Hynes 1970). Fisher and Likens (1973) reported that 99% of the annual energy in Bear Brook, New Hampshire, was allochthonous. Where currents rush over stony substrates, attached algae and mosses thrive and contribute to the total stream photosynthesis. It is often pointed out that the benthic plants, algal or those belonging to higher categories, are unusually productive because they are constantly supplied with nutrients from upstream sources. Since there is no accumulation of nutrients, the stream plants depend on constant renewal from the drainage area.

The invertebrates of running water include representatives from most of the large taxonomic groups found in inland waters. A few groups are confined to flowing water. The blackflies (Simulii-dae) serve as a good example of the latter; the larvae and pupae of these dipterans are practically limited to swift, moving water. They belong to the riffles of streams rather than the pools.

Hynes (1970) stressed that the stream substratum is a major factor in controlling the distribution of lotic animals. If the substrates are shifted and moved about by the current, the instability reduces the biota.

The fauna of stony streams has a cosmopolitan aspect, according to Hynes (1970). Sponges, cnidarians, triclad flatworms, oligochaetes, molluscs, and malacostracan crustaceans have representatives in stony brooks throughout the world, but the most remarkable constituents of the brook fauna are the insects. Nine insect orders contribute generously to lotic habitats and some, such as the stoneflies (Plecoptera), have all their families represented in streams. In the pools, where substrates are softer, the uniformity of the fauna is less evident, although the hemipterans known as waterstriders (Gerridae) are cosmopolitan, skimming about on the surfaces of quiet pools as well as on flowing waters.

To the North American it seems bizarre that crustaceans of marine origin occur far inland in rocky streams, but they do in warmer regions. Decapod crustaceans, such as crabs and shrimps belonging to the Palaemonidae and Atyidae, occur in streams to the south—in Mexico, for example (Darnell 1956; Miles 1967).

A striking feature of the biota of fast-flowing water is morphologic adaptation. Hynes (1970) listed 11 categories under this heading. Flattening and reduction of body size permit animals to escape the current by hugging close to the substrate, where water velocity is greatly reduced, or to escape the flow by hiding beneath stones. Small size alone seems to permit tiny species—rotifers, nematodes, and protozoans—to deal with current by escaping it in rocky cracks and fissures; they show no special morphologic adaptations that set them apart from their lentic relatives. Among the microscopic plants, however, flattened algal thalli, closely fixed to the stony substrate, are typical of the periphyton of swift water.

Some mayflies (Ephemeroptera), planarians, and leeches are remarkably adapted to current through flattening. Other invertebrate and vertebrate species are streamlined. The trout and other fishes that swim against strong currents are often cited as examples of this adaptation; their bodies are fusiform and round in cross section, offering reduced resistance to the flow. In torrential streams some organisms show morphologic configurations that permit them to hug the bottom in the face of current. One of the most striking examples is the rare minnow *Gila cypha* from the Colorado River of Arizona (Miller 1946). Its body is grotesquely humped just posterior to the head, an arching that holds it close to the bottom as it heads into the current by acting as a hydrofoil. In addition, the body of *G. cypha* is streamlined and round in cross section; its caudal peduncle is long and narrow, and it has lost nearly all its scales, thereby decreasing friction.

Other morphologic adaptations are associated with holding fast in currents; hooks, friction-pads, sticky secretions, ballasting with stony cases in some

caddis flies (Trichoptera), and massive shells in bivalved molluscs serve to maintain position. In many instances, two or more of these features are combined; stony-cased caddis fly larvae of the genus *Helicopsyche* glue themselves to stones, and larval blackflies spin silken meshes that stick to rocky substrates and then hold themselves in position by grappling into the silk with a circlet of posterior hooks.

The feeding habits of many rheophilous animals are particularly interesting; some lotic species feed by simply scraping algae from the stony substrate, and others let the flow bring them their sustenance. Larval blackflies possess fan-like mouth structures that are held outstretched to catch drifting particles in the flow above the relatively quiet boundary layer where they are attached. Members of the trichopteran Hydropsychidae are noted for spinning nets that entrap fine particles brought by the current. They are considered to be typical of stream communities and are especially abundant in the effluent waters of lakes.

An excellent place to collect *Hydra* is in rocky streams near their origin at the outlet of lakes. There, these carnivorous cnidarians are well supplied with microcrustaceans brought to them via the outflow current.

Because many rivers are ancient systems, they have evolved a diverse and sometimes endemic fauna. The unionid clams of the upper Mississippi River and the unique clam fauna of the Cumberland River in Kentucky and Tennessee are good examples. The latter, especially, has been decimated by impoundment and flooding of the stream.

4

Ecosystems, energy, and production

THE COMMUNITY CONCEPT AND ECOSYSTEMS
A few historical aspects

In the history of ecology there have been some variations in terms and concepts that deal with communities of organisms. Communities are not so rigidly defined as in the past even though Hutchinson (1967) elected to reserve community for conspecific groups. At present the term "community" can be used loosely to refer to all sorts of assemblages of plants, animals, and microbes that have colonized particular locations. Common usage permits one to speak of such contrasting and different-sized gatherings as microbial soil communities or upland prairie communities.

Three well-marked theories about the community have been discussed and argued during the past half century. Phillips (1935) is associated with the champions of the idea that "the biotic community is a complex organism," its species and trophic levels being comparable to cells and tissues of a plant or animal body. Surprisingly, the English ecologist

Tansley (1935), who gave us the useful word ecosystem, rejected Phillips' "complex organism" definition as unnatural "because animals and plants are too different in nature to be considered as members of the same community." Phillips' phrase, "the biotic community wherein plants and animals are intimately integrated associates," however, makes sense in light of modern knowledge. It seems to be in harmony with Tansley's ecosystem, which applies to the sum of the living and nonliving components of a community and their close and complex relationships.

The community certainly represents a high level of biologic organization but probably is no more than analogous to a superorganism. We are left now with the ecosystem—an acceptable mixture of Phillips' biotic community and the nonbiotic (physicochemical) environmental factors.

Energy is received by and flows through the ecosystem to be used only once, but minerals and nutrients are used time and time again as they pass from the biotic to the nonbiotic segment of the ecosystem, thus revealing the unity of its living and nonliving components. Lindeman (1942b) discussed the blurred lines between the living community and the nonliving environment by emphasizing the difficulty one encounters in determining the status of "a slowly dying pondweed covered with periphytes, some of which are also continually dying." He wrote further that the organic-inorganic cycle of any nutritive substance is so completely integrated that to consider a lake primarily as a biotic community appears to force a biologic emphasis upon a more basic functional organization.

Community succession

Communities may alter with time, and one group of species may replace another; but if important environmental factors persist, they can remain practically unchanged. This is not to say that communities are static entities. Succession is always a dynamic ingredient: one community is replaced by another as time passes. Succession, ideally, is a progression culminating in the climax, a comparatively stable phase that maintains itself indefinitely, provided far-reaching climatic changes do not occur. (Because of shoaling, most lake basins are stages in a series preceding the ultimate terrestrial community.) The concept of a subclimax community, occupying territory that will later support the climax and indeed paving the way for it by altering edaphic or light factors, comes to us mostly from plant ecologists.

Paleolimnologic evidence implies that past stable lake stages were in equilibrium with their climatic and edaphic surroundings. These lakes were oligotrophic as well as eutrophic in nature. Increased erosion in the drainage basin, often due to man's forest clearing and farming, upset the equilibrium, and the lakes rapidly changed to states nearer the eutrophic end of the spectrum. A similar upset occurs when fertilizers are added, but at present there is no satisfactory evidence that a natural, gradual accumulation of nutrients dictates an inexorable trend from oligotrophy to eutrophy. A lake brought to eutrophy by addition of nutrients will revert to its original condition if the nutrient supply is withheld. This has been documented in a series of papers on Lake Washington by W. T. Edmondson (1969 and 1972b), the last of which briefly details the chronology of this lake's condition. Furthermore, many old, now shallow lakes still have oligotrophic water (in the sense of Weber 1907) and scanty plankton populations despite their filled-in condition.

The idea that high species diversity and an exact balance of organic material gained and degraded characterize climax ecosystems (Patten 1959) is weakened by the concept of oligotrophy as the subclimax to eutrophy. Eutrophication results in lower species diversity than that seen in most oligotrophic lakes, and the annual degradation of the organic matter produced is more nearly complete in oligotrophic lakes than it is in eutrophic waters. Obliteration of the basin is a type of succession achieved despite the trophic nature of the lake. It is a separate phenomenon from the hypothetical sequence: oligotrophy → mesotrophy → eutrophy → senescence → terrestrial stage.

Retrogressive succession or rejuvenation is not denied to lakes. Dredging, deepening, aerating, removing sapropelic ooze, and destroying large areas of emergent vegetation are artificial techniques by which lakes are restored and their old age postponed (Bjork 1972).

A further type of retrogressive community evolution can be brought about by arrival of some new organism. The fungus blight that destroyed the chestnut *Castanea* reduced diversity in the deciduous forest of eastern North America by removing an important component of that ecosystem. In aquatic communities, retrogression or destruction sometimes follows willful or inadvertent introductions of alien fish species. Extensive introductions of the North American centrarchid, *Micropterus salmoides* (the largemouth bass), have resulted in disaster in some instances. The most distressing case is that of the ruination of the complex biota of Lake Atitlán, Guatemala (Geyer 1973).

The piscivorous cichlid *Cichla ocellaris* in South America is comparable to the largemouth bass in feeding habits. In 1967 it was introduced in Gatun Lake, Panama Canal Zone, about a decade after *Micropterus* was placed in Atitlán, and its impact on the resident biota has been far reaching. Zaret and Paine (1973) have documented second- and third-order changes throughout the lake community that followed the great reduction of smaller fishes, secondary consumers,

caused by the voracious *Cichla*. Modifications at the herbivorous zooplankton level were shown by changes in the frequencies of the two morphologic types of the cladoceran primary consumer *Ceriodaphnia cornuta* (one of which is superior to the other in the absence of fish predation). Other tertiary consumers, including piscivorous birds, were reduced where *Cichla* prevailed in the lake.

Succession, then, can be interrupted, and a diverse community structure that evolved over great spans of time can be destroyed when equilibrium is upset. In short, community succession is not always progressive, and we must guard against the concept of oligotrophy always leading to eutrophy, senescence, and death.

Food chains and ecospecies

Functional units of species with nutritional interdependence compose the community biota. First there are the primary producers that capture solar energy to produce energy-rich organic molecules upon which other ecosystem members ultimately depend. (This scheme is modified in situations such as cave communities, where organic material is brought in from the outside. Leaves and other organic detritus washed in, or guano deposited by roosting bats that forage outside during night hours, might form the basis for much of the energy transferred and degraded within the cave. The ultimate dependence is on photosynthesis, however, and the distinctions between the cave community and those of an epigean world are blurred.)

Community herbivores and omnivores utilize the primary producers for food and, in turn, pass on some of their energy to the carnivores. The herbivores, especially, are designated primary consumers; the omnivores are mixed, functioning as both primary and secondary consumers. Carnivores function as secondary, tertiary, or quaternary consumers, although rarely are there more than three levels of carnivores. They are served by the energy from more than the immediate trophic level below, so that their categories are somewhat indistinct.

Microorganisms gain energy by decomposing the dead tissues of producers and consumers alike, thus recycling nutrients and minerals to the system and effecting the final degradation of energy. This generalization, however, oversimplifies a complex situation, for the bacteria themselves may be consumed by other members of the community who gain energy from them.

From one point of view, the functional or trophic role of a species within a community is more important than the species itself. The role may be the same in communities that are geographically separated; the species playing the role, however, can be quite different. Thus organisms may be ecologic equivalents, although not closely related. The word *ecospecies* applies to such plants or animals that have nearly identical functions in separate communities. Two examples will suffice.

In many permanent saline lakes in most parts of the world, the brine shrimp *Artemia salina* is present. This species is an efficient osmoregulator and can live in salt solutions surpassing 20%. It feeds especially on species of a hardy green flagellate, *Dunaliella,* characteristic of hypersaline lakes throughout the world. In the saline waters of Australia, *Artemia* is replaced by an ecologic and physiologic equivalent, *Parartemia zietziana* (Bayly and Williams 1973).

In North America there are many species of fishes belonging to the sunfish and bass family, the Centrarchidae. Many are deep bodied and laterally compressed, and appear nearly circular when observed from the side. Various feeding habits are associated with the different species. Some feed on insects and microcrustacea; others are mollusc feeders; and some are piscivorous. Moving southward into Mexico and Central America, the centrarchids drop out, and representatives of another family appear. They belong to the Cichlidae, a diverse group remarkably resembling the centrarchids. All the trophic roles played by centrarchid species farther north are matched by the cichlids.

Biogeochemical aspects of ecosystems

Early efforts to understand the dynamics of an ecosystem focused on the chemical nature of organisms with respect to their environment. Later the quantitative roles of organisms in major chemical cycles became an important goal in ecologic research. This was essentially a biogeochemical approach. Biogeochemistry originally described the study of organisms in relation to mineral formation, but now it ranges from soil science and geochemistry to ecology, where it explores the interactions among the biosphere, atmosphere, lithosphere, and hydrosphere. Recently the use of isotopic tracers has helped quantify some relationships between living and nonliving components of ecosystems.

The total mass of the biosphere is much less than that of the atmosphere, hydrosphere, and the crustal portion of the lithosphere—a million times smaller than the last, for example. The biosphere is in dynamic equilibrium with these components of the physical environment, and the geochemical importance of organisms must not be underestimated. Although relatively common atoms compose the bodies of organisms, a few essential elements are so scarce that demand surpasses supply at times, and growth is thereby limited.

The chemistry of aquatic plants and animals is much like their surroundings, although some atoms are remarkably concentrated in the organisms. Redfield (1958) reviewed data showing that the relative composition of phosphorus and nitrogen in marine plankters is nearly identical to the ratio in seawater. The relative abundance in the organisms is 1:16, almost matching the mean of 1:15 in seawater samples.

The term cycle is applicable to both biogeochemistry and ecology. The chemical parts of an ecosystem can enter, leave, and reenter living systems repeatedly. Sometimes there may be a loss, as when silicon locked up in diatom frustules is sedimented and buried by subsequent deposition of other material, but this is only temporary on geologic time scales. Nutrients and other minerals are continually recycled through biotic communities.

Energy flow in ecosystems

A fish carcass lying at the water's edge is biomass and is the result of production within the lake. It contains minerals, nutrients, and chemical energy that will be transferred to the next enterprising scavenger that combs the beach.

Two common errors need to be corrected with regard to such a situation. First, the biomass (in this instance, best considered wet weight) is not production; the time factor is missing, and rate is an integral part of the concept of production. (A peep into the hen house reveals fifteen eggs, but nothing can be said about production until it is known how many days' accumulation they represent.) Second, only the minerals in the fish's body will be recycled without diminution; the energy will be passed on, but it cannot be utilized time and time again. The energy in the fish corpse is a tiny portion, perhaps less than 0.1% of that which was fixed by the green autotrophs in the system and transferred to the herbivorous invertebrates that served as the fish's diet. Some of it may nurture a scavenger, but, ideally, energy will not revert back to the herbivores and certainly not to the phototrophic plants, nor to the sun. The bulk of it moves unidirectionally through the ecosystem, eventually to be lost to it. Energy must, therefore, be continually put into an ecosystem to forestall its collapse.

Communities are complex, however, so that a small fraction of energy can, seemingly, flow backward, rather than forward as in the ideal concept of discrete trophic levels. The disintegration and decay of a carnivore body could contribute bits of detritus, coated with decomposers (bacteria) to the detritus feeders and to herbivores that are somewhat omnivorous (Fig. 4-1).

The second law of thermodynamics is relevant here. It specifies the direction in which energy flows, and it states that disorder, or entropy, tends to increase with time. It teaches that order becomes disorder, that randomness increases, and that structure and concentrations tend to disappear. It foretells elimination of all gradients, equalization of chemical and electric potentials, and leveling of contrasts in heat and molecular motion, unless work is done to prevent this.

The Nobel Prize–winning physicist Schrödinger (1945) wrote a book that is still fascinating and relevant 3 decades later. He underlined the improbable state of organization—the living system—that characterizes the organism. He asked how an organism avoids decay and postpones that state of entropy we call death. His answer was that we continuously feed on negative entropy, the reciprocal of disorder. We take in orderliness in the form of complicated organic compounds, utilizing much of their contained energy. In ecosystems the primary producers have their most important source of negative entropy in solar radiation. The sunlight that supports the green plants is the orderliness that' ultimately maintains the entire ecosystem, allowing it to stave off the final decay of entropy.

The second law of thermodynamics states that energy flows from a region of concentration to one of lesser concentra-

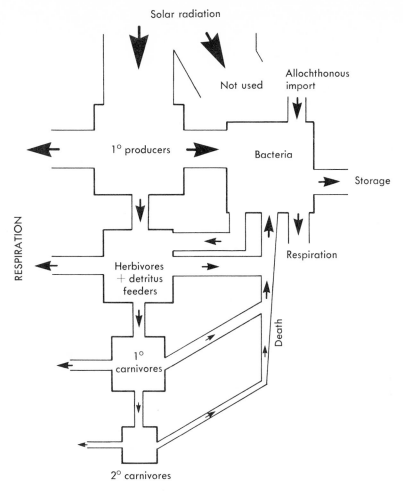

Fig. 4-1. Schematic portrayal of energy flow through an aquatic ecosystem.

tion, not the reverse, and that it is degraded as it is transformed, some being lost at each step downward. In animal metabolism, energy from well-structured food molecules is used for growth and work; but some energy is not utilized, and much is lost and dissipated as low-temperature heat.

Although it is incorrect to equate an aquatic ecosystem with an organism, there are similarities. The lake with all its inhabitants resembles an organism in that it is a "highly improbable aggregation of energy . . . , inherently ordered and comprising an infinitude of physical and chemical gradients" (Patten 1959).

The lake ecosystem accomplishes work like a live plant or animal, something impossible for a random system that lacks gradients and has a high degree of disorder, or entropy. The organism and the ecosystem are in a thermodynamic steady state: energy entering both systems is used for growth and maintenance or is stored. Eventually it is degraded. The degraded energy is entropy, dissipated as waste products and heat.

In ecosystems there is, however, more than just a dynamic balance with negative entropy being taken in to compensate for the natural losses of thermodynamics. Any complex system, such as a trophic level, also acquires energy to make up for the losses it will suffer to other trophic levels. Plants and animals not geared to sustain such losses would be doomed.

The trend to seek a common denominator in ecosystem ecology has led to increased use of the calorie. Solar radiation, plant and animal tissue, respiration, and other metabolic output can all be quantified as calories. Improved apparatus for direct calorimetry of very small samples has led to better results than those derived from earlier attempts with wet oxidants such as $K_2Cr_2O_7$. From the many determinations summarized and listed by Cummins and Wuycheck (1971), it has become obvious that the caloric content of all tissue is not alike; there are important systematic, as well as ecologic, differences. The 1971 list permits a new precision in converting mass to energy equivalents.

The grand mean of aquatic primary producers is 4,639 cal/g of ash-free dry weight. The diatoms with 5,310 cal/g surpass the bluegreens (4,882 cal/g), which in turn exceed the chlorophytes that average 4,780 cal/g. The invertebrate consumers, averaging 5,470 cal/g, have a greater energy content than the plants upon which they depend. In all organisms the energy in a gram is less if it is dry weight including ash; for this reason ash-free, dry weight is the best base for conversion to calories.

Community metabolism

There is a technique by which communities can be appraised in a manner analogous to quantifying an organism's metabolism. The community metabolism is measured for a period of time. The gross or total photosynthesis (P) is determined during the daylight hours and compared with total respiration (R) during a 24-hour period. From this a P/R ratio can be established without knowing specific rates of photosynthesis and respiration

for individual organisms in the system. The methods of measuring are dealt with later. It is sufficient to say here that oxygen increment during daylight hours reflects net photosynthesis; it is assumed that some oxygen produced is consumed by respiration before being assayed. Gross primary production is proportional to the total oxygen evolved. Since respiration dominates at night while oxygen is consumed, the nocturnal consumption of oxygen (when darkness is 12 hours) is doubled to represent total diel respiration (R). Half this daily respiration is added to the net photosynthesis, the sum being gross primary production (P).

The P/R ratio may vary from day to day, season to season, or year to year, but its long-term mean tells something of the ecosystem's nature. In North America Odum (1956) is usually credited with developing the idea of a P/R proportion to define a community type. Winberg (1972) suggested that this concept was expressed in Russia 2 decades earlier in terms of autotrophic or photosynthetic processes in relation to all those that are the opposite—heterotrophic phenomena. The destructive events, by which the results of primary production are utilized and degraded, are mirrored in total respiration. When the ratio is unity, all organic material produced by autotrophic organisms is destroyed by destructive processes, and a dynamic balance is achieved.

Oligotrophic lakes typically have P/R ratios not differing significantly from 1.0 (Fig. 4-2, *A*). These communities are in one kind of equilibrium: the solar energy received and converted to highly organized organic molecules, negative entropy, is approximately matched by conversions to entropy, although small amounts of organic material are stored in the bottom deposits. An ecosystem such as Silver Springs, Florida, must then be considered a community in dynamic equilibrium, for a balance is achieved be-

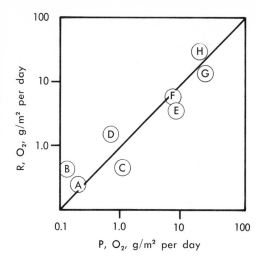

Fig. 4-2. Log-log plot of P/R ratios. On diagonal line, P/R = 1.0. Above the diagonal indicates heterotrophy; below the line, autotrophy. *A,* Unpolluted portion of Lake Päijänne, Finland (Tuunainen and associates, 1972); *B,* grossly polluted portion of Lake Päijänne; *C,* enriched, eutrophic portion of Lake Päijänne; *D,* Root Spring, Massachusetts (Teal 1957); *E,* Severson Lake, Minnesota (Comita 1972); *F,* Montezuma Well, Arizona (unpublished data); *G,* ponds of tertiary-treated waste water, Arizona (Foster 1973); *H,* sewage lagoons in the Dakotas (Bartsch and Allum 1957).

tween the organic matter produced and that destroyed or leaked downstream each year (Odum 1957). Similarly, unpublished studies on Montezuma Well, Arizona, show that it is in a similar balance: its photosynthesis is nearly matched by respiration (Fig. 4-2, *F*).

In eutrophic lakes the P/R ratio is substantially greater than 1.0 (Fig. 4-2, *C* and *E*). Autotrophic organisms produce much more organic material than can be accounted for by respiration. There is a balance, however, because the excess organic substances are stored as sediment, awaiting some future time to be oxidized. Communities with P/R > 1.0 are designated autotrophic; photosynthesis of organic molecules surpasses their destruction by heterotrophic processes. Many fertilized fish ponds and enriched sewage lagoons are good examples of this type (Fig. 4-2, *G*). Their primary productivity is high,

and only a part is consumed by heterotrophic events, termed respiration here. Thus Foster (1973) found that Arizona ponds enriched by treated sewage water converted 2.80 kcal/cm^2 of the annual solar radiation to organic molecules via photosynthesis. Of that primary production, 1.44 kcal was destroyed in community respiration; the storage in the sediments was about 1.3 kcal/cm^2, accounting for most of the rest.

In such highly productive ecosystems, temporary halts in the input of solar energy stops the synthesis of organic molecules, and the degradation of stored energy assumes predominance. Thus, during cloudy periods and during winter when ice and snow cover shallow eutrophic lakes, the P/R ratio often falls below unity.

Aquatic ecosystems to which allochthonous organic molecules are added in substantial quantities have P/R ratios significantly below 1.0 (Fig. 4-2, *B, D,* and *H*). The structured potential energy of those molecules entering community metabolism to be degraded did not come from autochthonous primary production. As a result, respiration, in the broadest sense, surpasses photosynthesis, and the community can be termed heterotrophic. The heterotrophic events surmount the phototrophic action of green plants, just as they do in shallow, darkened, ice-covered lakes.

Saprobicity, the total of all the processes that are antithetical to primary production, is another classification of heterotrophy. A sequence of saprobic conditions from oligosaprobic to mesosaprobic through polysaprobic corresponds roughly to a spectrum from pure oligotrophic to extremely polluted conditions. There is an α and β level for each division so that six categories represent the trend. The saprobic scheme is usually employed in discussions of polluted waters and their saprobionts, the indicator species ranging from the most tolerant β polysaprobic species to the least tolerant (Caspers and Karbe 1967).

Dystrophic lakes receiving humic substances from external sources are usually heterotrophic. Winberg (1963), summarizing work done by himself and other Russian limnologists, points out that dystrophic Lake Glubokoye, surrounded by bogs and with heavily stained water, has a low annual productivity and, despite some variation, typical heterotrophic P/R values. One year the mean ratio seemed to be 1.04, but usually the figure was much less. It was 0.82 the following year, for example.

Macan and Worthington (1951) have referred to Cedar Bog Lake, Minnesota, as dystrophic despite Lindeman's (1941) statement to the contrary. The quotient of the primary production and the sum of respiration from most trophic levels gives a value of about 3.7. The overall P/R ratio is lower than this, for neither bacterial respiration nor days of winter anaerobiosis are included. Nevertheless, Cedar Bog is autotrophic, producing more than it respires each year. Its community metabolism is not typical of dystrophy.

Within a single Finnish lake, Päijänne, a series of areas from oligotrophic to polluted can be discerned (Tuuainen and associates 1972). Päijänne has a maximum length of 120 km and is polluted at sites along the irregular shoreline by pulp mill influents and by water entering from a nearby polluted lake. Twenty years before the report, Lake Päijänne was oligotrophic, but by 1970 changes were evident. Some areas were still relatively clean, with P/R values averaging near unity (Fig. 4-2, *A*); another area showed the eutrophicating effects of sewage: P/R = 2.42 (Fig. 4-2, *C*); and others reflected the organic load and perhaps toxicity, imposed by pulp mill wastes: P/R = 0.04 to 0.51 (Fig. 4-2, *B*).

A similar relationship is seen sequentially in streams where pollution and recovery are involved. Immediately below the source of pollution, heterotrophic processes predominate (P/R < 1.0), the pollution being so great that there is no photosynthesis. Organic matter decomposes while flowing downstream, and gradually photosynthetic algae appear and begin to function. In a region best termed the early recovery zone, the nutrient-rich algae produce organic material in excess of its decay to create an autotrophic segment. In healthier reaches farther downstream, both primary production and respiration lessen, and the P/R figure approaches unity, perhaps much like conditions just above the pollution source.

Many healthy streams are heterotrophic, their biotic communities relying on the import of deciduous leaves from adjacent trees as a major source of energy. The report of Hall (1972) on the community metabolism of New Hope Creek, North Carolina, is perhaps typical. The annual mean P/R ratio is 0.60, but both photosynthesis and respiration vary from season to season. Both are low during winter, but with the approach of spring, photosynthesis peaks sharply beneath the still denuded trees, and the stream becomes nearly autotrophic. The new leaves bring about shading in May, thereby reducing photosynthesis. The stream is heterotrophic all summer. Then in October heterotrophy reaches its height when falling leaves serve as a new allochthonous import of potential energy.

Teal (1957) published results of work on Root Spring, a small *limnocrene* (a pooled spring) in an article that has become a classic in the history of investigations of community metabolism and ecosystem energetics. Root Spring, lying but a few kilometers from Walden Pond in Concord, Massachusetts, is supplied by cold water from adjacent banks of glacial drift. As is typical of small springs and brooks, there is no plankton, but benthic algae contribute to the input of energy via photosynthesis. However, the major source of organic input for the little eco-system (diameter about 2 m!) is leaf litter from nearby apple trees and other plant debris that falls into the pool, accounting for 76% of the annual energy supporting the spring community. As a result Root Spring is heterotrophic, with a P/R figure of about 0.30 (Fig. 4-2, *D*).

Steinböch (1958) proposed *allotrophy* as a term to describe conditions where the main energy source comes from out-side the lake. Allotrophic lakes are, of ne-cessity, heterotrophic on the basis of the P/R ratio. Wind-blown organic material is especially significant in some desert basins. Hutchinson (1937) coined *anemo-trophy* to describe certain allotrophic, arid land pools that receive their primary energy-rich carbon compounds via the wind.

TROPHIC-DYNAMIC ECOLOGY

Lindeman's posthumous paper (1942b) marked a turning point in ecology. The article was an outgrowth of his PhD dis-sertation based on research at Cedar Bog Lake and of his association (after comple-tion of the Minnesota work) with the Yale group, where an unpublished manu-script by G. E. Hutchinson was especially influential. Lindeman's paper (published after his untimely death at the age of 26) has become one of the most cited works in the literature of ecology. His effort seems to have crystallized earlier studies of energy flow through ecosystems and has stimulated further investigation of the dynamic approach to the study of communities. In retrospect there were flaws in his conclusions where he over-simplified and used terminology that is no longer in favor; but after Lindeman, the study of energy transfer in ecosys-tems came into its own.

The problem of efficiency

Measurements of energy passage in communities are notoriously difficult, yet subsequent studies agree with Linde-man's opinion that energy conversions from trophic level to trophic level are rather inefficient in ecosystems. From the energy available to a trophic rank, only a small part is incorporated into individ-ual bodies; thus some energy is lost. Such low efficiencies of conversion can be inferred from the second law of ther-modynamics. Lindeman (1942b) was con-cerned with progressive efficiency, the ratios of energy used by successive tro-phic levels. This is expressed as a per-centage by:

$$\text{Efficiency} = \frac{\lambda}{\lambda - 1} \times 100$$

The formula applies to different types of efficiencies; Lindeman used it to compare the degree to which one level (λ_n) utilized the energy resources available to it from the previous level (λ_{n-1}). Fol-lowing Lindeman's concern for progres-sive efficiency, there was an eruption of efficiencies—growth efficiencies of indi-vidual species determined from laborato-ry feeding experiments, and a host of other types. Twenty of these categories of efficiency from earlier authors are pre-sented in a list by Koslovsky (1968); still other types have been suggested.

The efficiency concept may be worth pursuing, but there are many inherent problems in it. The first trophic level, phototrophic plants utilizing radiant en-ergy, is easier to analyze than the subse-quent categories where omnivory ob-scures precise grouping and there is not always strict dependence on energy from the λ_{n-1} level. Furthermore, as Darnell (1961) observed, there are ontogenetic changes in food habits of fish. In Lake Pontchartrain, Louisiana, he found that a fish may be, successively, a detritus feed-er, an herbivore, and a carnivore as it ages, thus shifting from category to cate-gory through time.

Recently Slobodkin (1972) discussed some aspects of ecologic efficiency, the ratio of energy assimilated at one level to the energy assimilated at the next lower level. In his earlier publications he had contributed to the belief that there might be an optimal, constant, maximum efficiency that communities evolve. But in his essay of 1972 he states that we have no reason to believe that ecologic efficiency is constant and that there is much evidence to show it is not.

PRIMARY PRODUCTION

All production within an ecosystem stems from the energy in organic substances that autotrophic organisms create from inorganic raw materials. In some instances the organic energy was produced earlier and stored, as in leaf litter on a forest floor, or was imported as allochthonous energy produced elsewhere by autotrophs. With this in mind, the energy approach to studying ecosystems has the goal of balancing the whole energy budget and assumes that: first, there is an increase in organic compounds during a period of time and, except for import, only primary production can bring this about; second, there is a decrease in that stock as it is respired by organisms in aerobic environments, fermented in anaerobic surroundings, or oxidized chemically without the assistance of organisms; and third, any difference between accrual and subsequent diminution of chemical energy can be accounted for by either storage or some sort of export from the system.

There are two sorts of autotrophs or primary producers, the phototrophs and the chemotrophs, similar in their need for an energy source and utilizable carbon compounds. The chemotrophs are the so-called chemosynthetic bacteria, not all of which can be ranked as primary producers. There is a confusing hierarchy of these forms united only in that their energy comes from chemical bonds. These bonds may be inorganic, organic, or mixtures of organic and inorganic compounds used simultaneously. More-

over, their sources of carbon may be carbon dioxide, organic molecules, or mixtures that make possible nine types of chemotrophy. Of these, perhaps only combinations where energy from the chemical bonds of inorganic substances is used to build organic compounds of the bacterial cell from carbon dioxide can be called autotrophy and likened to primary productivity.

When the materials used by bacteria to acquire energy come from without the lake ecosystem, chemosynthesis is, to a slight degree, analogous to photosynthesis taking place within the lake; both require energy resources from outside. It cannot be equated with photosynthesis, however, because the energy source for such chemotrophs comes from decomposition of organic stuff produced originally by phototrophic organisms. In such instances, chemosynthetic bacteria are bringing about a decrease of the total energy in the ecosystem rather than adding to its store. They are playing a part in the utilization and degradation of the energy of primary production, typical of what is termed secondary production. Some limnologists believe this generally holds and that all kinds of chemotrophic biosynthesis should be designated secondary production.

Bacterial production of particulate food for grazing zooplankters must be extremely significant in some habitats where algal populations do not seem sufficient for supporting the existing zooplankton. Sorokin (1965) presents a picture of the trophic role of microorganisms, starting with flourishing heterotrophic bacterial populations effecting the initial decay of phytoplankton cells in upper waters and near shore where macrophytes, the phytobenthos, live and die. A great portion of the decay occurs in the water. When organic remains reach bottom in eutrophic lakes, there are two stages of mineralization. Anaerobic decomposition in sedimented matter results in release of reduced products such as H_2S, NH_4^+, Fe^{++}, CH_4, organic acids, and alcohols containing much of the energy of the initial organic material. The next step occurs at anoxic-aerobic boundaries, whether at sediment-water interfaces or higher in the hypolimnion, where the reduced products are oxidized. Both the anaerobic decomposers and aerobic oxidizers build their bodies from carbon dioxide or from carbon in such compounds as methane. As a result, the uptake of carbon dioxide in the dark is a rough measure of bacterial biosynthesis. Such assays show that the mass of microbial cells made available to animals is great.

The most important lacustrine producers are phototrophs; photosynthesis creates the bulk of the new organic compounds. Littoral macrophytes (with associated epiphytic algae), benthic algae, and phytoplankters convert radiant energy to potential chemical energy. Except for shallow lakes, the phytoplankters assume the most importance as producers.

According to Williams (1970), photosynthetic bacteria may make substantial contributions to primary production in certain saline inland waters. This is especially true in meromictic lakes where aerobic-anaerobic boundaries lie near the surface. Here green and purple sulfur bacteria reduce carbon dioxide to organic molecules, using light energy for the process. Since the electron donor is something other than water, bacterial photosynthesis differs from the typical green plant type. The various types of photosynthesis may also differ in other ways: oxygen is not always evolved; different wavelengths of light are used; different pigments function; and photosynthates vary. However, all photosynthesis depends on radiation for energy and converts stable inorganic compounds to energy-rich, but unstable, complex organic molecules—negative entropy in the

sense of Schrodinger (1945). Rabinowitch (1948) expressed this conversion in this manner for green plants: "In endlessly repeated cycles the atoms of carbon, oxygen, and hydrogen come from the atmosphere into the biosphere. . . . After a tour of duty which may last seconds or millions of years in the unstable organic world, they return to the stable equilibrium of inorganic nature."

The production of photosynthetic organisms must be defined carefully, because the word "productivity" has been used with different meanings. To some authors it goes without saying that production is net production or effective production, the growth increment. Perhaps this has been true more of Russian scientists, who in recent years have treated gross production as a superfluous concept (Winberg 1971). Others have felt that gross productivity is of considerable interest even though it includes metabolic loss.

There is, however, a problem if we delimit net primary production in plankton communities to gross production minus the plant's own respiratory use of newly formed organic products. Separating algal from bacterial and zooplankton respiration is a formidable task with the rather crude experimental apparatus used in lake studies, although it can be effected easily in the laboratory. Perhaps it is better to consider the totality of the plankton community without unnaturally abstracting the algal members. Thus, net production would be the difference between gross production and the respiration of zooplankters, bacteria, and algae tested during some period of time. With or without this approach, the net increment is still not known precisely, because, without doubt, some new organic energy may have been passed to a second trophic level during the testing period. If lake systems were axenic algal cultures, uninhabited by animals, the problem would be simplified.

Biomass

The Eltonian pyramid is usually an excellent generalization to portray relationships among an ecosystem's trophic levels, whether constructed in terms of numbers, mass, or energy. The concept was first presented in a book written by Elton (1927) and has become ingrained in the field of ecology. The base of the pyramid is made up of the autotrophs that synthesize their tissues from inorganic compounds; typically these are green plants. The next layer is composed of heterotrophs, the herbivores that require the autotrophs for food. Above this are predaceous heterotrophs that feed on the herbivores. Secondary carnivores make up the next higher level, and so on. Because much energy is expended in metabolism at each level, the mass of living material produced decreases at each higher level. On an annual basis, at least, the trophic structure of an ecosystem takes on the form of a pyramid (Fig. 4-3, *P*). (In a pyramid constructed on an energy basis, solar radiation would form the broad base in the best tradition of the ecosystem concept.)

An instantaneous sample of a simple ecosystem might yield data quite different from the ideal, where plant biomass surpasses that of the herbivores, which in turn is greater than the carnivore biomass. Possibly a closer approach to the ideal could be found in terrestrial communities than in aquatic ecosystems. The phytoplankton producers differ from their terrestrial counterparts; the mean biomass of

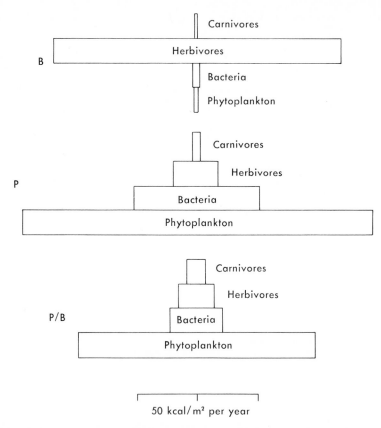

Fig. 4-3. Eltonian pyramids from oligotrophic Russian lake Krivoïe. *B,* Mean annual biomass; *P,* annual production; *P/B,* quotient of annual production and mean annual biomass. (Data from Winberg 1972.)

plankton algae may be exceeded a hundred times by annual production. Of course, the standing crop does not reflect annual production (Fig. 4-3, *B*).

Biomass or a sampled standing crop must not be confused with production, even though it can serve as a rough index to it; biomass is static. There are several methods of expressing it. Of these, wet weight requires no special treatment. Dry weight is found following oven drying at 80° to 105° C until a constant mass is achieved. If a dry sample is burned in a muffle furnace at about 500° C, only the ash content remains. Above 500° C some carbon dioxide may be driven from $MgCO_3$ and $CaCO_3$, leaving MgO and CaO, and also some potassium and sodium may be lost, thereby reducing accuracy. The difference between dry weight and ash weight ("loss on ignition") is an approximation of organic content, termed ash-free dry weight. Some authors have presented biomass in terms of ash-free wet weight, a description of the unlikely occurrence of a wet, organic plant or animal body lacking salts.

A further way of determining phytoplankton biomass is to extract and measure the chlorophyll from membrane or glass-filtered cells, using acetone as a solvent. The mass of the ash-free phytoplankton substance from which it came may have been some 35 times greater.

Assimilation numbers

After being warned of the error inherent in considering biomass the equivalent of production, the student must be aware of an important exception. Knowing the mass of chlorophyll is very close to knowing primary production. This applies especially to chlorophyll *a*. Its abundance tells a great deal, and because it is lively stuff, it is possible to establish empirically its relation to photosynthetic production.

Two men (Ryther and Yentsch 1957),

working at the Woods Hole Oceanographic Institute on Cape Cod, experimentally demonstrated something that had been suspected by Ryther and some earlier authors: a fairly constant relationship exists between chlorophyll and photosynthesis at any given light intensity. Thus, primary production studies, accompanied by collections and assays of chlorophyll *a*, permit calculation of an assimilation number. The milligrams of C fixed per m^3 during an average hour of daylight is divided by the mg of chlorophyll *a* in the same volume:

$$\frac{mg\ C\ per\ hour}{mg\ chlorophyll\ a} = assimilation\ number$$

Similarly, the average hourly photosynthetic rate beneath a square meter of lake surface could be divided by the chlorophyll *a* present beneath the same area. The quotient would be an assimilation number expressed in terms of unit area. In the same manner the oxygen released in the presence of a given mass of chlorophyll *a* can be calculated. This yields a number almost three times greater than the carbon result.

After a mean assimilation number has been established from research expeditions to some body of water, the mass of chlorophyll *a* within the illuminated portion is all that needs to be determined for future primary production assays. (However, a radical change in the composition of the algal community would negate this.) Multiplying the biomass of chlorophyll *a* by the assimilation number supplies a reasonable estimate of photosynthetic rate, precluding the need for tedious oxygen or carbon procedures. Thus McConnell (1963), studying a small Arizona impoundment named Peña Blanca Lake, settled upon 2.04 as an oxygen-chlorophyll assimilation number. Following this, he limited his field investigations of primary production there to determining the lake depth where about 1% of the incident solar radiation remained and to quantifying the chlorophyll in the stratum bounded by the surface and that depth.

Nutrients and temperature (controlling enzyme activity) affect photosynthetic rates directly as do age and adaptation of the cells. Furthermore, as phytoplankton populations increase, shading limits photosynthesis. Talling and associates (1973) suggested that an upper limit of gross production equals no more than 17.8 g C per m² per day, or the release of about 47 g of oxygen. This rate of production must be extremely rare because when chlorophyll concentrations roughly exceed 70 mg/m³ most of the incident light is absorbed within a meter of water, limiting the photosynthetic capacity of the community.* The figure put forth by Talling and his co-authors came from a tropical lake unusually high in salts and the raw stuff of photosynthesis, inorganic carbon.

In conclusion, then, when the biomass of most organisms is determined, a static parameter results. Coefficients converting it to production are arbitrary in light of our present state of knowledge. An exception is plant biomass, quantified as chlorophyll a, where assimilation numbers are known. These coefficients lead to translating standing crop to production rate.

Efficiency of primary production

The efficiency with which green plants convert radiant energy to potential chemical energy is low. An exact figure does not apply to all chlorophyllous communities, but 1% or 2% is often quoted. It depends, in part, on the manner by which efficiency is calculated. The general formula would be:

$$\frac{\lambda_n}{\lambda_{n-1}} \times 100$$

where λ_{n-1} represents solar radiation

and λ_n equals the energy in the primary producers. There are several ways in which the sunlight in the denominator could be treated: total incident sunlight, the visible radiation useful for photosynthesis (from about 380 to 720 nm), light penetrating to the community after correcting for reflectance and backscattering, light absorbed by the plant cells, and light absorbed by specific photosynthetic pigments. Each of these leads to a different index of efficiency for the plants.

Similarly, the numerator could be either the energy fixed during photosynthesis (gross production) or this energy minus respiration (net production). There are then ten possible producer efficiencies, a somewhat disenchanting number. Lindeman (1942b) compared solar radiation with gross primary production in Cedar Bog Lake, coming up with an efficiency of 0.1%. Had he corrected for the fact that only about one half of the incident wavelengths are useful in photosynthesis, the efficiency would have been doubled. Further corrections for reflectance (conservatively, 5%) and the diminishing radiation, after it strikes the lake surface and passes through water, would raise the efficiency of gross production even more.

Generalizations about the efficiencies of plants in capturing solar energy, calculated as the ratio of gross production in relation to total radiation per unit area, reveal that terrestrial communities often do a better job. Aquatic phototrophs are distributed downward from the surface upon which light impinges, and, as a result, their energy resources are diminished. The plants are less efficient than the animals that ultimately depend on them, yet another aspect invites attention. Ratios of energy expended in relation to gross production show that many terrestrial as well as aquatic primary producers respire only about 15% to 25% of the energy they fix. This indicates that their

*Parenthetically, 1 g of chlorophyll a per m² of lake surface is a high figure, although rare reports from unusually fertile habitats have indicated amounts 5 to 10 times this. Most lakes have far less.

inefficiency in capturing the energy available is compensated for by their ability to convert it to effective biomass.

PATHWAYS TO SECONDARY PRODUCTION

All ensuing transfers, transformations, and degradations of energy following primary production must be termed secondary production, the production of heterotrophs, which is supported by the net or effective energy synthesized by autotrophic producers. There are two main routes by which energy flows from the primary producers of ecosystems, one of which has been emphasized far beyond the other. The first, a commonly cited textbook example, involves grazing of green organisms by the herbivores; the energy of photosynthesis is passed on to the consumers. The second pathway, which has been neglected to a great extent, involves energy flow from dead plant material. For example, the livestock raiser feeds his herbivores via both the green, grazing pathway and the dead-hay route. The nonliving plant detritus in aquatic systems has a further dimension, the abundant microorganisms associated with it.

The term *seston* has been used in aquatic ecology for decades. It is defined as particulate material present in the water and includes both living plankters and their corpses. There are net seston and nannoseston, depending on particle size, and each is roughly defined by whether it is retained by a plankton net. The nonliving fragments have been called *tripton,* but now *detritus* is applied more frequently. Even the meaning of that word has been broadened as the notion of its importance has grown.

Organic detritus is of diverse origins, its plant components representing ungrazed material. The organic carbon compounds in plant detritus may be far in excess of those in an ecosystem's green cells at any given time, but the energy has not been completely lost to the consumers. Undigested plant material present in detritus passes through the gut of an animal, perhaps to be devoured subsequently by other species. This does not violate the second law of thermodynamics; energy is not reversing its flow in the system. The chemical energy in the plant cells has not been used yet, no matter where it has been since its formation. In part then, detritus consists of particles of plant and animal origin.

Wetzel and co-workers (1972) introduced a broader definition of detritus that covers more than particulate dead matter. They included the dissolved carbon-containing substances excreted by living plants and animals, as well as the soluble material leaking from decaying plant-animal detritus. There is abundant evidence that some algae can take in this soluble material, performing as heterotrophs.

Another characteristic of dissolved organic material was described by Baylor and Sutcliffe (1963), who found that air bubbling through filtered seawater brought about the formation of tiny plate-like aggregates of organic composition. They showed that these aggregates alone could sustain the filter-feeding brine shrimp *Artemia.* In a paper appearing directly after Baylor and Sutcliffe's report, Riley (1963) went further to show that these amorphous organic aggregates, formed by adsorption of soluble organic matter on bubbles and other surfaces, soon include bacteria and phytoplankton cells and increase from 5 μm to several millimeters in length.

Hynes (1969) detailed a similar phenomenon for the plant debris entering brook ecosystems. Leaves rapidly lose weight as soluble material leaches out. This substance rapidly becomes particulate; particles of 1 μm soon aggregate to form clumps 10 times as big. Earlier research (Fredeen 1960) has shown that blackfly *(Simulium)* larvae, typical of fast currents, filter out and utilize such tiny morsels as food. Meanwhile, the decaying leaves gain weight by absorbing nitrate, and a fungal community develops on them. As is pointed out later, these fungi are an important source of food energy for some arthropods in the stream, and later a bacterial flora flourishes on the feces of these animals to create another energy stock.

Now the definition of detritus includes matter composed of: planktogenic, pond-weed, and allochthonous fragments; feces and an associated bacterial flora; particles derived from agitation of soluble organics and an attached microflora; dissolved organic mixtures that can be used directly by some algae; and heterotrophic bacteria growing on silt particles. Rodina (1963) showed that lake detritus includes billions of microbes per gram, representing many physiologic groups, and that it suffices for supporting laboratory populations of *Daphnia.*

Most students of ecosystems have considered the bacteria as decomposers, fitting in somewhere at the end of the scheme, where they degrade the corpses of producers and consumers alike. This process of degradation is especially important in mineral and nutrient recycling. An awareness of the role of detritus changes such ideas drastically. Decay or mineralization of dead organisms is effected by microbial action; this is what builds bacterial cells. These cells can then be utilized by the filter feeders assigned to the primary consumer level in trophic chains. As a result, much less of the primary production is lost to the animals than was suspected by early investigators of energy flow in ecosystems. Bits of detritus may pass through the guts of consumers many times, apparently resistant to digestion. The animals are gaining energy, however, from ingesting bacteria, microbes that can break down the chemical-bond energy within the detri-

tus and pass it on within their cells.

A similar relationship was reported recently from a lotic ecosystem where other colorless organisms make available the energy of allochthonous detritus. Bär-locher and Kendrick (1973) showed that autumn leaves that have fallen into brooks support a rich fungal population. The amphipod *Gammarus pseudolimnaeus* often congregates in packets of these leaves and derives most of its nourishment from the fungal mycelia.

In ecosystems, then, an important role of microorganisms is to break down stubborn organic substances and make them available to animals, much like what goes on in the stomach cavities of a ruminant. In some introductory remarks preceding a symposium on the importance of detritus in aquatic ecosystems, Mann (1972) said, "I wonder if it would be more correct to say that plants are usually consumed by microorganisms, which in turn are consumed by animals, rather than to give the usual story about plants, herbivores, and carnivores."

SECONDARY PRODUCTION

The secondary producers cover a varied spectrum of organisms that accomplish their life activities by diminishing the stock of energy ultimately made available to them by primary producers. Dismissing the part played by bacteria in secondary production, we are left with the animal members of the community, including herbivores, omnivores, and predators. These are the true heterotrophs, ranging from ciliates to the sharks found in some freshwater lakes. Modes of feeding are so diverse among heterotrophs that assignment to discrete trophic levels is difficult, although we tend to categorize these animals as primary, secondary, tertiary, and quaternary consumers.

From examining trophic relations of the animals in an ecosystem, it is obvious why food "chain" gave way to food "web" in the parlance of biologists, the latter term designating more complexity. Taxonomic categories often include animals of contrasting feeding habits, assignable to different trophic levels. The calanoid copepod *Diaptomus* (see Fig. 3-8, *E*) feeds on limnetic phytoplankton in a manner reminiscent of its marine relative *Calanus*, which it closely resembles. Another calanoid, *Epischura* (see Fig. 3-8, *C*), often present in the limnoplankton, bears a superficial likeness to *Diaptomus* but preys upon it. To confound the issue further, some *Diaptomus* species in small mountain ponds attain unusual sizes and, as R. Stewart Anderson (1967) recently discovered, have abandoned the herbivorous way of life to feed upon smaller congeneric forms with which they coexist.

In addition, feeding habits change throughout life in many species, and there are marked seasonal aspects in diet for others. Long-standing generalizations about the niche occupied by a species in an ecosystem often do not hold up. Coregonid fishes, for example, are notably zooplankton feeders in lakes, but they turn to consuming bottom fauna at times.

Estimating secondary production of individual species

The measurement of secondary production is difficult for a multitude of reasons. There is no hourly rate to be established as in studies of photosynthesis, and standing crops contain no chlorophyll *a* to be converted to dynamic rates by assimilation numbers. Another inconvenience stems from the fact that some aquatic animals are perennial, while other species require only a week or so to complete a life cycle.

The simplest measurement, based on the annual take of economically important forms, such as fish and the larger molluscs and crustaceans, is not really simple even when forthright procedures are followed. If a known number of fish are introduced to a small pond early in the year and harvested later, a small part of the annual production can be computed. This quantity is termed yield and gives only a rough approximation of net production. Mortality prior to capture, which is part of the yearly production, was not taken into account. The portions taken up by predators or removed by bacterial decomposers and scavengers can only be guessed without additional data. Further complications arise from reproduction and the appearance of a new generation of individuals, many of whom died during the year. To all of these variables could be added metabolic loss, another part of gross production.

According to Mann (1969), this problem was first attacked with success by the Danish marine biologist Boysen Jensen, working with the bivalve *Solen* and other benthic invertebrates. His technique was based on the yearly difference between numbers and individual masses of a given age class of the clam. It was rationalized that the production in time could be approximated by:

$$P = (N_1 - N_2) \times \frac{w_1 + w_2}{2}$$

N_1 and N_2 are the numbers of animals per unit area at the beginning and end of the year, respectively, and w_1 and w_2 are the corresponding mean weights of individuals. The product of the average weight and the number of individuals that disappeared represents the production that had been either consumed by members of higher trophic levels or that had perished and been mineralized by microorganisms.

Boysen Jensen's approach to estimating production, with various refinements, has served subsequent workers. It is especially useful for reckoning production in populations with long life cycles. The problem becomes more difficult when animals have short life cycles and are constantly producing young, as is true for many plankters.

Edmondson (1960) published a scheme

for estimating production rate in planktonic rotifers. The problem in working with such animals is that samples taken at intervals could contain identical numbers yet tell nothing about the number of intervening generations and the population's production. Similarly, the ratio of eggs carried to females in the samples reveals nothing of the birth rate nor how often eggs were produced. Edmondson studied the rotifers in the laboratory, subjecting females carrying newly extruded eggs to different temperatures and noting the varying times it took the eggs to hatch. With information gathered on effects of temperature on duration of embryonic development, the lake temperature at time of collecting became a significant datum. The number of eggs produced per female per day, B, was calculated by $B = E/D$, where E stood for the number of eggs per female in the plankton sample and D was the duration of the embryonic stage. Thus, if 40% of the females carried single eggs, E would be 0.4. If the temperature were such that the value of D was 4 days, production would be 0.1 eggs per female per day. At some higher temperature, implying complete embryonic development in $1/2$ day, the same egg/female ratio (E) would represent eight times the daily production of the former case.

Edmondson went further to estimate an instantaneous birthrate, $b' = \ln (B + 1)$, and a coefficient of population increase, r', from counting the populations, N, on two successive dates, t_0 and t_1, r' being:

$$\frac{\ln N_0 - \ln N_t}{t}$$

From these calculations the death rate, d', was estimated as:

$$d' = b' - r'$$

With rotifer biomass data on hand, the production could be fixed as the product of mortality and mass.

Edmondson's rotifer technique can be applied to other plankters that carry their eggs until hatching and hold them after being killed and preserved; most copepods are especially suitable for such investigation. Actually, the method had its beginnings with Elster (1954) and Eichhorn (1957), who worked with calanoid copepods and showed the dependency of embryonic duration on temperature.

As data accumulate, it may become possible simply to apply the concept of the van't Hoff temperature coefficient, the Q_{10} value denoting the degree to which a process is accelerated for each 10° C increase. There are remarkable similarities in the temperature-development curves among some groups of related

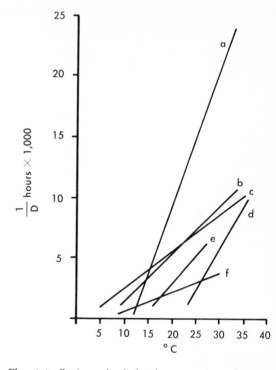

Fig. 4-4. Reciprocal of development time, from hatching of egg to maturity, in relation to temperature. *a, Moina* sp. (Brown 1929); *b, Simocephalus* sp. (Brown 1929); *c, Daphnia* (Brown 1929); *d, Eulimnadia antlei,* southwestern, temporary-pond conchostracan (Belk 1972); *e, Streptocephalus seali,* anostracan from humid-region temporary ponds (Moore 1957); *f, Diaptomus pallidus,* calanoid copepod from permanent lakes (Geiling and Campbell 1972). (Adapted from Winberg 1971.)

species, although divergences can be expected because of special adaptations to cold water or to transitory ponds (Fig. 4-4).

The literature on appraising magnitudes and rates of secondary production has grown to remarkable proportions in recent years and cannot be treated further here. The works by Mann (1969), Winberg (1971), and Edmondson and Winberg (1971) are recommended as excellent sources for further details.

Estimating secondary production at the trophic level

A unifying goal in studying ecosystems is the balancing of an energy equation for every component of each trophic level and thence for each level as a unit. Therefore, the best approach to the complexities of community secondary production is probably the study of individual species in the laboratory to gain information that will aid in interpreting quantitative field data. Some important facts to be assembled in such investigations are: caloric equivalents of dry weights; respiratory rate as a function of temperature, age, stage of development, and size; and growth efficiencies under various conditions.

Consideration of certain basic assumptions generally shows what knowledge should be sought. First, the food requirement for an individual can be quantified as: (1) calories as the sum of energy used in growth, (2) metabolic loss via excretion and respiration, and (3) the energy not used and therefore eliminated with the feces. Second, net production during the life cycle can be quantified as the sum of (1) somatic body growth, (2) reproductive-organ and gamete production, and (3) the energy in molted exoskeletons of many invertebrates.

Teal (1957) studied individual organisms of the Root Spring fauna both in the laboratory and isolated in bottles submerged in the spring water. From the data acquired, he was able to approximate what was going on at each trophic level in the spring by correlating information derived from field collections. Comita (1964) spent many months studying *Diaptomus siciloides* in the laboratory and came up with an annual energy budget for the species. With these data, he later calculated energy relations of the entire plankton community (1972). Many field samples implied five generations of *Diaptomus* per year. Extrapolation from laboratory data permitted Comita to make judgments about the annual energy flow in the entire lake for this species, the most important primary consumer.

The great amount of work necessary for measuring secondary production in aquatic invertebrates, many with several overlapping generations each year, has inspired search for applicable generalities. For example, the relationship between production (P) and mean biomass (B), expressed as the P/B ratio, recalls the assimilation number in primary production, both of which can be set down in kcal/m^2 per year. Work is in progress to see whether P/B values lead to applicable indices that will serve in translating biomass to some dynamic growth rate. Studies to date have shown that the P/B number is greater in smaller species of a taxonomic group: for example, species of chironomids with diminutive larvae have a higher figure than those with larger larvae. Furthermore, cladoceran P/B ratios surpass those of the copepods, and daily rates for both groups are lower in the cold water of northern lakes, except for some stenothermal species that thrive at such temperatures (Winberg 1972).

Studies of growth efficiencies have established values for ratios such as P/C, production in relation to total food consumed, and P/A, the production divided by *assimilated* food. The former has been symbolized K_1, equalling gross growth efficiency, and the latter is K_2, the net growth efficiency. P/C may be subject to more variability than P/A; yet Mann (1969) states that P/C figures for entire populations are better for showing magnitude of energy flow in and out of a given trophic level.

Biomass and efficiency of secondary producers

The Eltonian pyramid can be developed to model individual numbers, individual sizes, biomass, mean energy content, and annual production rates of successive trophic levels. Ideally, there is a diminution upward from the base, although in the case of individual body sizes, the pyramid might balance on its vertex. In an aquatic pyramid of mean mass, the base might be the dissolved solids in the water, followed by layers representing primary producers, bacteria, and the animals. In agreement with the generalization that biomass differs from production, a pyramid based on biomass may be imperfect, whereas production data provide good building blocks for an ideal pyramid (see Fig. 4-3).

A generality that is useful, yet only approximate, is to consider a loss of 99% from solar radiation to primary producers, and from then on, as energy flows from one trophic level to the next, a loss of 90% at each exchange (see Fig. 4-1). This means that biomass, or production of the first carnivore level, should be about 1% of primary production or 0.01% of solar radiation. An approximation of such a condition was shown by McConnell (1963), who found that the harvest of centrarchid fishes from Peña Blanca Lake was about 0.98% of the photosynthesis. This generality about energy flow be-

tween trophic levels is ecologic efficiency, the P/C ratio for all members of a trophic level collectively. It is only a rough approximation because loss of energy varies from 70% to 95% in transfers from plants to herbivores, and herbivores to carnivores. Nevertheless, the principle that animals are more efficient than plants in utilizing energy available to them still applies. Slobodkin (1972) questions the universitality of the 10% loss in energy exchanges while denying the probability that evolution could stabilize ecologic efficiencies, but he points out that animal effectiveness in taking prey, for example, is subject to evolutionary selection.

Lindeman (1942b) believed there were grounds for the notion that efficiency increases from the herbivores to the top carnivores of an ecosystem. This idea has not found support in subsequent research on individual P/C or P/A figures (Odum 1957).

Another ratio, R/P (respiration in relation to gross production), shows that, typically, animals spend a greater part of their energy on respiration than plants do. Furthermore, in many instances it appears that carnivores outdo the herbivores in this respect.

The search for general principles continues, but certain verities have stood the test of time. The magnitude of secondary production depends on the rate at which organic compounds are synthesized in primary production; and, as Deevey (1951) reminded us, managing a fish pond to take only the top carnivores for food is akin to raising peacocks for sustenance, but eating only the tongues!

5
Lake origins

The area of limnology dealing with lake origins can hardly be differentiated from geology, and particularly the branch termed geomorphology. Hutchinson (1957) devoted a chapter to the subject of lake origins, assigning them to 11 major categories; only 2 were not geologic. (The 11 main classifications were fractionated to 76 subdivisions, and 12 of these were divided further.)

Some geologic phenomena that build lakes have been somewhat restricted to certain times, climates, or geographic areas. As a result there are definite districts where lakes of similar age and origin are now clustered, or were in the past.

Categorizing the methods by which lakes are born can be oversimplified, because processes often interact to create and flood basins. A further complexity in this geologic aspect of limnology is that there have been some dramatic recent changes in opinion about what factors caused certain lakes to be formed.

The concave nature of a lake's basin leads inexorably to accumulation of sediments and thus to eventual death of the lake. Erosion and wind bring in allochthonous materials; settling materials formed within the lake itself contribute a portion to the bottom deposits. The trend is toward a terrestrial community where the lake once stood. Some lakes are fleeting features of the landscape, while others occupy such deep depressions that millions of years would be required for their filling.

GLACIAL LAKES
Background of glaciology

Important and fundamental contributions to limnology have come from studies of glacial lakes. For this reason, glacial events as lake-forming phenomena are considered first. North American limnology owes much to early workers who investigated glacial lakes such as Lake Mendota, Wisconsin, Cedar Bog Lake,

Minnesota (Fig. 5-1), and Linsley Pond, Connecticut.

A short introduction to some geologic terminology is appropriate. We are living in the Holocene epoch, as the Recent epoch is generally called. It is the time following the last glacial period, a postglacial span during which our modern soils and landscapes were fashioned. The Holocene's beginning commenced with the ending of the Pleistocene epoch some 10,500 or more years BP ("before the present"), the time being subtracted from 1950 AD. Together the Holocene and Pleistocene epochs comprise the Quaternary period, which was preceded by the Tertiary period. The Pleistocene was marked by four great ice ages, of which the last, the *Wisconsin,* is of limnologic interest in North America. It corresponds to the North European *Weichsel,* the Pol-

Fig. 5-1. Cedar Bog Lake, Minnesota, the senescent kettle lake made famous by Lindeman (1942). Bog forest and sedge mat occupy most of the former basin. (Photo by Donald B. Lawrence.)

ish and USSR *Varsovian,* and the *Würm* glaciation of the Alps. Perhaps 17,000 years BP the Wisconsin ice began to dwindle, with deglaciation completed to a great extent 6 or 7 thousand years later. At the glaciers' maxima about 31.5% of the world's land area was covered. Today the glaciers, existing in cold regions that receive abundant snowfall, cover about 10% of the land (Flint 1957).

The ice sheets of Pleistocene glaciation left the upper latitudes of the Northern Hemisphere well endowed with lakes. Immediately beyond the ice margin in periglacial areas, tundra and permafrost prevailed, and local glaciers developed in mountains farther south. Climatic conditions were such, farther from the ice and beyond the permafrost, that lakes developed in basins that are now dry or contain saline relicts only.

The Pleistocene was a period of greater precipitation, lower temperature, and marked cloudiness as compared with the present, and most important, it was a time of reduced evaporation—a pluvial age. Pluvial lakes owed their existence to the climatic trends that produced glaciers to the north and at higher altitudes, but the depressions they occupied were products of phenomena other than glacial activity.

Lakes associated with existing glaciers

Certain lakes exist only when in contact with active glaciers. This type of lake is, of course, much scarcer at present than in the past. Pools of water lying in the icy depressions on glaciers, or collecting beneath to form bizarre subglacial lakes, and streams dammed by advancing tongues of ice from mountain glaciers are good examples of such types today. The literature concerned with these lakes stresses their impermanence due to impounding ice that gives way to release waters with a rush.

Summer visitors to the Columbia Ice Fields in western Canada may have seen

another characteristic type. A pool of water lies at the glacier's extremity in a depression bounded by the ice and a morainic dam below.

Lakes formed near glaciers

Waters associated with active glaciers are perhaps curiosities, but lakes that exist now because of long-gone glaciers are near the heart of limnology. Of these, some lakes formed because of colder past climates or because of the proximity of glaciers, and indeed this type of lake— the *periglacial frost-thaw basin*—is being produced today.

Lozinsky (1909) introduced the term *periglacial* to refer to the cold climate beyond glacial ice sheets. According to Péwé (1969), the modern periglacial zone is marked by permafrost areas, where the ground is permanently frozen, only a relatively thin upper layer thawing in the summer. Geologists find evidence for former periglacial environments in unusual soil configurations called ice-wedge casts. These indicate the former presence of vertical, wedge-shaped veins of ground ice. Mean annual temperatures from $-1.0°$ to $-2.0°$ C are a prerequisite for the existence of ice wedges, but their active growth requires temperatures from $-6.0°$ to $-8.0°$ C.

The physiographic province known as the Arctic Coastal Plain in Alaska covers more than 67,500 km², lying adjacent to the Arctic Ocean from 69° to 71° North latitude. In it are tens of thousands of elliptical lakes, oriented on NW-SE axes and, on the average, pointing N 12° W. Their basins are above permafrost, where subzero temperatures are prevalent not far below the soil surface. Limnologists have explained the genesis of these elliptical lakes by localized melting that forms tiny pools. Loss of insulation by damage to plant cover may initiate this. Each pool grows, according to Hopkins (1949), by migrating in the direction of the strongest summer winds, caving in newly melted material on the downwind side. Hopkins' explanation may oversimplify the orientation of the lakes because the long axes of most lie at right angles to the modern summer wind. Livingstone (1963a) gives a good account of the Arctic Coastal Plain lakes and the theories and controversy concerning their alignment.

A district of mostly extinct lakes in the New Jersey coastal plain is composed of hundreds of basins stretching from the Raritan River at New Brunswick, about 8 km south of the greatest advance of the Wisconsin ice, to the tip of Cape May, 65 km farther south. These lakes are shallow, about 3 m, and in many cases filled with peat. They range up to 2.5 km², but most are much less expansive. The presence of many ice-wedge casts in the soils of this part of New Jersey leaves little doubt that these are periglacial frost-thaw basins that formed near the continental ice mass more than 10,000 years ago (Wolfe 1953). They are irregular in outline and unoriented, quite unlike the Alaskan periglacial lakes that are still forming today.

Pingo is an Eskimo word applying to certain hills rising above the surrounding tundra. A pingo is formed when water under pressure ascends through gaps in the permafrost, freezes, and lifts an ice dome that is covered with alluvium and tundra vegetation. During uplift the alluvial cap ruptures, and the ice, no longer insulated, melts to form a crater that may contain water. Likens and Johnson (1966) described an unusual lake in a pingo near the small Alaskan settlement named Circle. The pingo is 450 m in diameter. The thaw crater in its center is 13.8 m deep and contains 8.8 m of water forming a nearly circular lake, quite different from the oriented lakes of the coastal plain farther north.

Lakes formed where glaciers existed

Relevant terminology. Ice, moving slowly down mountain slopes, spreading out over the piedmont regions, and perhaps joining other ice masses to form expansive sheets, is not clean. It carries rocky material of many sizes, from boulders to silty particles, and it scours and pushes materials ahead as it advances. When the ice melts, the rocky debris is left behind.

Glacial *outwash* applies to material carried from and beyond the ice as a glacier retreats by melting. A melting, isolated ice mass, stranded by its retreating parent ice sheet, can also produce outwash material. This may be designated as *drift,* a general term for any accumulation of direct or indirect glacial origin, including boulders, sand, and gravel. The word *moraine* designates drift deposited directly by a glacier; outwash, therefore, is not morainic.

Lakes in ground moraine. Ground moraine is the drift left on a surface over which a glacier has moved. Upon melting, the glacier leaves an expansive region of irregularly surfaced drift, perhaps containing masses of detached ice like raisins in a cookie. Such dead ice blocks may persist for centuries because of the insulation afforded by overlying drift, but eventually melt, leaving water-filled pits. *Kettle,* or *pit, lakes* occupy such depressions. The irregular low spots in the ground moraine contain water if the climate permits. Thus, in recently deglaciated regions such as the Ungava Peninsula of Quebec, much of the northern area is water. Shallow lakes with irregular shorelines are abundant. Erosion subsequent to deglaciation has not altered them much or filled them in. Farther south, in the Great Plains physiographic province, a later stage is seen. In the rolling plains of North Dakota, for example, prairie sloughs represent deeper ground-moraine lakes of the past. Many have been obliterated in the last 10,000 years.

Kettle lakes may be many hundreds of years younger than one might expect. They do not necessarily form immediately after the glacier's recession. Insulated by an overburden of drift, the detached ice mass persists long after the parent glacier has disappeared from the region. A typical plant succession may follow, supported by the drift above the residual ice. Herbaceous species, appearing first, give way to alder thickets, which are followed in turn by forests. As a result, cores of sediment taken from some North American kettle lakes yield spruce needles, twigs, bark, and other evidence of a boreal forest *below* the sediments of lacustrine origin (Florin and Wright 1969).

Lakes formed by morainic impoundment. Several categories of morainic lakes are formed by ponding rather than by ground moraines. A glacier, moving down a valley, blocks and impounds a tributary, and long after its ice has wast-

ed, a damming lateral moraine is left behind. Lakes resulting from such impoundment are not rare, but a commoner type is formed by a terminal moraine, marking the farthest extent of the ice. In many such cases, however, *corrasion,* mechanical erosion, was also involved. Thus, the grinding abrasion of a tongue of ice moving down a river valley converts it from a V-shaped trough to a typical glacial valley, U-shaped in cross section.

Fremont Lake (Fig. 5-2) in the Wyoming mountains illustrates the interplay of corrasion and morainic ponding (Rickert and Leopold 1972). The elongate lake, which must be one of the finest pristine lakes remaining in the United States, is in a trough of granite, scoured by glacial debris and ice and plugged downstream

Fig. 5-2. Fremont Lake, Wyoming, an ultraoligotrophic glacial lake formed by corrasion and morainic damming. View toward the terminal moraine that impounds the lake. (Photo by G. Heilman.)

by a terminal moraine. The lake covers 20.6 km² and is 185 m deep.

More complicated, the eleven Finger Lakes of New York state are narrow bodies of water, semiparallel, oriented north-south, and impounded at *both* ends by drift. They were formed in river valleys, gouged out by ice to depths below sea level in the two deepest, Seneca and Cayuga lakes. The southern limits are blocked by complex terminal moraines of a Wisconsin ice advance somewhat older than the moraines at the northern shores.

Lakes formed by hydraulic force on drift. During temporary decreases in the rate of glacial wasting, recessional moraines are left behind. Where retreats are marked by several rate changes, complex and jumbled morainic hills eventually form. Such morainic mounds and valleys in Itasca State Park, Minnesota, are called the Itasca Moraine. Hundreds of lakes, ponds, and bogs occupy depressions in that region. Many of these existing lakes are elongate, a characteristic that leads to the proposal that melt water, streaming under pressure beneath the ice, washed out deep elongate basins in the drift. This explains the morphology of Lake Itasca itself and a topographic continuation of its southeast arm, a narrow, deep valley, dry now except for a few deeper depressions that contain isolated, well-protected lakes. One of these, Demming Lake, is best known, thanks to the work of Hooper (1951) and Baker and Brook (1971). Hydraulic force, then, is another glacial activity in lake building. Hutchinson (1957) discussed examples of this phenomenon that occurred in Denmark, Germany, and Poland.

Glacial scour lakes. Although emphasis has been placed on basins in drift depressions and ponded by drift barriers, corrasion as a lake-forming force needs attention. The striking corrasive effect of ice moving down valleys is seen in modern *fjords*. They are restricted to coastal areas of high relief where there was severe Pleistocene glaciation. Towering cliffs rise abruptly above deeply scoured, elongate, narrow passageways. Fjords commonly connect with the sea, but many are lakelike, above sea level, and separated from marine waters by rocky sills at their outer ends. The process of isostatic elevation (uplift after having been depressed by ice) is very important in the genesis of a fjord lake. The fabled Scottish Loch Ness is one of these.

Great Slave Lake in the Northwest Territory of Canada is the deepest lake in North America. Its surface is 150 m above sea level, but its maximum depth is reached about 464 m below sea level. This basin is largely the result of corrasion beneath a great mass of continental ice. A more remarkable example is the Norwegian Mjösen, a glacial scour lake with its shoreline 395 m above sea level, but having maximum depth at 720 m, a point 325 m below mean sea level.

Familiar examples are the Laurentian Great Lakes of North America, which owe a great part of their origin to glacial corrasion, although tectonic events were also involved. Lake Superior, especially, lying in an enormous Precambrian syncline, might be better classified as a lake of mixed origins.

Cirque lakes. At the very head of a mountain glacier is an abrupt crevasse, the Bergschrund of German authors. It is bounded by the ice and an abrupt, nearly vertical headwall of rock. Daily freezing and thawing of the melt water at the base of the crevasse and of rain and melted snow trickling down the headwall shatter bits of the rock from it. In addition, the glacier grinds the rock beneath it, perhaps by rotational slip of the ice. The result is a cirque, typically with a concave floor that meets the headwall sharply above and is bounded below by a lip or threshold of rock. These armchair-shaped hollows can hold cirque lakes. In English-speaking regions the word *tarn* has become a specific name for these appealing mountain lakes.

TECTONIC LAKES

Tectonism refers to the earth's crustal instability and all its behavior. Warping, faulting, fracturing, buckling, folding, thrusting, and quaking are words that apply to deformation and adjustment of the earth's shell; they describe tectonic phenomena. From crustal movements come depressions that can hold water, making up, in some cases, the most remarkable lakes of the world.

Graben, fault-trough, or rift lakes

A *graben* is a depressed, usually elongate block of the earth's crust lying between faults and adjacent highlands. Typically the graben or fault-block is untilted, forming the flat bottom of a trough. Its development was preceded by crustal fracturing called faulting (Fig. 5-3). Two parallel faults or rifts isolated a block that sank lower to become the graben. In addition, its depression may have been relatively increased by attendant crustal uplift of land on either side. The ideal symmetrical graben forms a steep-walled,

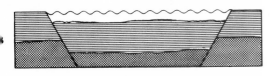

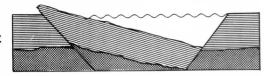

Fig. 5-3. Formation of graben lakes. **A,** The rocks before faulting; **B,** a lake occupying a symmetrical graben; **C,** lake occupying a graben with a tilted fault-block.

flat-bottomed lake such as Lake Tahoe, California-Nevada.

The most remarkable graben lakes are two ancient bodies of water, Baikal of Siberia, with an unsurpassed depth of more than 1.7 km, and the second deepest, Tanganyika of East Africa.

A giant fracture system known as the midocean rift has been studied in recent years and traced around the world. Some branches of the rift go inland as conspicuous terrestrial features. The Red Sea trough and its northward continuation, the Jordan–Dead Sea Rift, are part of the system. From the south end of the Red Sea, the African Rift valleys commence. Two enormous rents in the earth's crust compose these African Great Rift valleys. The eastern rift extends south for 1,500 km to Tanzania, containing many more small lakes than the western valley. Nyasa, 760 m deep, and Tanganyika, with a maximum depth of more than 1,400 m, are the most remarkable of the African lakes and occupy depressions in the western rift.

The tectonic lakes of the African Rift valleys, are not so idealized as Lake Tahoe, for asymmetry is common among them. With respect to sea level, the lowest part of the African Rift valleys, if indeed it belongs to the same system, holds the Dead Sea, its bottom being 793 m below sea level. Utah's Great Salt Lake also occupies a graben and is reminiscent of the Dead Sea.

The large freshwater lakes in the Nicaraguan Lowland, Lake Nicaragua and Managua, are in an area famed for volcanic activity. At one time they were believed to represent results of Pleistocene and Holocene volcanism, being remnants of a Pacific bay isolated through damming by volcanic cones and ashfalls. The occurrence of sawfish, tarpon, and a shark, erroneously assigned Pacific affinities, strengthened this idea. However, the modern concept is that the lakes occupy a late Tertiary–early Quaternary graben, and the evidence for a marine past is lacking. The disastrous earthquake of 1972 in Nicaragua emphasized that the lakes are in a region of tectonic as well as volcanic activity.

Uplift lakes, the result of epeirogeny

Epeirogenesis is the term applied to wide-reaching tectonic events that raise large crustal blocks and sometimes bring about the formation of enormous basins. It is a slow process when compared with orogeny (typical mountain building by folding and thrusting of the earth's crust). The prime example of an epeirogenetic lake is the Caspian Sea, with the greatest area of them all. It appears to have been originally a submarine depression. During the Tertiary it was raised to inland status, cut off from the sea, and subsequently freshened.

The major high-altitude lake in the world is Lake Titicaca, lying across the boundary of Peru and Bolivia high in the Andes more than 3,800 m above the sea. It is fed largely by snow melt. A rather rapid epeirogenesis was one of the tectonic events in the history of the lake. Its basin, a low spot in a great plateau of inland drainage known as the Altiplano, is thought to have been raised on high from altitudes but a few hundred meters above the Pacific during and since the Tertiary.

Floridians are proud of Lake Okeechobee, which, they point out, is the largest body of fresh water entirely within the boundaries of one state. (The dilute nature of the water must be stressed in order to take Great Salt Lake out of the competition.) Okeechobee occupies a shallow depression in land that was lifted by epeirogeny from below the sea surface. It holds water largely because of the damming effect of an accumulation of plant material.

Earthquake lakes

Reelfoot Lake, Tennessee-Kentucky, came into being almost overnight in 1811, or at least the mythology of the region tells us this. A series of earthquakes created lowlands into which Mississippi River water spilled. The wooded, subsided areas received waters richly endowed in nutrients. The largest depression is Reelfoot, noted for its exceptional sports fishery. Much of the basin is now marshland, and because of erosion from adjacent farms, the lake is shoaling in rapidly.*

LANDSLIDE LAKES

Many lakes are known throughout the world that owe their existence to the impoundment of stream valleys by rock slides, mud flows, or other mass movements of soil and rock. The lakes formed by such impoundment are often short lived because a stream obstructed by such a barrier might eventually overflow and destroy it.

Mountain Lake, Virginia, has been the scene of summer biology instruction for many years and the site of some interesting limnologic research. Hutchinson and Pickford (1932) showed that Mountain Lake's morphology overrides its edaphic heritage, displaying many aspects of eutrophy despite its nutrient-impoverished water. Roth and Neff (1964) summarized the pertinent preexisting literature on Mountain Lake and published the results of their own extensive limnologic study there.

Mountain Lake is the only natural lake of consequence in the unglaciated Appalachians. Sometime during the early Holocene a mountain valley was dammed by a landslide of sandstone. Its level may have fluctuated much since then, but now it is about 32 m deep. It has not

---

*Because this shallow lake is studded with tree trunks and stumps, a unique boat has evolved on its shores in response to their threat. The Reelfoot skiff is rowed in the normal fashion, but because of an extra pivot and joint in the oar-oarlock mechanism, the oarsman moves forward rather than blindly backward.

breached the slide-rock dam, because it is fed by no more than precipitation, seepage, and underwater springs.

Although most landslide lakes are solitary, Martin (1960) studied an entire high-altitude lake district of this type in Costa Rica. The lakes are boglike, in some instances completely filled in. They are found in narrow valleys at altitudes where precipitation is high, but stream flow is not continuous. Landslides are common along the steep-sided valleys, impounding runoff to form numerous small ponds. Many of these have been able to run the course of their life cycles to extinction because stream flow has not been great enough to destroy the landslide dams.

LAKES FORMED BY VOLCANIC PHENOMENA
Geography of volcanic lakes

Volcanism has modified and shaped past landscapes in many areas of the world and continues to do so today. The depressions owed to volcanic activity, then, occur in many countries, and their formation is in no way related to climate. To keep basins full, however, a water source is needed, and today there are dead volcanic lake districts in arid zones where lakes flourished in the pluvial climate of the Pleistocene.

Important contributions to limnology have come from studies of volcanic lakes.

For example, a large portion of Japan's limnologic endeavor has been focused on lakes formed by volcanic activity. Also, much of what is known about tropical limnology is based on studies of volcanic lakes in Java, Sumatra, and Bali (Ruttner 1931) and the Central American lakes investigated by Juday (1916), Deevey (1957), and Armitage (1958).

Volcanoes are common in areas of tectonism. Thus, among the graben lakes of the African Rift valleys, there are many small lakes occupying depressions created by volcanism.

Crater lakes

The deepest lake in the Unted States is Crater Lake, Oregon, occupying a *caldera* (Fig. 5-4), a collapsed volcanic crater formed when underlying magma (molten rock) flows out. Other crater lakes are contained in *maars* (from the German Maare), formed by subterranean explosions that created low rims but left little cinder and lava material. Many of these explosion craters form deep circular lakes with relatively small areas. The Lac d'Issarles in France is 108.6 m deep with an area of 92 ha. Pulvermaar in Germany holds a lake covering 35 ha and 74 m deep. Thienemann's important contributions to the concept of lake typology and theoretic limnology, it must be remembered, came from studying explosion craters. In the Eifel lake district, the im-

Fig. 5-4. Crater Lake, Oregon, a magnificent caldera lake and the deepest body of water in the United States. (Courtesy National Park Service.)

Fig. 5-5. A, Zuñi Salt Lake, New Mexico, an eroded maar with secondary cinder cones. **B,** The lakelet in the cinder cone at the Zuñi maar. (Photos by J. Platt Bradbury.)

portance of mean depth in separating eutrophic conditions from oligotrophy became evident to Thienemann.

In western New Mexico, the Zuñi Salt Lake, which Bradbury (1971) studied recently, is a maar that was formed by volcanic explosions in the late Pleistocene. It is quite different from the deep holes occupied by most maar lakes. A subsequent explosion or explosions caused lava and cinders to well up and fill the crater as secondary cinder cones were produced. The main lake occupies an area of 60 ha with a maximum depth of 1.0 m. From it emerge three secondary cones, one of which is almost perfect, having undergone very little erosion and containing a small circular lake (Fig. 5-5), which seems to be a comparatively unmodified crater, rather than a collapsed caldera. Its enclosed pool lies above the level of the main lake and has a mean depth of 3 m. Such a crater lake, present in an unmodified cinder cone, is rare. Most are contained by maars or calderas.

Lakes in lava depressions

Usually lake-holding depressions in lava flows are caused when the upper layer cools, forming a crust over the hotter magma beneath. The latter may drain out leaving space into which the crust sags. The result is a shallow depression. Collapse following the withdrawal of magma created quite a different type of depression in the magnificent, deep (340 m) Guatemalan Lake Atitlán, studied by Deevey (1957). Cauldron subsidence, the name given to the process whereby this lake was formed, involves the lowering of a great cylindrical block, fractured peripherally, into a chamber created by the outflow of molten rock.

Coulee lakes

The word *coulee* is commonly used in the American Southwest to refer to dry gulches and arroyos. The geologic word,

however, refers to solidified volcanic flow and not to the valley it impounds.

Coulee lakes are formed by lava impoundment. Perhaps the molten material pours across valleys to dam river channels or blocks only gentle depressions. An excellent example of a coulee lake, a newcomer among ancient rift lakes, is Lake Kivu between the African nations of Zaire and Rwanda. A river that flowed north to Lake Edward on its way to the Nile was blocked by a late Pleistocene lava flow. The magnificent, deep (480 m) Kivu was the result. It did not breach the lava dam, but subsequently overflowed southward and now drains to Lake Tanganyika.

A little lake district on the Colorado Plateau near Flagstaff, Arizona, is present because of past volcanic activity. Most of the lakes are nearly extinct, reviving during rainy years. Some are impounded by lava dams or occupy much eroded calderas; others occupy shallow depressions in sheets of lava. Nearly all the methods by which volcanism creates lakes can be demonstrated in this area.

SOLUTION LAKES
Lakes in carbonate substrates

Basins created by dissolution and removal of material may later hold water to become lakes or ponds. Usually the carbonates of calcium and to a lesser extent magnesium are the solutes. Because calcium carbonate is soluble in aqueous solutions, and especially when the water is acid, karst features may develop in climates where there is ample precipitation. The term *karst* refers to the sum of surface and subsurface aspects that characterize regions where carbonate rocks and particularly the common limestone are exposed. Generally, in karst regions there are underground passages and channels, increasing permeability to such an extent that surface streams are scarce. *Cryptorheism,* meaning hidden drainage, prevails; soils are scanty; and the topography may be rugged and pock marked by the collapse of surface rocks into subterranean caverns.

Water collecting in surface depressions may seep into joints and cracks in the limestone below, enlarging the lines of weakness and draining the surface. Circulating water removes soluble material and weakens overlying layers, eventually creating depressions called *sinks, dolinas,* or *swallow holes.* They may be cone shaped, shallow and dishlike, or steepwalled, resembling wells. At times they connect with underground channels and contain water continuously or irregularly. Soils and debris tend to wash into the sinks, choking them so that they hold water even when the groundwater table drops. Such systems are unstable, however, and there have been exciting instances of plug failure in a sinkhole followed by the abrupt drainage of its lake to subterranean passages.

One of the world's most extensive karst tracts is the level Nullabor Plain of southern Australia, but at present watering places are scarce in that arid region. The karst terranes of deserts are relics because corrosion of limestone continues only as long as a supply of acidic water exists. Commonly it is carbonic acid formed by the hydration of CO_2. Karstification proceeds most efficiently, therefore, in humid limestone regions.

The Tertiary limestones capping central Florida have created the best North American example of a large lake district due to solution. Because the topography is low and the climate humid, the water table is high and lakes are common. Many of these are nearly circular, typical of solution collapse basins. Others lie in basins formed by coalesced dolinas and are, therefore, less regular in shape, being somewhat like a figure 8, if two were formed together, but much more complex in shape if more sinks were involved. At least one of the Florida lakes is more than 30 m deep, but most of them are probably 5 m or less. A recent article concerning a detailed study of 55 of these lakes and ponds contains a short summary of the limnologic contributions that have come from the Florida lake district (Shannon and Brezonik 1972).

Typical also of karst landscapes are large springs situated at widespread intervals, discharging great quantities of water from enormous arterial channels formed from enlargement of solution crevices and fractures in limestone. Silver Spring in Florida, where H. T. Odum (1957) did his classic study of community energy flow among trophic levels, is one of these.

Most of the Yucatán Peninsula in Mexico has a flat karst topography overlying limestone. Much of the rock is exposed and fluted by solution depressions. There is no surface drainage; therefore, steep-sided solution basins known as *cenotes* serve as water sources. When these circular sinks connect with the water table, they form natural wells. (The ancient Mayans built temples by some of the cenotes that they considered sacred. As a result, these solution lakes have provided rewarding opportunities for modern underwater archeologic research.) Limnologic research on the cenotes has been rare, but it began with Pearse and associates (1936), who studied 30 of them ranging in depth from 0.5 to 54 m. Back and Hanshaw (1970) compared the cenotes with the sinks of Florida.

Parts of the states of Indiana, Tennessee, Kentucky, and Missouri are noted for their karstic topographies and cave districts. Although small water-filled dolinas are not rare, many of the associated aquatic habitats are underground streams and lakes, and most of the research done on them has been faunistic in its approach. In southwestern Kentucky some dry sinks connect with subterranean waters during the early spring when the water table rises. At that time, water flows out to cover low depressions (which will be cornfields later in the year), and two aquatic communities mingle. The cave fish *Chologaster* emerges from the caverns below to feed on the rich crustacean fauna of the epigean temporary pond. Then it returns to the underground habitat as the water recedes, having enjoyed a vernal banquet most cave species never experience.

The Kaibab Plateau in northern Arizona is capped by a remarkably flat, thick layer of limestone. As a result, a little-known lake district composed of sinks occurs north of the Grand Canyon of the Colorado. It must be pointed out, however, that it is composed of small ponds, many of them transitory, that have attracted no biologists except those interested in fairy shrimps, copepods, and larval salamanders. In well-watered areas this "lake" district would receive even less attention.

Lakes in salt-collapse basins

Calcium carbonate and to some extent magnesium carbonate are the common solutes in karst regions. Corrosion, or chemical erosion that requires acidity, has been the main agent. Other substances that are readily dissolved by water without carbonic acid can also play a part in lake formation. For this reason, solution lakes occur at times in noncalcareous regions. Salt karst lakes formed by the dissolution of evaporites such as NaCl and $CaSO_4$ are widespread. They may be more common than hitherto suspected.

The origin of the circular Colombian lake called Laguna Quatavita was reevaluated recently. It had been considered the result of a meteorite, but Dietz and McHone (1972) could find no evidence for impact and believe it was formed by the sapping of a deep-lying salt pocket by

Fig. 5-6. Montezuma Well, Arizona, either a limestone sink or a salt-collapse basin. (Photo by Art Clark.)

ground water. The authors stress the occurrence of many such sag lakes elsewhere.

Montezuma Well in Arizona (Fig. 5-6) has been described as a solution basin originating from collapse of a limestone cave. There is some evidence that this could be the case, but the depression is the only one of its kind in the Verde Valley, a region exhibiting no typical karst topography. Lange (1957) suggested that a lens of salt beneath brittle limestone was the solute. Water entering the salt pocket caused expansion that cracked the overlying rocks. Next the salt was carried away in solution by underground seepage, and the fractured rocks collapsed, producing a circular hole with steep walls of limestone. The modern lake occupying this depression is similar to those of the Yucatán cenotes. Several small localized deposits of salt (NaCl, Na_2SO_4, $CaSO_4$) are known in the Verde Valley and are similar to the theoretical pocket that lay beneath the brittle limestone in which the well lies today.

The Bottomless Lakes of New Mexico, far from fathomless, are solution basins aligned linearly in the Chalk Bluff formation east of Roswell. They form a small salt karst region. These solution basins were fashioned in material of gypsum and anhydrite (both sulfates of calcium); only minor amounts of limestone are present. They are steep walled and bring to mind the Yucatán cenotes and Montezuma Well. At least one of them was formed from the coalescence of two adjacent depressions, and at times of low water, the basins become two unnamed lakes separated by a dry strip.

PIPING: FALSE KARST LAKES

The Chuska Mountains lie across northwestern New Mexico and northeastern Arizona. They are topped by a flat layer of sandstone in which there are many unusual water-containing depressions. Some interesting studies in palynology and paleolimnology have come from this lake district (Bent 1960; Megard 1964), and the origin of the lakes is especially remarkable. Wright (1964) attributed the depressions to the geologic process of piping, which produces tubular subsurface drainage channels in insoluble clastic rocks (rocks composed of fragments that have been moved individually from their place of origin), simulating what results when solution occurs in calcareous rocks. Cemented sandstone layers collapse into the vacuities produced by the piping of uncemented sand out to the steep escarpments that bound the mountains.

In the case of solution basins formed by collapse, water removes $CaCO_3$ or $CaSO_4$ molecule by molecule. In piping, sand is removed grain by grain by suspension in moving water. The piping could not occur, however, without the proximity of precipitous slopes. The Chuska Mountains are steep-sided mesas. Tunnels developing in their sandstone cap serve to carry loose sand away and permit it to be dumped down the mountain slope, leaving water-filled depressions with such colorful names as Whiskey Lake and Dead Man Lake.

Another lake district that may owe its existence to piping is seen along one part of the Mogollon Rim in Arizona. This steep and scenic escarpment marks the abrupt southern edge of the Colorado Plateau. Along the Rim are a series of lakes and lake remnants that can be termed the Potato Lake series after Whiteside's (1965) paleolimnologic study of a small dystrophic lake by that name. Most occupy depressions in the Coconino Sandstone.

LAKES OF AEOLIAN ORIGIN

In arid regions of today or in regions of marked aridity in the past, the erosive force of wind has left its mark; in some instances lake basins have been formed. (The climatic requisite for them is the op-

posite of that needed for karst formation.)
Several categories of lakes occupy concavities fashioned by aeolian forces.

Moses Lake in the cold desert of eastern Washington is an example of a lake
that originated by damming of streams by
drifting wind-blown sand. Depressions
among dunes may contain water, especially if the wind has scooped away sand
to approach or expose the water table.
The Sand Hills region in some western
counties of Nebraska contain many small,
in some instances very saline, waters
occupying interdune basins.

A lake district composed of thousands
of shallow depressions in the panhandle
of Texas and adjacent eastern New Mexico has been considered an example of
wind work. This probably oversimplifies
the forces that built these depressions,
but wind has modified all of them to
some extent, according to Reeves (1965)
who studied them in detail. They are
commonly called buffalo wallows, because large hoofed mammals may have
aided in their formation. After a period
of precipitation, rain-filled depressions
attract herds that trample the soil, thereby destroying stabilizing plant growth
and deepening the basin. Later, when the
depression is dry, the wind removes
dried soil, a process called deflation.* In
South Africa basins of this type are called
pans; Hutchinson and co-workers (1932)
published an important limnologic report
on them.

FLUVIATILE (RIVER) LAKES
Ponding by deltas

Rivers, which are lotic environments,
create standing-water habitats, or lentic
environments, by various actions. Impoundment of a stream can be effected by
wind, ice, lava, landslides, man, and

---

*These basins could be termed zoogenic as well be-
cause of the importance of animal erosion in their
formation. Thus, in the examples shown, deflation
basins owe their origins to more than wind.

beaver, but a second river can do the
same. A good example in North America
is Lake Pepin, a wide place in the Mississippi River where the current is slowed
and the river somewhat widened. The
river lake was formed by the Chippewa
River flowing from Wisconsin and depos-
iting material where the current slack-
ened to create a partial dam across the
Mississippi River. In the past, Lake Pepin
was noted for its pelecypod fauna that
supported a nineteenth and early twentieth century pearl button industry and
for its fish, the most noteworthy being
the spoonbill *Polyodon*. The lake is cur-
rently noted for its swarms of emerging
chironomid dipterans—midge flights that
often assume nuisance proportions.

Flood plain lakes

In the mature reaches of a stream
course, where gradient is much reduced
and there is a broad flood plain over
which the river has wandered in the past,
other fluviatile lakes may be found.

Levee lakes. Levee lakes are shallow,
often elongate bodies of water that lie
parallel to the stream bed and are separated from it by strips of higher land. The
barrier is a natural levee of river sediments, deposited at times of high water,
although occasionally breached as water
is delivered to the lateral levee lake.

Oxbow lakes. A second type of flood
plain lake is the oxbow lake formed from
isolated loops of meandering, mature
streams (Fig. 5-7). These crescent-shaped
basins are usually deeper than the levee
lakes because they occupy old segments
of the river, which may reach lower than
adjacent depressions in the flood plain
where levee lakes form.

The North American fluviatile lakes,
associated with mature alluvial plains
and gentle gradients, are most abundant
in the Central Gulf states. Relatively
speaking, they assume even more importance there because there are no glacial,
tectonic, or volcanic lakes nearby.

Fig. 5-7. An oxbow lake, Minnesota. (Photo by G. Heilman.)

Evorsion (pothole) lakes

Evorsion is defined as the complex mechanics of pothole erosion, streambed abrasion that occurs under vortices and eddies in torrents or beneath waterfalls. A category of fluviatile lakes associated with torrential flows and cataracts includes the evorsion lake. Stones, driven by hydraulic pressure and swirling in circular fashion, cut vertically into the stream bedrock, gradually forming a pothole.

In 1956 Eggleton wrote the first detailed limnologic report on Fayetteville Green Lake, New York. Since then several more studies have been made on this unusual lake. Called a "plunge-basin" lake, it was formed beneath a waterfall during a recessional stage of the late Wisconsin. The main portion of the lake occupies a deep cylindrical cavity.

Edmondson (1963) and his students studied another important group of evorsion lakes in eastern Washington. They are the Grand Coulee lakes, lying in linear fashion beneath an enormous escarpment over which the ancestral Columbia River cascaded. The lakes display a sequence of salinity, and studies made on their biota have provided insight into osmotic and ionic tolerances of many aquatic organisms.

SHORELINE LAKES

Wave action at shorelines constantly molds and modifies lake basins; this is especially obvious in newly created lakes. There are also good examples of shoreline lakes formed where barriers of sand are thrown up to cut off bays from the sea. These are especially frequent along drowned coastlines. Likewise, sand spits, partitioning a single body of water into two lakes, are not rare. Geologists have been concerned with the origin of such lakes, but no outstanding limnologic contributions have come from shoreline lakes.

Lake Rudolf in the desert of northern Kenya is important in anthropology because its shores have yielded consequential primate remains pertaining to man's ancestry. Some limnologic reports from this lake emphasize the difference between the main lake and Ferguson's Gulf. The Gulf is nearly isolated by a growing spit of sand, molded by wind and wave. Dissolved minerals are less concentrated in the open lake than they are in Ferguson's Gulf, which has its own character even though not yet completely separated as an individual lake by shoreline phenomena.

Beach pools are particularly common examples of shoreline lakes, representing isolated remnants of the main lake. They were included in a most important study by Cowles (1899), who blended geology and botany in a dynamic investigation of sand dunes and vegetation at the south shore of Lake Michigan. (Cowle's paper, published in four installments, contributed much to the development of the concept of community succession.) A minor portion of his work treated the early formation of beach pools and their subsequent fate. These ponds, more or less parallel to the lake shore, result from movement by both wind and wave. Cowles also wrote about the lakes that formed at mouths of rivers along the east shore of Lake Michigan: silt and sand brought by the rivers are dropped in the lake shallows where currents slacken; waves pile the sand up along the beach; and winds pick up the material to form dunes that divert and pond the rivers to produce lakes near their mouths. Thus the birth of these shoreline lakes is due in part to both fluviatile and aeolian forces.

LAKE BASINS IMPOUNDED OR EXCAVATED BY ORGANISMS

Geologists consider organisms as important geomorphic agents but relatively minor lake builders. Nevertheless, a few kinds of plants and animals have contributed to limnologic habitats, and their contributions should be mentioned.

Dams of *Sphagnum* and other bog plants have been reported to impound some Nova Scotian lakes (Hutchinson 1957). Perhaps many other northern lakes occupy depressions in peaty deposits. Certainly small pools enclosed by bog-mat plants are very common but distinct little ecosystems. At Lake Itasca one can dock a boat and disembark at the margin of floating bogs that have obliterated former bays of the lake. There, in isolated little pools, are peculiar flora and fauna, the latter including the bizarre cladocer-an *Bunops.* Members of the biotic community in these little ponds are quite different from their counterparts in the adjacent open lake.

Golubić (1969) detailed the events whereby $CaCO_3$, precipitated from solution in spring brooks, is trapped by algae and mosses. The species that are adapted to being buried and encrusted respond by growing vigorously upward from the cemented layers only to be subjected to further encrustation. There are various results, including the formation of plant-limestone barriers and terraces that create pools. Later Golubić (1973) pointed out the extreme importance of bluegreens in precipitating calcium carbonate, both in fresh water and seawater.

There are rare Pacific freshwater lakes surrounded by coral reefs, the antho-zoans being the primary architects (Hutchinson 1957). Other invertebrates, including polychaetes and gastropods that build tubes and attached pelecypods such as *Mytilus,* serve to build the walls higher above the coral. Calcareous algae such as *Lithothamnion* and *Porolithon,* especially on the seaward side, raise the rims even higher and serve to cement and protect the invertebrate remains below.

Higher plants also build interesting micropools. The biota of tiny pools held by the carnivorous bog pitcher plants and the crustaceans and protozoans in the axils of epiphytic bromeliads in Florida, Jamaica, and other warm humid areas of the New World have been studied (Maguire 1971).

Some species of mosquito live as larvae in water-filled tree holes. Perhaps seven or eight animal phyla, as well as bacteria, fungi, and algae are known from such habitats. Maguire (1971) reviewed the literature on this subject and discussed the relationship of such miniscule lakes and their biota to wider ecologic problems of dispersal, immigration, establishment, and extinction, all being problems of colonization.

Mammals are the main lake engineers among the Chordata, but some mention should be made of the pools fashioned by alligators in the southeastern United States. These reptiles excavate only small concavities, but they may be of paramount importance in the survival of alligators and other aquatic animals of the southern swamps during dry periods.

Beaver damming and man's similar activity are well known. In both instances streams are impounded with subsequent flooding of streamside vegetation and widespread effects on riparian communities. Controversy has accompanied the actions of both *Homo* and *Castor.* The effect that beaver ponds have on trout streams (elevating temperatures of impounded waters and silting in former stretches of moving water) has been attacked as well as defended. Similarly, the ponding of streams by man has resulted in controversy.

Avakian and Fortunatov (1972) undertook the formidable task of tallying the world's man-made lakes. The number of large reservoirs has tripled in the last 25 years, while the volume has increased fivefold. The authors estimate about 10,000 reservoirs with individual capacities greater than a million cubic meters and a total volume approaching 5,000 km³!

In some artificial lakes, man has done more than simply impound running water. He has excavated the basin in addition. Bulldozed farm ponds and arid land stock tanks are typical, although very small and sometimes transitory bodies of water.

Certain man-made excavations contain water, although they were not made for this purpose. Water-filled rock quarries and gravel pits come to mind immediately. One of the most interesting examples is Hot Lake, Washington, occupying an old epsomite mine (Anderson 1958b). The mineral was mined intensively during World War I, and later the abandoned diggings filled with water. Similarly, most of Holland's lakes are contained by shallow cavities where peat was harvested. They are examples of resurrected lakes.

Another category is the natural concavity inundated by accident. The Salton Sea of California fills a depression that once held pluvial Lake Cahuilla. Carpelan (1958) has told the story of this unique lake in interesting detail. In the spring of 1905, the inadvertent diversion of the Colorado River's main flow into the dry basin by way of newly dug irrigation canals initiated the creation of a modern lake. Two years later the flow was stopped, but not before a new body of water covering more than 1,000 km² had come into existence. Its level has fluctuated since then but now seems to be fairly stable. The saline Salton Sea survives to date because the input from irrigation systems approximates the yearly evaporation of about 2 m.

LAKES FORMED BY EXTRATERRESTRIAL OBJECTS AND THOSE OF PUZZLING ORIGIN

The spectacular, instantaneous formation of a lake basin by meteoritic impact and explosion may be a more common method of lacustrine genesis than has been suspected. According to Nininger (1972), the high frequency at which stony and metallic objects arrive from outer space has been accepted only recently. In 1967 Barringer listed 31 "identified" meteorite craters and 40 suspected to be of such origin. The New Quebec Crater Lake is typical of lakes formed by meteoritic impact. Its high rim and circular outline are unique among the irregularly shaped lakes in that barren glaciated landscape more than 61° N latitude near the tip of the Ungava Peninsula in Quebec.

The Carolina Bays, distinct water-filled as well as extinct basins, numbering up to at least 500,000, are puzzling. They occur in an area of 65,000 km² in the southern half of the Atlantic coast of North America. There is an extensive literature on them, and their origin has been attributed to everything from wind action to the nesting and schooling activities of shallow-water fish. One theory holds that they might be the result of our planet's encounter with a shower of stony meteorites when that part of the continent was under shallow seas. Their NW-SE alignment recalls immediately the thaw-basin lakes of Alaska, but there is no reason to believe that the Carolina Bays ever had a permafrost underlay. Their derivation is still unsolved.

ADDITIONAL ORIENTED LAKES

The thousands of oriented thaw basins in the Alaskan Arctic Coastal Plain have been known for many years as the prime example of a district of oriented lakes. There are other such districts owing their origins to different phenomena. In the Beni Basin of Bolivia there are 2,000 basins remarkably square to rectangular in outline. Most of them are aligned about N 48° E and at right angles to this, N 41° W. Plafker (1964) explained this lake district on the basis of a system of longitudinal and cross fractures in the crystalline rocks underlying the flat, poorly drained Beni Basin, and he suggested that new lakes are still being created by new faults. This may not be unique, for there are several hundred basins in the Old Crow Plain, Yukon Territory, Canada, that seem to be this type. Most of them are oriented in a northwest direction, and a smaller number are aligned at right angles.

IMPORTANT RELICT LAKES

An enormous lake formed in North America between retreating Wisconsin ice and the height of land that separates Hudson Bay drainage from the Gulf of Mexico drainage. It covered 540,000 km² from eastern Saskatchewan to western Ontario and south to include eastern North Dakota and northwestern Minnesota. This was Glacial Lake Agassiz. Its sediments cover a greater area than any lake existing today, although the lake may never have been flooded completely at one time. It lay in a well-drained area termed *exorheic,* an area of open basins whose rivers ultimately reach the sea. Remnants of the lake persist today as separate bodies of water, such as Lake Winnipeg, Lake Nipigon, and Lake-of-the-Woods.

Pluvial lakes, all probably of the Quaternary age, existed south of the continental ice sheet. They were characterized by sensitive responses to climatic changes and by considerable fluctuation in level. In the Great Basin of North America there were at least 120 of these lakes, the two largest being Bonneville and Lahontan. The former is now represented by old shorelines far from water, glistening evaporites of the extensive Bonneville salt flats, and a few saline remnants, of which the Great Salt Lake of Utah is most important. The most striking Lahontan remnant is Pyramid Lake, Nevada, which, along with other bodies of water in the Lahontan Basin, figures in the history of desert limnology (Hutchinson 1937). Pluvial lakes existing on other continents are similar to our own. For example, the saline Lake Urmia, an Iranian counterpart of Great Salt Lake, occupies an undrained depression of tectonic origin.

The Spanish word *playa* (beach) is applied to the intermittent lakes, now mostly dry, that were the pluvial lakes of the past. Many of these inland desert basins are bright with salts and are known also as *salinas.* Certain playas are economically noteworthy, yielding valuable salts. Searles Lake, California, is one of these.

Remnants of pluvial lakes occupy closed basins in arid regions characterized by internal drainage. Closed basins can exist only where annual evaporation surpasses the precipitation; in such climatic regions the rivers, if present, never reach the sea. These are termed *endorheic* areas because they are undrained by streams. The realm of desert limnology, by definition, coincides with regions where closed basins are found (Cole 1968).

6

Shapes and sizes of lakes

The diverse origins of depressions that contain bodies of water known as lakes and ponds and the phenomena that create the morphologic features of these concavities have been discussed. The physical dimensions of a lake interact with climatic and edaphic factors to determine the nature of the lake as an environment and, thus, its inhabitants.

The methods of measuring and analyzing the physical dimensions of a lake are termed morphometry. Many aspects of the lake's fauna and flora can be studied without this knowledge, but to venture into theoretic limnology and to determine some indices of productivity, morphometric data must be known.

The purpose of this chapter is to blend discussions of lake-basin dimensions with their origins, the modifications that occur with aging, their effects on the trophic nature and inhabitants of the lake, and basic morphometric techniques.

THE BATHYMETRIC MAP AND ITS DATA

An outline of the lakeshore, with submerged contours, drawn to scale is a ne-cessity for calculating morphometric data. Usually such a bathymetric map is easily produced by tracing the shoreline from aerial photographs, thus precluding standard, time-consuming surveying methods. An examination of an aerial photo usually reveals landmarks of various types—perhaps a stretch of straight highway or two promontories demarking a nearly straight line of shore. From these landmarks one can arrive at a scale by driving an automobile from point to point and noting the final odometer reading to determine the distance (although the accuracy of this method may be questionable). A calibrated line, or a transit and stadia rod, can be used to measure the distance walked along the shore between conspicuous points. Welch (1948) treated map making in great detail, outlining many ways of arriving at the shoreline configuration and other lake dimensions. Whatever method is used, if all measurements are translated into metric units from the beginning, ensuing calculations will be simplified.

With an outline of the lake (Fig. 6-1) and a proper scale, at least five bits of information can be deduced about the lake even before subsurface configuration is known.

Symbols representing lake measure-

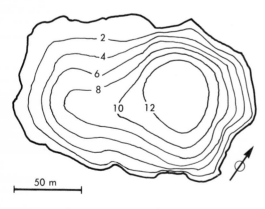

50 m

Fig. 6-1. Bathymetric map of Lake 230, Experimental Lakes Area, Ontario. (Adapted from Brunskill and Schindler 1971.)

ments have been in common use since Hutchinson [1957] brought them together for a wide audience in his first volume of the *Treatise.*

Surface dimensions

Maximum length. The distance across the water between the two most separated points on the shoreline is, of course, the maximum length *(l)*. It can be determined simply from the outline map with a ruler. It may or may not be a significant dimension; the wind-effective length has more limnologic importance. The relation of the long axis of the lake to the direction of prevailing winds is obviously worth considering, and the greatest distance wind can sweep uninterrupted across the lake surface should be reckoned. The maximum length might be intercepted by islands or promontories, so that the actual fetch of the wind becomes far less. The surrounding topography may be such that the lake is sheltered by hills, resulting in little actual wind action on its surface. The exposure of a lake to wind has a direct effect on water movement, and thus indirect effects on the biota within the lake.

Breadth. The width of a lake *(b)* is determined by measuring, at approximately right angles to the axis of maximum length, a line that connects the greatest distance between two opposite points on the shore. The mean width *(b̄)* can be found if the lake area is known; it is the quotient of area divided by maximum length.

Surface area. Surface area *(A)* is an extremely important dimension, for it is at the surface that solar energy enters the aquatic habitat. Furthermore, many types of data from within the lake are referred to a unit of area, making possible meaningful comparisons among different-sized bodies of water.

With a map of the lake's outline and an appropriate linear scale, there are at least four ways to determine the area. An inexpensive procedure is to draw this outline on graph paper, with the scale of the grid spacing being known (Fig. 6-2). Summing the squares, estimating the fractions thereof, and multiplying by the proper factor would serve to estimate the lake area.

The polar planimeter is an instrument designed for deriving areas of flat surfaces. With it the shoreline is traced in a clockwise direction, and dial numbers are read when completed. These dial readings can be compared with the results of tracing a square or circle of known area. The planimeter is calibrated in square inches or cm², and from the map scale the actual lake area can be calculated. Welch (1948) gives explicit directions for planimeter use and many other morphometric procedures.

Another rapid way of determining area is to use an accurate balance. If the lake outline is drawn on paper of fairly uniform density, it can be cut out and weighed to yield a mass that can be compared with confidence to the weight of a known area cut from the same type of paper. Ratios derived in this fashion probably have as good a degree of accuracy as those achieved by planimeter.

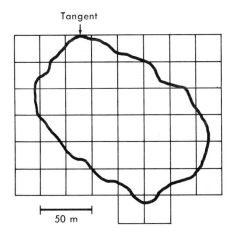

Tangent

50 m

Fig. 6-2. Outline of Lake 230, ELA, superimposed on grid. Twenty-six intersections and one tangent shown; grid spacing 25 m. Shoreline = 26.5 × 0.785 × 25 m = 520 m.

The methods of ascertaining area from a map have been discussed in some detail because they can be applied to many other limnologic calculations.

Length of shoreline. The length of the shoreline *(L)* can be determined from the map by stepping off segments with dividers or by sticking pins in place around the shoreline and connecting them with a thread that can be measured later. A map measurer or rotometer may also be used. This instrument is essentially a wheel and dial that indicates the linear distance the wheel rolls.

Olson (1960) outlined another method of finding the dimension *L*, which leads us back to the map sketched on the graph paper grid (Fig. 6-2). It is preferable that the long axis of the lake be inclined to the grid lines and not parallel to one set. One counts the times that the shoreline crosses grid lines, summing all horizontal and vertical intersections and tallying any point of tangency as one-half an intersection. The sum of intersections multiplied by $\pi/4$, or 0.785, and then by the actual distance represented by the grid spacing yields *L*. Olson discusses many concepts of morphometry and reveals methods of achieving all lake dimensions from a map imposed on a grid without specialized equipment.

Shoreline development index. The development of the shoreline (D_L) is a comparative figure relating the shoreline length to the circumference of a circle that has the same area as the lake. The smallest possible index would be 1.0. The formula from which the index is derived is:

$$D_L = \frac{L}{2\sqrt{\pi A}}$$

Both *L* and *A* must be in consistent units for this computation—meters and m², or km and km².

Solution basins, volcanic lakes in various craters, some deflation basins, and the rare depressions owing their origin to meteoritic impact and explosion are all nearly circular, with indices approaching unity. Good examples are: Montezuma Well, the Arizona solution basin (see Fig. 6-10). D_L = 1.04; Crater Lake, Oregon, a volcanic caldera, 1.27 (closer to 1.10 if an island that adds to shoreline and decreases area is ignored); the Javanese maar Ranu Pakis (Ruttner 1931), 1.02; the south African deflation basin Avenue Pan (Hutchinson 1957), 1.01; and the modern rim of the dry Meteor Crater, Arizona, has a D_L of 1.02.

Some glacial lakes, such as those in kettles, are nearly circular, but others have irregular shorelines characterized by higher shoreline development indices. The elongate Finger Lakes of New York, formed by glacial ice scouring and deepening valleys, have high shore development values. For example, Cayuga Lake has a D_L value of 3.3. Similarly the elongate, somewhat rectangular lakes found in grabens have high D_L values; for example, that of Lake Baikal is 3.4.

River impoundments, whether natural or man made, often back water up tributaries, creating irregular dendritic outlines with much shoreline in relation to surface area. By contrast, despite marked shoreline regularity, a narrow, elongate lake can have a high index (Fig. 6-3).

Although a newly formed lake basin derives its outline from the events that gave rise to it, the shoreline will change with aging. Currents and waves within the lake tend to erode promontories, reducing shoreline irregularities. Protected bays are the first lake parts to fill in and become portions of the terrestrial environment. As the bays are eliminated and irregularities are removed by events occurring within the lake itself, D_L values are reduced. Conversely, the arrival of sediment via an incoming stream might result in a delta projecting into the lake. If part of the delta eventually emerges as water level lowers, it contributes more irregularity to the shoreline and, perhaps, increases the D_L index.

The development of shoreline may play some role in determining the trophic nature of the lake because shallow water is the most productive. Most photosynthesis occurs in the upper, illuminated stratum of a lake. Furthermore, in this upper zone near shore, there is a proximity to the decomposition products from the bottom sediments that cannot be equalled in offshore regions. Moreover, the arrival of terrestrial nutrients to the lake is, to a great extent, a shoreline function. It is tempting to theorize that, of two lakes alike in most features except shoreline development, the one with the highest D_L would be more productive. We must know other facts about lakes, however, before placing much significance on a D_L value. Certainly a low index reveals an approach to circular outline. But when one learns that the shallow, productive Canadian Lake Winnipeg has the same shoreline development index (3.4) as the far different, tectonic Lake Baikal, it becomes obvious that caution should govern interpretation of the index.

Subsurface dimensions

Contour mapping. To this point, morphometric data have been derived entirely from an outline map drawn to scale. Subsurface contours must be established and plotted before the bathymetric map

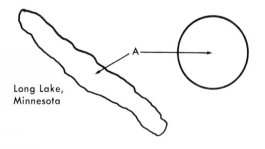

Fig. 6-3. Elongate lake showing comparable circle with the same area, *A.* The shoreline-development index of the lake is greater than the DL of the circle, 1.0.

Long Lake, Minnesota

is complete and before one can proceed with other morphometric work.

There are several methods of finding depths and their positions within a lake. With echo-sounding equipment readily available, it is possible to move by boat from one landmark to another, keeping the speed constant and timing the entire journey. Time intervals are assumed to be proportional to linear spacing for the purpose of plotting depths along the transect. Also, the position of the sounding station on the lake surface can be estimated by triangulation. Echo-sounding devices permit the rapid accumulation of many depth data.

On northern lakes during winter, holes can be bored or chopped in the ice at measured intervals along transects between known points on opposite shores. If echo-sounding equipment is unavailable, sounding with weight and calibrated line can prove effective.

A simple method employed in surveying small lakes is to row a boat on a straight course between points on opposing shores, sounding the bottom at intervals, such as at every 10 strokes. One should transect the lake many times, keeping in mind that a shallow stratum contains greater volumes of water than a deeper layer of the same thickness; therefore, shallow strata should not be neglected during sounding operations.

Whatever method is used, a matrix of points will eventually appear on the map. Contour lines can be plotted by interpolation or, more rapidly, by computerized programs. In small lakes a contour interval of 1 or 2 m may be appropriate. In large lakes the contour lines may be shown at 5- or 10-m intervals.

With contours plotted at regular intervals, the area bounded by each line (or isobath) is determined by one of the methods suggested earlier for obtaining area bounded by z_0, the total area, A. With these data assembled, it is possible

to learn more particulars of a lake's morphology.

Maximum depth. Depth is indicated by the symbol z. Thus z_0 is the surface, a depth of zero; its contour is the shoreline. The first subsurface contour would be z_1, followed down the basin slope by z_2, and so forth. While sounding the lake, a parameter of popular interest, the maximum depth, z_m, should be found. This is the datum most people search for and inquire after in studies of lake dimension.

It is interesting to note that people are prone to accept fantastic tales of enormous depths. The so-called Bottomless Lakes, occupying a string of solution basins in gypsum rocks, are said to have acquired the name from New Mexican cowboys, who sounded them with lariats tied to inadequate weights and could not sense when bottom contact was made. Henry David Thoreau wrote of Concord farmers fathoming Walden Pond with rope, measuring their capacity for credulity rather than the lake parameter z_m; as their test line coiled on the sediments below, they continued to measure it out from above. Thoreau, we must believe, did a better job; about 100 years later, Deevey (1942) found Walden's z_m to be 31.3 as compared with Thoreau's datum, 31.1 m.

It is apparent that as a lake ages and accumulates sediments, the maximum depth lessens and the volume of deep water diminishes even more strikingly (Deevey 1955).

Relative depth. Rarely in the literature on lake dimensions have authors presented the relative depth (z_r). This is the ratio of the maximum depth in meters to the average diameter of the lake surface (m²). The following formula has the computation for percentage built into it, for the ratio is expressed in that manner.

$$z_r = \frac{88.6 \times z_m}{\sqrt{A}}$$

Among the larger lakes of the world

the relative depths are less than 1%. In calderas, maars, fjord lakes, and solution basins there are some high values for z_r. The caldera Crater Lake has a notably great relative depth, about 7.5%; this is very similar to that of the circular, deep meteoritic New Quebec Crater, 7.6%. Montezuma Well has a surprising z_r of 17%, but this is outmatched by Devil's Ink Well, one of the Bottomless Lakes; this small circular solution basin's z_r is 23.2%. Small maar lakes, such as Pulvermaar in Germany and d'Issarlès in France, have high relative depths. The dimensions given by Hutchinson (1957) permit the calculation of 11% and 10% for the two explosion craters, respectively.*

Cryptodepressions. Frequently the maximum depth of a lake is below sea level; the portion of the basin beneath sea level is called a cryptodepression (z_c). For example, the surface of Cayuga Lake lies 116 m above mean sea level; its maximum depth is 133 m; and, by subtraction, it has a z_c of 17 m. The surface of the saline Dead Sea, is 399 m below sea level; therefore, its entire basin is a cryptodepression.

Volume. The volume of a lake *(V)* can be calculated when the area circumscribed by each isobath is known. One method involves formulas such as the following:

$$V_{z_0-z_1} = \frac{1}{3}(A_{z_0} + A_{z_1} + \sqrt{A_{z_0} \times A_{z_1}})(z_0 - z_1)$$

From this, the volume of water between the shoreline contour *(z₀)* and the first subsurface contour *(z₁)* is found. A_{z_0} is the total area of the lake, and A_{z_1} is the area limited by the z_1 line. If the values are at 1–m intervals, the value of $z_0 - z_1$

would be 1 m; this is not a negative figure but is simply the vertical contour interval. Volumes of succeeding strata are now determined one by one and summed. The next would be $V_{z_1-z_2}$, the volume of water occupying depths bordered by the first two subsurface contours. This method is based on adding layer after layer of water, each a truncated cone or one frustum of a large imaginary cone that is the entire lake. Though a tedious, cumbersome procedure, it eventually yields the total number of cubic meters of water within the lake.

Hypsographic curves. An easier method of computing *V* is to construct a curve on graph paper (Fig. 6-4). The area of this curve, or of parts of it, can be determined by any one of the methods outlined before. In this instance, however, area beneath the curve designates volume, for the area bounded by each contour line has been plotted against the depth of that

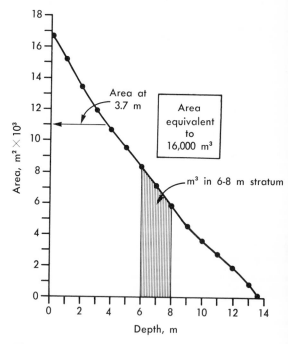

Fig. 6-4. Hypsographic curve for Lake 230, ELA. Area beneath curve represents the volume of the lake. Further data that can be acquired from the plot are indicated.

---

*It is not surprising that small bodies of water can have high relative depths compared with those of large lakes. There must be many small ponds with areas approximately 2,000 m² and maximum depths of 2 m, but no lakes are known with areas of 2,000 km² and maximum depths of 2 km. They would have identical relative depths, 3.96%.

contour. Thus, at zero depth, z_0, A is plotted; at z_1 the area limited by that contour, A_{z_1}, is designated, and so forth. The points are connected, ending finally with a curve at z_m where area is zero. The total area beneath the curve, essentially the product (m³) of m² × m, is the important lake dimension, V.

This hypsographic curve provides many other data as well. For example, in Fig. 6-4 it can be seen that vertical lines from all depths intersect the curve; from this any stratum in the lake can be delineated so that its volume can be computed. Furthermore, a horizontal line from any point on the curve intersects the vertical axis to show the area inside a contour drawn at that depth. Therefore, if the

Table 6-1. Morphometric data from Lake 230, Experimental Lakes Area, Ontario

Depth (m)	Area (ha)	Percent	Product (A and depth)
0	1.67	100	0
1	1.52	91.0	1.52
2	1.35	80.8	2.70
3	1.19	71.2	3.57
4	1.07	64.1	4.28
5	0.957	57.3	4.78
6	0.837	50.1	5.02
7	0.713	42.7	4.99
8	0.588	35.2	4.70
9	0.460	27.5	4.14
10	0.359	21.5	3.59
11	0.274	16.4	3.01
12	0.192	11.5	2.30
13	0.094	5.6	1.22
13.6	0	0	0

Data from Brunskill and Schindler 1971.

Table 6-2. Morphometric data from Lake 230, Experimental Lakes Area, Ontario

Stratum (m)	Volume (m³ × 10⁴)	Percent	Cumulative percent
0-1	1.60	15.38	15.38
1-2	1.43	13.75	29.13
2-3	1.27	12.21	41.34
3-4	1.13	10.86	52.20
4-5	1.01	9.71	61.91
5-6	0.90	8.65	70.56
6-7	0.77	7.40	77.96
7-8	0.65	6.25	84.21
8-9	0.52	5.00	89.21
9-10	0.41	3.94	93.15
10-11	0.32	3.08	96.23
11-12	0.23	2.21	98.44
12-13	0.14	1.35	99.79
13-13.6	0.02	0.19	99.98

Data from Brunskill and Schindler 1971.

area of a plane 6.2 m below the surface is needed, a vertical line drawn from 6.2 m on the horizontal axis would intersect the curve above at a point marking that area.

Further useful data that could be obtained and tabulated with the depth-area curve of the lake include: the area at each depth, its percentage of the total area (A_{z_0} or A_0 = 100%), the volume of each stratum, and the percentage of the volume contained in each stratum (Tables 6-1 and 6-2).

Another direct hypsographic curve is drawn by plotting on one axis the volume above each subsurface contour and on the other, the contour depths. Percentage hypsographic curves are constructed by plotting the percent of lake surface area bounded by every contour line against the respective contour depths, or, in the case of the percentage volume curve, plotting against depth the percent of total lake volume lying above each contour (Fig. 6-5).

An additional dimension, the depth of the center of gravity (z_g), can readily be affixed from the percentage volume curve. This is done by marking the depth opposite the point where a perpendicular line from the 50% mark on one axis intercepts the curve (Fig. 6-5). Despite the fact that the horizontal location within the lake has been neglected, the parameter z_g has a use in certain calculations pertaining to physical limnology.*

Mean depth. The lake volume divided by its surface area obviously will yield the mean depth $(\bar{z})$ if the units employed are the same. Thus, the volume in m³

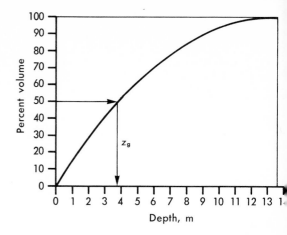

Fig. 6-5. Percent volume hypsographic curve for Lake 230, ELA. Center of gravity, z_g, indicated at depth where 50% of volume lies above and below. (Data from Table 6-2.)

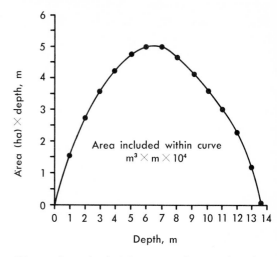

Fig. 6-6. Curve for deriving center of gravity for Lake 230, ELA. The plot of area × depth against depth yields m³ × m, which, when divided by volume in m³, gives z_g in m. (See footnote in left column below.)

must be divided by area in m², or two other comparable units should be used in the formula $V/A = \bar{z}$.

Mean depth has been considered an important dimension since Thienemann (1927) proposed that in German lakes a boundary between what he defined as oligotrophy and eutrophy lay at about 18 m. Lakes with $\bar{z}$ greater than 18 m showed features he had assigned to oli-

---

*Another way of deriving z_g is to plot the product of every depth and the area bounded by that depth contour as a function of depth (Fig. 6-6). Thus at z_0, the product is zero (0 × A); at depth z_1, there is a positive figure, $z_1 \times A_{z_1}$, to plot against the depth axis at z_1, and so forth. The curve finally encompasses a theoretical area that is m³ × m. Dividing this value by volume of the lake (V) in m³ yields the depth of the center of gravity.

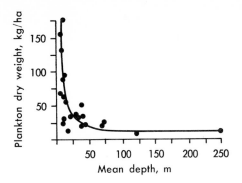

Fig. 6-7. Standing crops of plankton in kg/ha plotted against mean depths in various lakes. (Data from Rawson 1955.)

gotrophy; shallower lakes were more productive and belonged to the eutrophic series. Similar data have been documented by Rawson (1953, 1955) and Hayes (1957). In a series of diagrams, Rawson showed the dry weight of plankton, bottom fauna, and fish crops from many lakes plotted against the mean depths of the lakes. Rawson's plots form L-shaped curves, similar to hyperbolas (Fig. 6-7). There are two arms to the curves; their junction is not far from 18 m.

Earlier, Deevey (1941) had presented a diagram of bottom-fauna weights plotted against mean depths from 116 lakes in Europe and North America. That graph also suggests a group of shallow lakes characterized by variable but high biomass and a group of lakes deeper than 20 m with a relatively small mass of bottom fauna. Deevey came to the conclusion, however, that the supposed hyperbolic curve was the "result of noncorrelation within several very diverse bodies of data"—that correlation between bottom fauna and mean depth alone was poor, since the situation was much more complex and based on additional interrelated factors. With the data he had available to analyze from a series of Connecticut and New York lakes, Deevey found that, in addition to mean depth, the amount of phytoplankton beneath a unit area of lake surface and the average oxygen content

of the hypolimnion were closely correlated with the biomass of bottom fauna.

Gorham (1958b) further discussed mean depth and biologic productivity, pointing out that Rawson's data fit a curve of photosynthetic rate per surface area plotted against mean depth. He suggested that $\bar{z}$ is an important dimension in determining what proportion of a lake's volume is well lighted and within the photosynthetic zone. With photosynthesis as the basis of most productivity within the typical autotrophic lake, Gorham's conclusions seem reasonable.

Volume development. A further index to basin shape is the volume development, D_V. This compares the shape of the basin to an inverted cone with a height equal to z_m and a base equal to the lake's surface area. In a lake with a volume equal to this hypothetical cone, $D_V = 1.0$; a lake with a relatively greater volume would have an index greater than 1.0; and a basin with a smaller volume than such a cone would have an index below 1.0 (Fig. 6-8).

To arrive at D_V keep in mind that the volume of a cone is one third the product of basal area and height; A is substituted for the former and z_m for the latter. Since the actual volume of the lake is $A(\bar{z})$, the ratio of actual volume to the volume of the theoretical cone, $\dfrac{A(\bar{z})}{1/3\ A(z_m)}$, equals volume development. By cancellation, $D_V = 3\dfrac{\bar{z}}{z_m}$.

From the above it is apparent that the relation of mean to maximum depths in the case of an ideal cone, with D_V of 1.0, is 0.333.

Hayes (1957) examined morphometric data from 500 lakes and found the average D_V to be about 1.27. Gorham (1958a) assembled figures from many lakes of northern Britain and elsewhere that revealed volume developments greater than 1.0 as typical. Neumann (1959) used dimensions, given by Hutch-

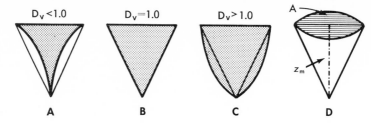

Fig. 6-8. Volume developments (D_V). D_V = 1.0 in **B**, where volume of lake is the same as that of an imaginary cone, **D**, which has the same area *(A)* and maximum depth, z_m, as the lake.

inson (1957) for 107 lakes, and found that the mean value of $\bar{z}/z_m$ was 0.467; this implies a D_V of 1.40. Koshinsky (1970) studied the morphology of 68 glacial lakes sharing a common history and geologic environment on the Precambrian Shield in Saskatchewan. Their average volume development was 1.23.

These averages show us that most lakes for which there are good morphometric data occupy depressions that are U shaped in cross section. Deevey (1955) pointed out that vertical profiles of at least deeper parts of lakes are more like segments of spheres than parts of cones. The flat part of the spherical slice is an imaginary subsurface plane parallel to the lake surface; the rounded part represents the bottom contour, and the resultant geometric figure has $D_V > 1.0$.

Neumann's analyses convinced him that the ideal lake is close to an elliptic sinusoid. This is a geometric body, its base (the lake area) an ellipse, and its surface (the bottom contour) a sinusoid, rounded like a sine curve. This model has a D_V of 1.39. Anderson (1961) found that the elliptic sinusoid model applied well to the Great Lakes, except for shallow Lake Erie, and Lake Superior, which has a very irregular basin.

The precision of the frustum-of-cone formula to calculate volume is reduced because of error due to convexity of the lake sides. If the lake is divided into many thin, horizontal slices, each considered a frustum of the conical model, the error due to convexity will be lessened,

but the construction and analysis of a depth-area curve (Fig. 6-4) is probably the best method for determining lake volume.

Can we look at a volume development index and visualize the type of lake from which it came? Probably not. In Minnesota, some rich lakes that lie in basins of calcareous glacial drift often have D_V of less than 1.0, while some lakes in the northeastern part of the state, occupying granitic ice-scour basins have indices greater than 1.0. It is easy to generalize that high D_V values are equated with elongate, steep-sided, deep basins, and with oligotrophy. When we consider the elongate Finger Lakes of upper New York, our conclusions are reinforced—Cayuga Lake, for example, has a D_V of 1.23, which is not remarkable but substantially above unity and not much lower than Lake Baikal's D_V of 1.29. Then we examine Lake Tahoe, within a deep, elongate graben and extremely oligotrophic; it exhibits a D_V of 1.87. Oligotrophic Crater Lake, although not elongate, is the deepest body of water in the United States; occupying a steep-sided circular caldera, it is characterized by a high index, 1.65.

The generalization, however, proves untenable when we note that shallow lakes with relatively great areas have the highest indices—these are saucer-shaped lakes rather than bath tubs, or deep, rounded pits. Lake Winnipeg and other remnants of glacial Lake Agassiz occupy shallow depressions and have D_V values even greater than those of deep and troughlike basins; Winnipeg's is 2.07.

Some Minnesota lakes rich in calcareous deposits owe their low D_V indices in part to shelves of marl precipitated in the shallows, altering the basin shape to such an extent that it looks much like that shown in Fig. 6-8, A. This brings to mind Hooper's (1956) report on some lakes of southern Michigan and how their water chemistry ultimately affected basin dimensions. Those with hard waters, high in $Ca(HCO_3)_2$, had steep subsurface slopes from 1.5 to 6.1 m, while similar lakes with softer waters showed gentle sloping within those contours. The difference reflected the presence or absence of a marl shelf in the shallows. The precipitous slope at the offshore edge of the marl bank was characteristic of the hard-water lakes.

But what of the volume development in these lakes? Are the marl shelves reflected in the D_V? Hooper found that this index correlated poorly with water chemistry. In fact, one of the highest indices was in a lake with the hardest water and with evidence of abundant marly sediments. A remarkably low D_V (0.65) had been reported earlier by Hooper (1951) in the soft-water Demming Lake, Minnesota. There are no marly shelves in this drift-basin lake. The low D_V index is the result of a relatively small volume of deep water due, to a great extent, to the original mass of ice that formed the kettle that Demming occupies and not to later events within the basin.

Perhaps not comparable, but of some interest in this discussion, is Mountain Lake, Virginia, with extremely dilute water and with no evidence of littoral marl deposits (Roth and Neff 1964). It is an elongate natural lake impounded by landslide debris. Its maximum depth, 31.5 m, lies in a relatively small depression at one end near the rocky dam. The result of this morphology is a D_V value of 0.93.

A similar phenomenon may explain why the larger Saskatchewan lakes on the Precambrian Shield have lower indices than the smaller lakes. For example, the mean D_V for the four lakes with areas surpassing 1,000 km² is only 0.57. Koshinsky (1970) considered the possibility that greater wave action and shore erosion associated with ice movements could have destroyed the U-shaped basin of large lakes. His final conclusion, however, was that the progressive lessening of D_V, which was associated with increasing area, may simply reflect the greater chance of larger basins encompassing aberrant, localized depressions.

Thus, volume development conveys useful information only if we know other facts about the lake. It is a comparative value that can be instructive, but caution must be observed in its interpretation. By contrast, A, V, z_m, $\bar{z}$, and D_L indices near 1.0 are data that tell something real about the lakes from which they come.

Basin slope. The degree of slope from contour to contour can be found if the lengths of all isobaths are known. The methods for determining the lengths of these contours are the same as those outlined for finding the shoreline. The slope, or tangent (Fig. 6-9), between any two contours is:

$$\frac{L_{z_1} + L_{z_2}}{2} \times \frac{z_1 - z_2}{A_{z_1} - A_{z_2}}$$

In this formula L_{z_1} is the upper contour's length, and L_{z_2} is that of the deeper contour; $A_{z_1} - A_{z_2}$ is the area enclosed by the two; and $z_1 - z_2$ is a positive figure, the

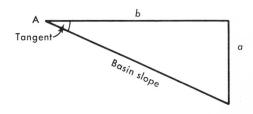

Fig. 6-9. Slope between contours in a lake shown as the tangent, A. In this diagram b is the distance from the shore to the spot above depth, a.

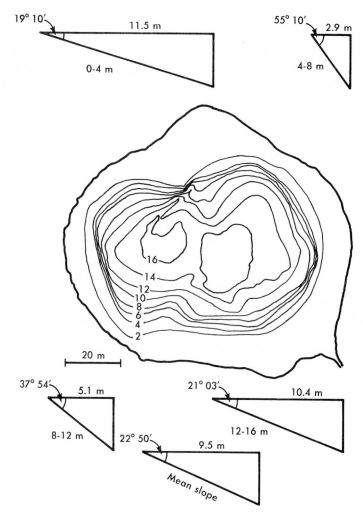

Fig. 6-10. Bathymetric map of Montezuma Well, Arizona, showing 2-m contour intervals. The differences in slope from 0 to 4 m, 4 to 8 m, 8 to 12 m, 12 to 16 m, and the mean slope of the entire basin are shown. Tangent and *b* values are indicated; all *a* values are 4 m.

height between the two isobaths, or the contour interval. The resultant calculations will be in decimal form and must be multiplied by 100 to be expressed as percentage.

The average slope of the entire lake bottom is sometimes determined, although it may have less ecologic import than the mean slope from shore to a given depth or the slope circumscribed by any two subsurface contour lines. Furthermore, there may be significant contrasts between the average slope and individual parts of the basin (Fig. 6-10).

The mean slope of the entire lake is found by the following formula, *n* being the total number of contours:

$$\frac{(\frac{1}{2} L_{z_0} + L_{z_1} + L_{z_2} + L_{z_3} \ldots + L_{z_{n-1}} + \frac{1}{2} L_{z_n}) \, z_m}{n \, A}$$

In simplest terms, mean slope is the average change in depth per unit horizontal distance. It is usually expressed as a percentage, but there are at least two other ways to designate it.

A lake bottom, for example, that has plunged to a depth of 30 m when it is at an average of 30 m from shore shows

100% slope within that distance; the angle of slope is, therefore, 45°. Henson and associates (1961) reported that the mean slope of the entire Cayuga Lake is 5.2%; this is an angle of 2° 58′. Expressed in another manner, the average slope of the lake is 52m/km or 5.2 cm/m.

A simpler approach to approximating the mean slope of a basin is founded on the assumption that the lake surface is circular, and, therefore, $\pi r^2 = A$. The following formula is derived from this assumption:

$$\text{Percent mean slope} = 100 \frac{z_m}{\sqrt{A/\pi}}$$

The steps used to arrive at this formula are:

$$\pi r^2 = A$$
$$r^2 = \frac{A}{\pi}$$
$$r = \sqrt{\frac{A}{\pi}}$$

Therefore:

$$\frac{z_m}{r} = \frac{z_m}{\sqrt{A/\pi}}$$

The trigonometric function for a right-angled triangle is (see Fig. 6-9):

$$\text{Tangent } A = \frac{a}{b}$$

The depth, z_m, is a; the radius, r or $\sqrt{A/\pi}$, becomes b; and the angle of A is assumed to be the average for the entire lake.

USES OF MORPHOMETRIC DATA

If a particular body of water is to be studied in detail, the results of all morphometric procedure should be tallied and kept on record for future use. This applies also to the hyposographic curve, the depth-area curve discussed earlier (see Fig. 6-4). These data will be useful in faunal, floral, and productivity studies. Some specific examples follow.

The accepted manner of expressing amounts of bottom fauna harvested by

dredge is numbers per hectare or per square meter; or, on the basis of mass, expressions such as kg/ha or g/m² are employed. It is also becoming common for these and comparable data to be expressed in terms of energy: calories per unit area appears regularly in limnologic literature. Whatever the unit of measure, lake morphometry is useful.

Assume that the profundal zone, where the dredging is being done, ranges from a depth of 22 to 40 m and that 18 one-meter strata from 22 to 23 m and 39 to 40 m have been sampled. Each dredge haul encompasses a fraction of a square meter,* so that counting and weighing the catch allows one to express numbers and masses in m², ha, or km². It would be valid to state, therefore, that in the sediments lying at a representative depth of 32 to 33 m there are, on the basis of sampling procedure, so many animals per square meter of bottom. The average number collected per dredge would have been used to calculate numbers within that stratum. It is not valid, however, to find the average per dredge throughout the entire profundal zone and simply express this without correcting for unequal areas at different depths. First, the numbers of animals (or their mass, if required) per unit area of any stratum must be multiplied by the total area of that stratum. If all the profundal strata are treated this way and summed, the total number of animals in the profundal zone is calculated. Dividing that sum by the total area of the 22 to 40 m region yields a permissible average figure; it can be stated that there are so many animals per hectare in the profundal zone because the areas of the various depths within it have been properly weighted.

Similarly, knowing the lake's area and the volumes of the various strata below

---

*Most Ekman dredges commonly used to sample soft, fine-grained sediments grab an area of about 225 cm².

it permit proper expression of other limnologic features. Assume, for example,
that photosynthesis occurs from the surface to a depth of about 5 m, below
which the process cannot be demonstrated. if we know the mg O_2 per liter
(g/m³) produced per hour within each
stratum, we can find the total produced
within the stratum by multiplying its volume by oxygen value. With summation,
the total amount of oxygen produced
within the lake during a certain period of
time is revealed, each stratum having
been weighted properly. If the sum is divided by the surface area of the lake, a
figure useful for comparative purposes is
derived, photosynthetic rate expressed as
g O_2 per m² per hour.

This method can be applied to many
other data, to mass or numbers of plankton organisms, to iron or sulfate, or to
whatever is being measured and studied.
The main point is that morphologic details of the lake must first be known.

Schindler (1971b) used morphometric
procedure to explain differences in trophic status among a group of neighboring glacial lakes in Ontario. He reasoned
that in most instances the nutrient input
to the lakes was only via runoff from the
drainage area, A_d, and precipitation on
the lake surface, A_o. The total catchment
area $(A_d + A_o)$ would be proportional to
the yearly supply, while lake volume
would serve to dilute it. Thus, the ratio
$\dfrac{A_d + A_o}{V}$ should be proportional, first, to
levels of nutrient and, second, to the biologic productivity dependent on nutrient
supply. The correlations were direct and
excellent when the chemical nature of
the sediments and water column, primary production, biomass, and some
other indices of productivity were com-

pared with the ratio. Such correlations
lend support to the concept that change
in morphology, as the lakes fills, leads
sometimes to an increase in nutrient per
unit volume and to a resultant rise in
productivity.

LAKE "SIZE"

When people ask the dimensions of a
lake, they wish to know the area, maximum length, and especially the maximum depth. Volume is rarely questioned,
and the common way of ranking the great
lakes of the earth does not consider that
dimension. We speak of "bodies of
water," yet rate the lake's size on the
basis of surface area. This is something
that, in retrospect, may make little sense.
On the other hand, there is only so much
surface to the planet Earth, and the
amount occupied by lakes is significant
to us. Moreover, solar energy arriving at
the lake surface marks the beginning of
lacustrine energy exchanges from one
trophic level to the next. As a result, we
express productivity in terms of surface
area: for example, annual photosynthesis
as carbon fixed per m² or yearly fish
growth as kg/ha. Even the total heat absorbed by the lake during the warming
period of the year is expressed as calories
per cm² of surface.

Some past controversy about the relative importance of surface area in determining the trophic status of a lake led to
work that has bearing on lake size. It had
been said that the enriching effect of runoff, entering at the shoreline, is diluted
in lakes of large area, and indeed, Thomas (1969) recently pointed out that central European lakes of small area are
more susceptible to pollution than larger
ones. However, the relationships between
area and other dimensions must be con-

sidered here. Hayes (1957) attempted to clarify the effects of area and other lake dimensions on such indices of productivity as fish yield and bottom-fauna mass. His analyses of morphometric data from 500 lakes led to the presentation of a formula and a plot showing a direct relationship between surface area and mean depth. This shows that large lakes are usually deeper than smaller ones, and we can generalize that lakes of great expanse are apt to have great volumes also. The relationship, Hayes found, did not apply well in small lakes; those with an area of 0.3 km² or less often had mean depths (and hence volumes) greater than expected.

Hutchinson (1957) presented, in tabular form, morphometric data derived from the greatest of the world's lakes. From these facts one can devise a list of the 10 largest lakes, with respect to area alone. Eight of these 10 would also appear on a list of the 10 largest, ranked according to volume.

Thus, lakes as three-dimensional bodies of water can be arranged with some success on the basis of their two-dimensional surfaces. There are exceptions. The most noteworthy may be the African equatorial Lake Chad, a tremendous lake covering more than 16,500 km². Its mean depth is about 1.5 m. This reveals that its volume is only about 25 km³, and it does not seem farfetched to say that Chad would be considered an insignificant swamp if it were less extensive.

Lake Baikal has a volume of 23,000 km³, surpassing by 11,000 km³ the volume of Lake Superior. The latter, however, has an area of 83,300 km², as compared with only 31,500 km² for Baikal. Which is the "larger" lake?

7

Light and the aquatic ecosystem

The arrival of solar radiation at the lake surface marks the beginning of the photosynthetic process below. In some lakes and streams organic detritus from outside surpasses the production of organic material within the water. Even in such instances, however, sunlight impinging on a terrestrial surface somewhere was the ultimate source of energy in the carbon-containing compounds delivered to the lake.

Except for well-known uranium fission and hydrogen fusion devices, one is hard pressed to list energy sources that do not depend on the sun. Perhaps the earth's internal heat and moon-pulled tides are the only other nonsolar sources of energy we can list.

It interests the limnologist to know first, how much radiation falls upon the lake surface within a span of time; second, how far it penetrates; and, third, how it can be used or how it affects aquatic organisms.

SOLAR CONSTANT AND NATURE OF LIGHT

To quantify the energy arriving from the sun, a value called the solar constant has been established on the basis of many careful assays. It varies somewhat, but 2.0 cal/cm^2 per minute is a good figure. It is a tremendous quantity of energy, which, if available to and used with 100% efficiency by phototrophic plants, would produce about 325 tons of vegetable material on a square kilometer of the earth's surface each hour. Much of this energy, however, does not reach phototrophic plants, for the solar constant applies to the sun's rays arriving at the outer limits of the earth's atmosphere. Energy is lost as the rays enter the atmosphere: sunlight is scattered, reflected and absorbed by molecules of carbon dioxide, ozone, and water. More than half the energy is lost, although some absorbed radiation appears again as long-wave radiation (greater than 5,000 nm), playing no direct part in photosynthesis.

Light arrives as a pulsating field of electromagnetic force composed of an endless series of waves speeding from the sun at more than 186,000 miles/second (299,790 km/second is more nearly exact). The light contains quanta of energy that are directly proportional to the frequency, or number of waves produced per second. There are myriad individual rays within the solar radiation, each with its own wavelength and characteristic frequency. A broad electromagnetic spectrum is formed by the entire range of waves radiated from the sun, but only a small fraction reaches earth. About half of these waves comprise visible light, although the *pyrheliometer,* the instrument employed to measure radiation, is equally sensitive to all arriving wavelengths.

Photosynthetic plants capture some of this electromagnetic force and convert it to chemical energy rather than let it escape as heat or fluorescence. They are not especially efficient at this conversion; perhaps almost 99% is lost, but it has been estimated that, if all the solar energy striking the earth's surface were utilized, 258×10^9 tons of glucose would

be produced every 12 hours of daylight. This could be more than the yearly energy requirements of all the animals on the globe today.

The length of each wave in the mixture that is sunlight can be expressed in various ways. The Angstrom unit (A) has been much used. It is $1.0 \text{ m} \times 10^{-10}$. The nanometer (nm) is employed more often now; it is $1.0 \text{ m} \times 10^{-9}$. At times the micron ($\mu$), or $1.0 \text{ m} \times 10^{-6}$ is the unit used to measure wavelengths. Thus a certain blue-green wavelength, containing the highest energy content of waves within the visible spectrum, is about 4900 A, or 490 nm, or 0.49μ . Representative colors selected from the continuum of the spectrum are: violet, 400 nm; blue, 460 nm; green, 520 nm; yellow, 580 nm; orange, 620 nm; and red, 700 nm. The longest ultraviolet waves and the shortest of the infrared rays are about 350 and 750 nm, respectively. Within this range, or perhaps from about 380 to 780 nm, the waves that can be detected by the human eye, are defined as "light." Rays shorter or longer than those within visible range are designated as radiation, not as light, even though other animals can detect them. This anthropocentric approach is commonly used.

The lengths and frequencies of the waves within light vary. As a result, their energy content differs. The size of a quantum of electromagnetic-radiation energy is directly related to its frequency. The short waves contain larger quanta than the longer, because they have a greater frequency. During the brief span of time that light travels 299,790 km, enough waves must be present to fill this enormous distance. Red light near the limits of our visual capabilities is about 750 nm; about 400 trillion of these waves span the distance light travels each second. Extreme violet light comes in waves about half the length of red light. Therefore, twice as many waves will be needed to fit into the great distance that is a light-second. About 789 trillion violet waves of 380 nm are required. Thus, the frequency of visual light ranges from almost 400 trillion at the red end of the spectrum to nearly twice that at the violet extreme. This explains the larger energy quanta in short waves.

LIGHT AT THE EARTH'S SURFACE

There are two sources of radiation, direct and diffuse. The former is from the sun; the latter is the light from clouds and sky.

Unfiltered pyrheliometers can measure incoming waves up to 5,000 nm, but most radiant energy from skylight and sun ranges from 290 to 3,000 nm, and there is little evidence that bluegreens and eukaryotes can utilize light outside the band of 380 to 720 nm. Only absorbed light can be used for powering chemical reactions. Chlorophyll, which is the key to photosynthesis in the bluegreen and eukaryotic plants, vigorously absorbs red and violet waves, reflecting the intermediate greens and yellows. This is, of course, why plants appear green to the eye, and why photosynthetic efficiency is highest in violet-blue and orange-red light.

It is worthwhile to think of radiation in terms of calories impinging on a horizontal surface of the earth. This is because a common denominator has been found in lacustrine community metabolism and ecosystem studies: the flow of calories from one trophic level to the next, expressed in terms of unit area of lake surface. It must be pointed out, however, that radiant energy customarily is described by another unit, the langley (ly). One ly is equal to one cal/cm^2. It is an amount that takes no account of time. We must, therefore, introduce the irradiance rate by considering ly per minute, per day, per year, or some other time unit.

In a valuable review on radiation and aquatic environments, Westlake (1965) suggested that we express irradiance in terms of the m-kg-sec system. This idea has merit, for it would lead to uniformity in terms of energy and power units. If Westlake's recommendation were followed, langleys per minute would be converted to $joules/m^2$ per second, or $watts/m^2$, by use of the factor 6.98×10^2. To report ly/min in cgs units (cm-g-sec) as $ergs/cm^2$ per second, the factor is 6.98×10^5.

LIGHT AT THE LAKE SURFACE

A portion of the energy reaching the lake surface does not enter the water, but is immediately reflected. This amount depends first upon the sun's angle of incidence, varying with the hour, the season, and latitude. From studies of an Oklahoma impoundment, Lake Hefner, Anderson (1952) developed the following formula to quantify reflectance *(R):*

$$R = aS_A^{-b} = 1.18\ S_A^{-0.77}$$

In the above, S_A is the sun's altitude, or angular height in degrees, while a and b are constants, 1.18 and 0.77, respectively. From Anderson's formula one can calculate almost no reflectance when the angle of incidence is zero (the sun is at its zenith) to a loss of 20% by reflectance when S_A is 10° (the angle of incidence is 80°).

The calculation of reflectance is complicated by factors such as wind sweeping across the water surface. Gentle ripples allow more light to enter than do surfaces whipped to whitecaps by strong winds. Moreover, the sun's angle becomes relatively less important with increasing cloud cover. The ratio of diffuse radiation from the sky to direct solar import increases with cloud cover.

In Phoenix, Arizona, the mean annual loss by reflectance is about 5% in summer and 12% in winter. This includes the back scattering from particles beneath the surface, taken into account in Anderson's formula.

LIGHT BELOW THE WATER SURFACE

Although water is a transparent liquid, light passing through it is weakened and eventually extinguished. A discovery made in the first half of the eighteenth century, now termed Bouguer's law, applies here. The principle is often attributed to Lambert, who rediscovered it soon afterward, in 1760. The law explains something about light passing through various thicknesses of an absorbing medium. When a parallel beam of monochromatic light enters chemically pure water, for example, it is absorbed exponentially; the absorption varies directly with the logarithm of the thickness of water through which the light passes. No exceptions are known to this. Light entering a homogeneous absorbing medium is decreased at a constant rate as it proceeds through each infinitesimally thin layer. These ideal conditions are not to be found in nature, where polychromatic light strikes a pond surface from many angles and penetrates heterogeneous layers.

Beer's law expresses the relationship between absorptive capacity and concentration of a uniform solution through which light passes. The absorbing capacity is directly proportional to the number of absorbing entities. This principle lies at the heart of the familiar spectroscopic method used in some chemical analyses. The light-path distance is held constant as concentrations of solute are varied. A beam of monochromatic light passing through a given distance of a solution is absorbed exponentially according to the concentration of solute. This is shown when standard curves of different strengths of a solution are prepared. The transmittance of light through the solutions, plotted on semilog graph paper, reveals a straight line, an exponential decrease from weak to strong solutions. The technique works best with an array of colored solutions and approximately monochromatic light. This method is weakened by entities that scatter rather than absorb light. Obviously nature seldom complies with the conditions of Beer's law. Light composed of many wavelengths impinges on the lake surface from many angles and is deflected as well as absorbed by materials that change concentration in the downward light path.

Despite imperfections, a combination of the two laws, called the Beer-Bouguer law, is used in limnology and oceanography. A *vertical absorption coefficient* quantifies the quenching of light as it passes from the water surface to some light-sensitive device arranged horizontally to receive the light from above. Here another factor invalidates strict application of Bouguer's law, for the length of the light path is not unequivocally known. The average distance traveled by rays arriving at a depth of 1.0 m is 1.2 m, much of the light having followed oblique paths. The angle of the sun, the diffuse radiation from the sky, and the scattering of light by particles within the water contribute to increasing mean distances traversed to a given depth. Vertical absorption coefficients are expressed, then, no matter what attenuates the light, as:

$$k = \frac{\ln I_0 - \ln I_z}{z}$$

This formula is derived from the equation

$$I_z = I_0 e^{-kz}$$

which shows the remaining intensity of light, I_z, having passed through a water of thickness in meters, z. The original intensity at zero depth was I_0.

Some confusion exists in nomenclature; the coefficient of absorption is often termed the *coefficient of extinction.* These terms, when used interchangeably, usually refer to calculations using natural logarithms. However, the coefficient of extinction accurately applies when a logarithm to the base 10 is used in the formula rather than a natural logarithm. The absorption coefficient, therefore, is 2.3 times greater than the coefficient of extinction.

In some lake research, data on optical density have been presented. This term, properly used, applies to procedure in photometry where light path, z, is expressed in cm.

$$OD = \log \frac{I_0}{I_z}$$

The sum of three coefficients contribute to the *total coefficient of absorption* in natural waters, so that the intensity of light at depth z is:

$$I_z = I_0 e^{-k_w} \times e^{-k_p} \times e^{-k_c}$$

Water can be analyzed in the laboratory, reducing the light path to 1.0 m. The coefficient of absorption due to pure water, k_w, can be approximated from data based on past experimentation. The remainder is caused by suspended particulate matter, k_p, and dissolved substances, k_c. Filtration or centrifugation eliminates the former and permits estimation of k_p and k_c by subtraction. The total coefficient of absorption is the sum of these three and is usually what is implied when limnologists and oceanographers write of extinction coefficients, absorption coefficients, and attenuation coefficients. Whatever the terminology, the log base used in calculations should be put forth clearly. Moreover, the use of some noncommittal term to express the diminishing of light as it penetrates lake water is to be commended. The word absorption is useful because it implies that natural logarithms have been employed in computing the coefficient; but with deflection playing a big part in light's decrease, there is good reason to use phrases such as the *coefficient of attenuation* or the *diminution coefficient*.

Rather than thinking only of light that is diminished in its journey through lake water, one can consider the part transmitted. Transmittance, T, is the percentage of incident light passing through 1 m. It is $100 \, e^{-k}$, where k is the vertical absorption coefficient. The transmittance of a given wavelength, λ, differs from that of other wavelengths. Thus, when λ is red light of 680 nm, $T = 100^{-k\lambda_{680}}$. In distilled water, $k\lambda_{680}$ is known to be 0.455; from this, $T\lambda_{680} = 100e^{-k} = 63.47$.

The following took place in an afternoon survey of Saguaro Lake, Arizona. A limnology class found that the light of mixed wavelengths remaining at a depth of 10 m was but 1.3% of the surface light. From this, the mean vertical coefficient, owing to absorption, back scattering, and other diminution factors, is 0.434, and transmittance, expressed as a percentage of radiant energy passing through each meter to that same depth, is $T = 100e^{-0.434} = 64.7$.

As the mixture of wavelengths making up the incident solar radiation penetrates lake water, it is extinguished exponentially, but wavelengths are absorbed differentially so that the spectral nature of light changes with depth. The ambient light may contain a spectrum of waves from below 300 nm to well over 800 nm. If it were to pass to a depth of 100 m in some improbable lake of distilled water, where the coefficient of absorption is due to water only, there would remain a range from about 350 to 570 nm. Within this, the greatest intensity would be in blue waves approximately 473 nm. The dim light at the depth would be mostly blue with a little violet and green (Fig. 7-1).

The abundant long rays in the incident light are absorbed rapidly. About 65% of the visible red rays are gone by the time the light commences the second meter of its vertical path in the water. The infrared waves, best described as heat, are absorbed in the first meter to an even

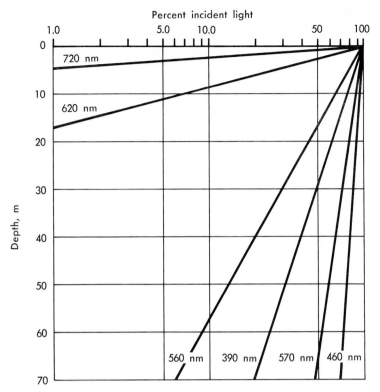

Fig. 7-1. The vertical paths of selected wavelengths through distilled water, showing differential penetration. (Modified from Clarke 1939.)

greater extent. As a result it can be said that, during the course of a summer, sunlight could warm hardly more than the upper meter of a body of water.

At the other end of the spectrum there are some waves shorter than 350 nm. These are the ultraviolet waves that were not filtered out by the atmosphere. Their relative intensity is not great, about 7%, and these waves become a tiny fraction of the subsurface spectrum.

Natural lake and sea waters contain light-quenching components that distilled water lacks. As a result, not only is the penetration of light reduced, but the alteration of spectral composition differs from that seen when light passes through pure water. Dissolved and suspended materials have selective actions on light that vary from lake to lake (Figs.

7-2 and 7-3). Of the three components of the total attenuation coefficient, only k_w remains the same. A generalization can be made that the higher the vertical attenuation coefficient, the greater the transmittance of longer wavelengths. Red, for example, penetrates relatively farther than would be expected. The light reaching the depths of what seem to be very clear lakes is often a green-yellow mixture, while in heavily stained waters orange may penetrate farthest. Vollenweider (1961) showed that, within limits, knowing the mean vertical extinction coefficient of the light allows for estimation of its spectral distribution. Fig. 7-4 portrays this generality and reveals the relative increased transmittance of longer waves as the attenuation coefficient rises.

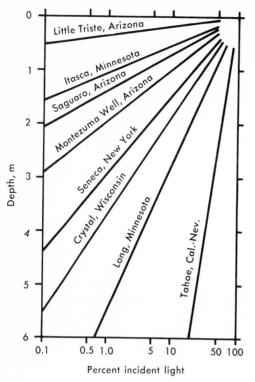

Fig. 7-2. Vertical penetration of light in various bodies of water, showing percentage of incident light remaining at different depths.

VERTICAL VISIBILITY, THE SECCHI DISC, AND THE EUPHOTIC ZONE

During the 1860's a report was published that detailed some experiments an Italian oceanographer had made with white discs. The investigator was named Secchi, and devices similar to those he worked with are now called Secchi discs. A disc, with the flat surface horizontal, is lowered into water on a calibrated line, and the exact depth at which it disappears is noted. This is the Secchi disc transparency expressed as a depth in meters, Z_{SD}. Obviously it is one-half the distance light travels to the disc and back up to the observer's eye.

One of Secchi's discs was more than 2 m in diameter; since then, people have experimented with various sizes. Usually in limnologic work a platter 20 cm in diameter is used. To make comparisons possible, the transparency should be determined between 10 AM and 2 PM and observed off the shady side of the boat. Secchi disc transparency depends on several factors: the eyesight of the viewer,

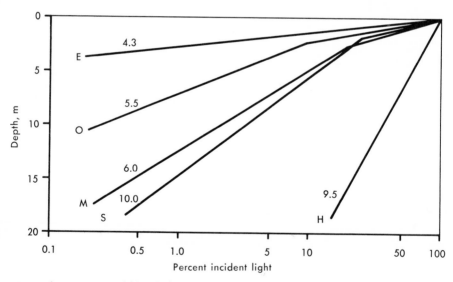

Fig. 7-3. Vertical penetration of blue light (400 to 490 nm) in the Laurentian Great Lakes: *E*, Lake Erie; *O*, Lake Ontario; *M*, Lake Michigan; *S*, Lake Superior; and *H*, Lake Huron. Figures on lines refer to typical Secchi disc transparencies in meters. Orange light penetrates farthest in *E* and *O*; green light in *M* and *S*; and blue light penetrates deepest in *H*. (Modified from Beeton 1962.)

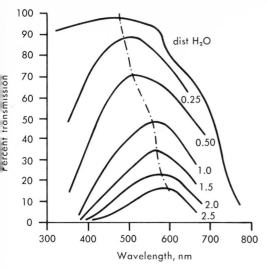

Fig. 7-4. Transmission curves as functions of absorption coefficients (indicated by figures on each curve). Dotted line shows wavelength with greatest transmittance, illustrating a shift toward increased transmittance of long waves as absorption coefficient increases. (Modified from Vollenweider 1961.)

the contrast between the disc and the surrounding water, the reflectance of the disc, and to a lesser extent its diameter. Still it is a valuable tool, and every lake investigation should include Z_{SD} data.

Secchi disc transparencies are extreme in certain lakes. The oligotrophic lakes New Quebec Crater, Waldo and Crater (both in Oregon), and Tahoe are noted for their transparencies: the Secchi disc is visible for 40 m at certain times. For many years, aptly named Crystal Lake, Wisconsin, was one of the clearest lakes known, with recorded Z_{SD} of 15 m; polluted Crystal Lake, Minnesota (near Minneapolis), belies its name with Secchi disc visibility never attaining 1 m. These data show how lake transparency varies.

The minimum intensity of subsurface light that permits photosynthesis has been set at about 1.0% of incident surface light. Thus, the region from surface to the depth at which 99% of the surface light has disappeared is called the *euphotic zone,* or simply the photic zone. The energy flux in this level is well within the photosynthetically active spectral band of 380 to 720 nm. Below this somewhat arbitrary depth, primary productivity is usually considered nil. However, shade-adapted algal communities carry on photosynthesis beneath the snow and ice of Alaskan and Swedish lakes in light intensities well below 1.0% of ambient light. Hobbie (1964) shows that about one half of the annual production of Lake Schrader, Alaska, came from winter photosynthesis at very low light intensities.

The euphotic zone can be ascertained between 10 AM and 2 PM with a subsurface photometer connected to a microammeter within the boat. The response of the photometer (in microamperes) at the water surface is considered as 100% of incident light, and subsequent readings at increasing depths are referred to this value. From the light percentages plotted on semilog paper, it is easy to establish the depth intercepted by the line where 1% of surface illumination remains (see Figs. 7-1 to 7-3).

Two British oceanographers, Poole and Atkins (1929), presented important data on Secchi disc transparency and the vertical absorption coefficient. They empirically determined a constant, 1.7, which, when divided by Z_{SD} in meters, gives the vertical coefficient of light absorption. Although this 1.7 constant has wide application, it does not always hold true, because it was derived from the average illumination at the Secchi disc depth in British Channel waters: specifically, 16% of the surface light. This percentage is not invariable for all waters, but it yields a 1% level of 2.7 times Z_{SD}, very close to the rule-of-thumb factor of 3.0, used by limnologists. From 3.0 can be inferred a Secchi disc transparency to a level where 21% of the surface light remains.

The factors 3.0 and 2.7 discussed above represent the ratio of the photic zone depth to the Secchi disc transparency (Z_{SD}). This ratio varies with stained and colored water and may not apply at all in waters where thick, turbid layers occur *below* the Secchi disc level. Illustrating this latter condition, Edmondson (1956) reminded us of some data published 4 decades ago by the Wisconsin team, Birge and Juday. In Crystal Lake, some Secchi disc depths from different seasons were identical, but the photic depths differed. At one time, they determined a ratio as low as 1.07. In that instance, a large population of the pigmented chrysophyte *Dinobryon* was found lying at and below the Z_{SD}, causing a rapid diminution of light below that level.

At Montezuma Well, the mean lower photic zone depth throughout the seasons is 3.1 times the Secchi disc transparency, with little variance (Cole and Barry 1973). Verduin (1956) presented data to show that 5.0 was a good factor to translate Secchi disc level to 1.0% surface light in Lake Erie, but this is unusually high for lakes. In some very turbid waters the euphotic zone $/Z_{SD}$ ratio is substantially above 3.0. In such cases, the white disc rapidly disappears from sight, but diffuse light, scattered by particulate matter, penetrates deeper than one would expect. Thus William T. Barry, in some unpublished research in Arizona, found that a shallow, muddy desert impoundment called Little Triste Pond had a mean Secchi disc visibility of only 6.0 cm. The average euphotic depth was 4.6 times deeper.

Effect of ice and snow cover

Although an ice cover terminates circulation and isolates the lake from the atmosphere, it does not put an end to light penetration. Actually, clear ice transmits light better than the water beneath it. When a surface layer freezes, particulate and especially dissolved electrolytic materials are reduced in the ice. This may be demonstrated by weighing the total residue following evaporation of a melted ice sample and comparing it with the

greater amount of material remaining after drying an equal volume of water taken from just beneath the ice.

A snowfall, however, alters conditions drastically, as Curl and associates (1972) demonstrated in a recent study of the absorption of solar radiation in alpine snowfields. The intensity of light present at a given vertical distance within new-fallen, powdery snow is less than in some types of older and denser snow. In the former, 99% of the incident solar radiation may be lost within 18 cm, but transmittance is increased sixfold in older, crystalline snow. In both instances, however, high reflectance or *albedo* (the percentage of light reflected) from the white surface is an important factor. A series of snowstorms at close intervals especially serve to darken the winter lake. The result in a rich shallow lake may be drastic oxygen depletion and a faunal catastrophe (see Chapter 10).

OPAQUE LAYERS AND THE HORIZONTAL TRANSMISSION OF LIGHT

Ordinarily the vertical transmittance of light can be plotted on semilog paper (see Figs. 7-1 to 7-3) with little or no obvious inflection in the resultant line,

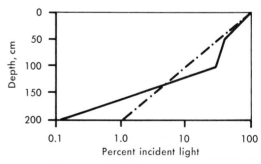

Fig. 7-5. Vertical transmittance of incident light on two occasions in Red Pond, Arizona. Solid line represents June 1964, when a stratum of purple sulfur bacteria was met about 100 cm below the surface. Dotted line represents light penetration in August 1964, when the bacterial concentration was absent.

especially beneath the upper meter where there is greater relative absorption of the fractions of total light. This is explained by the rapid diminution of long rays, with perhaps 50% of the total illumination disappearing in the upper 100 cm. Below this there is usually relatively little change in the percentage absorbed from meter to meter. Lake waters, however, do not fulfill the requirements of Bouguer's and Beer's laws in that they are not homogenous and do not present a uniformly attenuating medium. In some instances this is obvious when vertical light path is measured; a denser layer of particles may lie below the surface and absorb light much more effectively than overlying strata (Fig. 7-5).

With an instrument now called the transmissometer the vertical stratification of light-reducing entities can be shown. In the 1930's the physicist L. V. Whitney (1938) made some underwater measurements in Wisconsin lakes using a device that was the forerunner of this modern instrument. Briefly, it consists of a light source projecting a horizontal beam to a photocell receiver. Usually a distance of 1 m separates the two, but in waters of less clarity the distance can be lessened. A battery power source and a microammeter, receiving impulses from the photocell, are both in the boat. Transmittance just above or below the lake surface, or sometimes through a neutral filter, can be considered 100%; and as the instrument is lowered stage by stage, readings from the microammeter are recorded on this basis. Some workers calibrate the microammeter exponentially and record the results as optical density, the initial reading being zero. Plotting OD data yields a more meaningful curve because layers where marked light-extinguishing factors occur are shown as positive peaks (Fig. 7-6).

The transmissometer often reveals that the subsurface environment is indeed far from uniform; somewhat opaque layers may lie between layers of marked clarity. The phycologist Allan J. Brook and his students were among the first to study

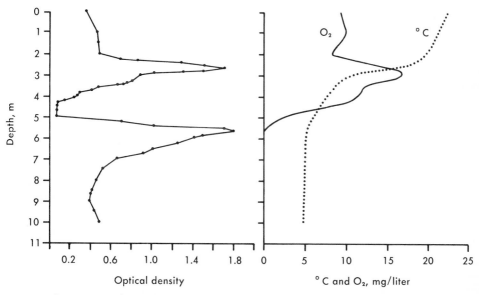

Fig. 7-6. Data from Arco Lake, Minnesota, 27 June 1970: optical density from use of transmissometer at left; temperature and oxygen profiles at right. The peaks in OD were due to a concentration of *Oscillatoria* at the upper level and a dense assemblage of sulfur bacteria below.

algal communities with a transmissometer, calling it a turbidimeter; their results were published in a series of articles (Baker and Brook 1971; Brook, Baker, and Klemer 1971). Samples taken where peaks of subsurface OD occurred contained large concentrations of phytoplankton, especially when from the lower metalimnion. Bluegreens were responsible for many peaks, but eukaryotic algae and sulfur bacteria accounted for others.

COLOR

Light coming from the lake surface yields an *apparent color* that is the result of many factors. Of these, the materials in solution and the particulate matter, both living and nonliving, are most important. The particulate segment can be termed sestonic. Reflections of subsurface objects in shallow ponds may also impart apparent color—light-colored sandy bottoms and dense, dark vegetation, for example.

Some reddish ponds are the result of suspended inorganic particles eroded from the surrounding soil. Organisms account for other red waters. A shallow saline pool in Arizona (Cole and associates 1967) is known as Red Pond presumably because of the purple sulfur bacteria not far below the surface (see Fig. 7-5), and at times schools of the brine shrimp *Artemia* are so thick that they intensify the reddish hue of the pond.

Oscillatoria rubescens, the bluegreen that heralds the onset of extreme eutrophication, sometimes colors the lake a reddish tint. "Blood lakes," although ordinarily small ponds, owe their name to surface scums of the flagellate *Euglena sanguinea*. Similarly, some ponds are bright green because of a superficial layer of some other species of *Euglena*. Phytoplankton populations consisting of diatoms or of the common dinoflagellate *Ceratium* give a dark yellow tint, and heavy blooms of bluegreens impart a green color.

Filtration removes the entities contributing to apparent color, leaving the so-called *true color* of the water. This ranges from clear blue to dark brown, or even to a blackish hue in hypolimnic waters containing ferrous sulfide.

The bluest waters are transparent and ultra-oligotrophic, low in both dissolved humic material and seston. The caldera Crater Lake, Oregon, serves as an example. Much of the color of such deep blue water comes from molecular scattering; light waves with the highest frequencies, especially, are scattered upward to view.

Waters with dissolved organic materials—humic substances leached in from soil, peat, or lake sediments—represent a cline of concentrations and color from green oligotrophic lakes, through the yellow of eutrophic waters, to brown, tea-colored bog pools.

Color standards by which natural waters can be compared and categorized have been developed. The Forel-Ule scale of colors is most often used. It consists of mixtures of different proportions of three solutions, ranging from the rare blue color I, a pure solution of cuprammonium sulfate, to the extreme brown color XXII. The latter and other browns and yellows are made from mixtures of cobalt ammonium sulfate, potassium chromate, and the above copper compound. An array of green shades, serving as standards, is made from various proportions of the yellow potassium chromate and the blue cuprammonium sulfate.

ABSORPTION OF LIGHT BY PLANT AND BACTERIAL PIGMENTS

Chlorophyll *a* is the master pigment in bluegreen and eukaryote photosynthesis. In living cells it absorbs light in two peaks, one between 670 and 680 nm and the other at about 435 nm. It is clear that long rays, making up the former peak, would be present in abundance in shallow water and that the short waves would penetrate deeper, permitting photosynthesis to occur at many levels. Since plants contain assortments of accessory pigments, other light waves that travel vertically in the lake also play a part in photosynthesis.

Accessory pigment molecules absorb energy quanta from light waves, become "excited" and energy-rich, and pass their excitation energy on sequentially. This energy eventually reaches chlorophyll *a,* although some has been lost by fluorescence at each transfer. Pigments absorbing short rays pass some of their energy to those absorbing longer waves, but not vice versa. The yellow carotenoids absorb blue light and pass it to the reddish phycoerythrins that absorb the longer wavelengths composing green light; they in turn pass energy to the phycocyanins, absorbing in the yellow-orange part of the spectrum. Chlorophyll *a,* found in all photosynthesizing plants except bacteria, is the final energy recipient. In addition, the molecules of chlorophylls *b, c,* and *d* have absorption peaks near, but different from, those of chlorophyll *a.* The result of all these organic pigments is that energy from light waves ranging from near 400 nm to at least 700 nm can be used in primary production by the higher plants. Because chlorobium chlorophyll in some green bacteria absorbs strongly near 755 nm, and bacteriochlorophyll *a,* found in purple and many green bacteria, absorbs in the red bands of 800, 850, and 890 nm, the spectrum from below 400 to 900 nm is available as an energy source to phototrophic organisms.

At great depths and in grottos and dimly lighted caves, blue-green algae are remarkable for their reddish color. Phycoerythrins, usually typical of the mainly marine red algae, are concentrated in them. This is an adaptation for absorbing the blue-green light that is still available after the filtering effect of the lake water and its components.

LIGHT PENETRATION AND AQUATIC PLANT ZONATION

Relationships exist among Secchi disc transparencies, euphotic zone, and the depths to which pondweeds and other macrophytes extend. Shading, which inhibits these plants, is the basis of a technique used to control them in fish-rearing ponds. Nutrients are added to increase the phytoplankton crop to such an extent that it acts as a light barrier.

Lake Tahoe has an unusually deep bed of macrophytes, supporting many invertebrate species and small fish, as well as a lake trout concentration. This is a unique plant community and one that is of extreme consequence in the economy of the lake. There is a danger that the response of phytoplankton to enrichment of the lake by domestic wastes and erosion could eliminate this complex benthic association by shading it; the results would be devastating (Frantz and Cordone 1967).

Schindler and Comita (1972) reported some abrupt changes in Severson Lake, Minnesota, that further illustrate the interactions of light penetration and plant growth. During a decade of summer observations, Secchi disc visibility always had been from 0.5 to 1.0 m, and submersed macrophytes were confined to depths no greater than 1.0 m. In 1965, following the first winter during which the lake became anoxic beneath the ice, *Daphnia pulex* made its initial appearance. Members of the growing population of this cladoceran grazed the phytoplankton to such an extent that by June a Secchi disc could be seen 4.5 m below the surface and a meter deeper in July. The rooted plants responded rapidly to the change in light environment and colonized the bottom to a depth of 3 m.

Table 7-1 shows various data on Secchi disc transparency (Z_{SD}) and the greatest depth inhabited by the associated macroscopic hydrophytes. Some of the most re-

Table 7-1. Relation between Secchi disc transparency and depths to which aquatic macrophytes grow in selected lakes

Lake	Secchi disc (m)	Deepest plant growth (m)
Crystal Lake, Minnesota	0.32-0.55	1.75
Sweeney Lake, Wisconsin	0.6-1.0	2.25
Lake Itasca, Minnesota	1.8	3.5
Montezuma Well, Arizona	3.1	7.5
Walden Pond, Massachusetts	6.0+	16
Long Lake, Minnesota	8	11
Weber Lake, Wisconsin	8	13.5
Lake Ontario, USA-Canada (1912-1914)	12 (est.)	46
Crystal Lake, Wisconsin	14	20
Waldo Lake, Oregon	28	127
Crater Lake, Oregon	38	120
Lake Tahoe, California-Nevada	33-41	136

markable deep-water communities known are included.

LIGHT AND AQUATIC ANIMALS

Light is important to aquatic animals as well as to plants, and a voluminous literature exists on these relationships. Animals can detect far lower intensities than those to which plants respond. Thus the larvae of *Chaoborus,* buried in the sediments well below the euphotic zone, rise to the ooze-water interface at sunset to reconnoiter the fading light. In its absence, or at some low threshold of light, a nocturnal migration to the epilimnion may occur, but too much light inhibits such a journey (LaRow 1969).

In an important paper, Smith and Baylor (1953) reported on experiments with light and Cladocera. They showed that diminishing intensities provoked upward swimming, while brightening caused downward movements. Moreover, they showed responses to blue, yellow, and red wavelengths that have ecologic significance. For example, blue light evokes a downward migration (this response is blocked in cold water, such as that of the thermocline layer) until sunset dimming

causes upward movement again. The reasons for some of these responses were reviewed by McNaught (1971), who pointed out that most cladocerans have visual pigments that absorb strongly at peaks of 430, 560, and 670 nm. In addition, they can respond to ultraviolet light because a fourth pigment absorbs maximally at 370 nm.

Photoperiodicity is a part of aquatic life cycles. Some less obvious examples are the initiation and cessation of diapause in *Daphnia* embryos (presented in a series of articles by Stross in 1971) and the termination or inducement of resting stages in freshwater cyclopoid copepods.

Löffler (1964) discussed briefly the common occurrence of pigmented Cladocera in high mountain waters and related this to ultraviolet radiation. Also, neuston-filtering species, such as the cladoceran *Scapholeberis* and the ostracod *Notodromas,* creep along beneath the surface film with their pigmented ventral sides up. (In contrast, their dorsal surfaces are pale.) *Daphnia middendorffiana* is pigmented because it is an inhabitant of high-latitude ponds where the atmospheric mantle is thin.

8

Density, layering, and lake classification

TEMPERATURE STRATIFICATION, LAKE REGIONS, AND WATER DENSITY

As solar radiation passes downward from the surface of a lake, it disappears exponentially (see Figs. 7-1 to 7-3), and the heating wavelengths are usually absorbed very rapidly. At the end of the yearly heating period, one might, a priori, expect the vertical temperature curve to resemble the light curve. This is not the case; in fact, a moderately deep lake sheltered from extreme winds would have a temperature profile quite different from the light curve (Fig. 8-1). The difference is readily explained by the wind mixing the upper layers of water and distributing downward the heat that had been absorbed in these surface strata. The result is a curve such as that shown in Fig. 8-2. It portrays *direct stratification,* with dense cold water lying beneath lighter warm layers, and shows the lake divided into three regions. The upper warm region, mixed thoroughly by wind to a more or less uniform temperature, is the *epilimnion.* At the bottom lies a colder region of heavier water little affected by wind

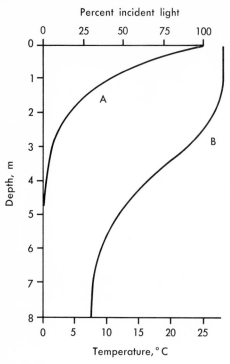

Fig. 8-1. Comparison of the vertical daytime light curve *(A)* and the temperature curve *(B)*. Tom Wallace Lake, Kentucky, 25 June 1952.

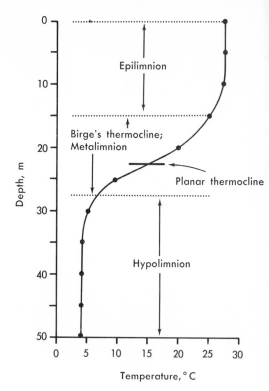

Fig. 8-2. Vertical temperature profile showing direct stratification and the lake regions defined by it.

action and, therefore, traditionally considered stagnant. This is the *hypolimnion.* Separating the two lake regions of more constant temperature is an intermediate zone, where temperature drops rapidly with increasing depth. Various names have been applied to this middle zone. Birge (1897) called this zone the *thermocline,* an appropriate term signifying a temperature gradient. The name *metalimnion* (changing lake), a contribution from Brönsted and Wesenberg-Lund (1911) and effectively accepted by Hutchinson (1957), is often used and has merit because it is not as rigid a definition as thermocline. Birge's term limited the middle zone to a region where temperature drops at least one degree Celsius with each meter increase in depth. Regardless of terminology, with a typical direct stratification there are, in a sense, three lakes in one: an upper lake, the

epilimnion; a middle lake, the metalimnion (perhaps in the present sense, more appropriately termed the mesolimnion); and a lower lake, the hypolimnion.

Hutchinson (1957) preserved Birge's word thermocline, but no longer to designate a broad region. Instead, he followed Brönsted and Wesenberg-Lund (1911), considering the thermocline to be an imaginary plane within the lake. It is located at a level intermediate between the two depths where the temperature decrease is greatest. This planar thermocline lies within the metalimnion or Birge's classical thermocline (Fig. 8-2).

The concept of a plane that separates an irradiated, wind-stirred upper lake, where primary productivity prevails, from a darker, less turbulent lower lake is useful. Organic material is synthesized in the trophogenic epilimnion; much of it sinks to the tropholytic hypolimnion to be mineralized by bacteria. An imaginary plane, the area of which can be calculated and through which organic particles theoretically drop, is useful in techniques of estimating lake productivity.

Because the word thermocline implies a gradient, perhaps it is not the best choice for such a plane, but there are also unusual situations where the modern term metalimnion is awkward. For example, a body of water much protected from air currents would have a summer temperature curve somewhat similar to the exponential light-absorption profile. In certain lakes that have come under study this is the case: a pronounced summertime temperature gradient starts at the surface; the epilimnion is poorly defined, shallow, or practically absent; and the metalimnion is the uppermost stratum. Here the word thermocline is more useful to describe the zone of decreasing temperature starting at the surface.

Momentarily neglecting their effects on animal and plant metabolism, temperature differences are significant because of the density contrasts that accompany them (Table 8-1). In general, we can say that under normal pressure, water is heaviest at 4° C when a milliliter weighs 1 g, the standard unit of density. Because of water's unusual molecular constitution, it becomes lighter as it cools below 4° C; the outcome is floating rather than sinking ice. Also, as temperature rises above 4° C, density once more decreases. Direct stratification (Figs. 8-1, *B,* 8-2, and 8-3) shows that warm water is buoyed up by cold, but a natural inverse stratification can be found beneath an ice cover. The ice at 0° C floats on water that warms progressively with depth to 4° C at the bottom.

The adjectives *isothermal* or *homoiothermal* describe a body of water of unvarying temperature. The temperature curve would be a straight vertical line, and theoretically the density would be the same throughout.

Table 8-1. Some temperature-density relationships of pure water at one atmosphere pressure and with density 1.0 at 4° C

°C	Density change × 10⁷	Ratio*
0-1	+588	7.25
1-2	412	5.08
2-3	243	3.00
3-4	78	0.96
4-5	−81	1.00
5-6	238	2.93
6-7	388	4.79
7-8	533	6.58
8-9	674	8.32
9-10	811	10.01
10-11	949	11.71
11-12	1081	13.34
12-13	1207	14.90
13-14	1328	16.39
14-15	1447	17.86
15-16	1564	19.30
16-17	1679	20.73
17-18	1790	22.00
18-19	1901	23.46
19-20	2008	24.79
20-21	2113	26.08
21-22	22.7	27.37
22-23	2319	28.62
23-24	2418	29.85
24-25	2517	31.07
25-26	2611	32.23
26-27	2707	33.41
27-28	2798	34.54
28-29	2888	35.65
29-30	2979	36.77

*The ratio above is:

$$\frac{\text{Density change between two adjacent temperatures}}{\text{Density change between 4° and 5° C}}$$

Thus, between 24° and 25° the density change is 2517×10^{-7}; between 4° and 5° it is 81×10^{-7}. The ratio is 2517/81 = 31.07. This means that the change between 24° and 25° is more than 31 times greater than the density change between 4° and 5°. By summation, the density change between 12° and 16° is 5546×10^{-7}.

FACTORS MODIFYING DENSITY OF WATER AND TEMPERATURE GRADIENTS
Temperature

Our knowledge of thermal phenomena in lakes and ponds has been derived mostly from studies of relatively dilute waters. In density computations the water is usually considered pure, and temperature is the major factor affecting density. Table 8-1 shows that under these conditions the density change between 24° and 25° C is more than 31 times greater than such a change between 4° and 5° C. This point is emphasized further by Fig. 8-3 in which the density gradient caused by pronounced temperature stratification in a cold-water lake is matched by the gentle inflection in a warmer lake.

Pressure

Pressure lowers the temperature of maximum density so that in a very deep lake the lowest stratum may be composed of water substantially below 4.0° C and even below 3.94° C, a more precise estimate of the densest pure water at one atmosphere. At the surface (at sea level) an atmosphere approximates a column of water 1,000 cm × 1 cm², 1 kg/cm². Actually, it is 1.032 kg, and it appears that every 10-m increase in depth equals roughly another atmosphere of pressure. On the average the temperature of maximum density is lowered about 0.1° C per 100 m. More specifically, the temperature of maximum density below 500 m of water is 3.39° C, and below 1,000 m it is 2.91° C.

Solutes (salinity)

Rawson and Moore (1944) studied some saline lakes in Saskatchewan and reported summer temperature profiles that on cursory examination appear normal: epilimnion, thermocline, and hypolimnion are delineated clearly. They differ radically from the norm, however,

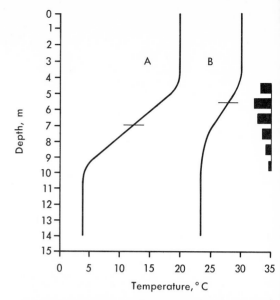

Fig. 8-3. Comparison of the temperature profiles of a cold lake *(A)* and a warmer lake *(B)* having identical density gradients caused by temperature. Density changes shown by histograms at right. Horizontal lines in curves represent planar thermoclines based on maximum temperature change.

in that the temperature of greatest density is depressed by high salinity, and hypolimnion temperatures fall below 0° C. For example, in the deeps of Manito Lake, the freezing point has been lowered to −1.1° C, and the maximum density is at −0.3° C. These apparent summertime anomalies are simply explained by the winter ice cap that melts at an unusually low temperature to expose a cold, salty body of water. Stirred by vernal winds, the lake becomes isothermal below the normal freezing point of water and does not gain much heat throughout before the surface strata warm enough to shape a stratification that traps cold water in lower levels.

Materials in solution, if abundant enough, result in other phenomena that appear anomalous to the student of dilute fresh water. Specific gravities are increased by solutes. In lakes with marked salinity with layering, the usual temperature-induced density relations can be re-

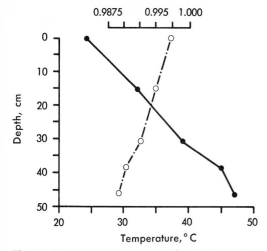

Fig. 8-4. Inverse temperature stratification in a saline desert pool. Solid line indicates temperature, ° C; broken line shows density of distilled water at the same temperatures. (Modified from Cole and Minckley 1968.)

versed: warm water may persist below colder strata if it contains enough extra salt. The outcome is an inverse stratification far from the 0° to 4° C range considered normal. Fig. 8-4 illustrates such an improbable condition in a shallow brine pool in Mexico; here an inverse temperature curve is explained by salt layering. A shallow pool of salty water concentrated by evaporation became overlain by a dilute layer originating from rain and runoff. The high temperature in the deeper part is readily explained by direct solar radiation penetrating the upper stratum. The saline bottom water accumulated heat, while the dilute upper layer reduced outgoing radiation and prevented evaporation from it. The contrasting densities prohibited anything but very slow mixing of the two layers.

Abrupt temperature gradients often accompany stratified saline waters, although decreases amounting to 0.1° C per cm are rare in the metalimnia of freshwater lakes, Small inland salt ponds often display gradients amounting to perhaps 0.5° C per cm but differ from the typical

metalimnion because the temperature rises with depth.

Suspended particles

Materials need not be dissolved to increase density of a water mass; suspended particles also are effective. A common example is that of a turbid, muddy stream entering a lake or joining a clearer stream. The muddy flow maintains a degree of integrity and can be followed by the eye. Thus, a *density current,* due to particles in temporary suspension can enter a lake, cut through colder water, and continue its downward path until reaching a level where its density is matched or surpassed. Unusual temperature stratification often accompanies such an event but is not lasting.

Anderson and Pritchard (1951) discussed the annual cycle of the turbid Colorado River as it flowed through the Grand Canyon to enter Lake Mead. During summer a down-lake flow along the bottom was observed and attributed to sediment-laden water. As the water cooled in autumn and winter, the flow was even more conspicuous, its density being augmented by lower temperatures. Salinity also played a role, and the spring runoff water, flowing down the Colorado, revealed its dilute nature by spreading out over the lake rather than sinking. Since the 1951 report, there have been alterations that may have changed this annual pattern. Because of the impoundment of the stream to form Lake Powell (which serves as a sediment trap), the Colorado River no longer flows through the gorge to Lake Mead as a remarkably turbid stream.

Another example of a density current due to turbidity comes from Lake Mendota. A bathymetric map constructed from soundings made many years ago by Birge and Juday had some bizarre contour configurations. A later survey utilizing sonar equipment for establishing depths showed that the soundings of the early workers had revealed a real feature, a subsurface gully. This had been formed by density currents from an inflowing stream eroding the bottom slope. One summer, following an unusual spell of heavy rainfall, the swollen stream, densely laden with silt and mud, flowed down the gully to unusual depths, introducing some oxygenated water to the hypolimnion (Bryson and Suomi 1951).

The classic example of a density current entering a lake is seen in Lake Geneva (Forel's Léman) where the entering Rhone has cut an elongate gully in the bottom of the lake for more than 6 km.

Particulate matter, like solutes, can bring about sharp temperature profiles in addition to imparting density. The gradient usually is the reverse, however, from what has been described from briny stratified pools. Very abrupt thermoclines have been reported from small turbid ponds in hot sunny areas. The particles in the upper layers absorb heat rays so effectively that pronounced vertical contrasts occur.

STABILITY OF STRATIFICATION

Direct stratification persists through much of the summer because the contrasting densities imparted by temperature can be mixed to homogeneity only by a tremendous amount of work. The summer wind is not powerful enough to do this, and we say that the lake exhibits *stability.*

The concept of stability is owed to Schmidt (1915, 1928), and although few authors have calculated stability in ensuing years, the term has become valuable in limnologic vocabulary and theory.

Very simply, S is the amount of work that would be required to mix an entire lake to uniform density without adding or subtracting heat in the process. If density is uniform from top to bottom, stability is zero: no work must be performed to promote homogeneity. Somewhere in the lake at any given time, there is a

point representing the depth of the center of gravity (z_g); above this point the water mass equals the mass of water below. Vertical contrasts in density, resulting from differences in temperature, salinity, and suspended particles, lower the center of gravity from its level when density is uniform throughout. Stability begins to increase as the center of gravity is lowered.

Theoretically, S equals the amount of work necessary to lift the entire lake from the actual z_g up to the level of z_g that would exist at uniform density. The work, implying a force and distance through which it moves a mass, is reduced to the absolute unit of work in the cgs system, the erg, and is related to unit area (cm²) of lake surface. Thus, stability could be expressed in terms of the dyne-centimeter per square centimeter. Customarily, however, acceleration is omitted from the dyne (a force that gives a 1-g mass an acceleration of 1 cm/sec per sec), and stability is presented as g-cm/cm².

Recently Idso (1973) discussed stability based on Schmidt's original formula, pointing out that, although the formula gives correct integrated values for the lake as a whole, there are inherent errors in it that lead to mistakes in some subsequent calculations. Idso proposes the following formula, which violates no physical principles and yields no negative work data:

$$S = \frac{1}{A_0} \int_{z_0}^{z_m} (\rho_z - \bar{\rho}) \, (A_z) \, (z - z_{\bar{\rho}}) \, dz$$

A_0 = A, the surface area in cm

A_z = The area (cm²) at some depth z (considered positive and in cm)

$\bar{\rho}$ = The final or mean density that would result from stirring the lake to uniformity (g/cm³)

ρ_z = The density at depth z

$z_{\bar{\rho}}$ = The depth in cm where the final or mean density $(\bar{\rho})$ exists prior to mixing

z_m = maximum depth in cm

z_0 = surface, or zero depth

Table 8-2 shows data from Tom Wallace Lake, 26 June 1954, that permit approximation of the stability of stratifica-

Table 8-2. Data and calculations of stability stratification in Tom Wallace Lake, Kentucky, 26 June 1954

I	II	III	IV	V	VI	VII	VIII	IX	X
z	T_z	A_z	ρ_z		$A_z/\Delta z$	$\rho_z A_z \Delta z$	$\rho_z - \bar{\rho}$	$z - z_{\bar\rho}$	(V × VIII × IX)
cm	°C	10^8 cm²	g/cm³	A_z/A_0	10^8 cm³	10^8 g	g/cm³	cm	g/cm²
50	27.7	2.150	0.99634	0.9188	215.0	214.21	−0.00165	−196.5	0.29789
150	26.7	1.800	0.99662	0.7692	180.0	179.39	−0.00137	− 96.5	0.10169
250	20.9	1.500	0.99804	0.6410	150.0	149.71	+0.0050	+ 3.5	0.00112
350	14.0	1.235	0.99927	0.5278	123.5	123.41	0.00128	103.5	0.06992
450	10.3	0.980	0.99700	0.4188	98.0	97.97	0.00171	203.5	0.14574
550	8.1	0.725	0.99987	0.3098	72.5	72.49	0.00188	303.5	0.17676
650	7.3	0.470	0.99992	0.2009	47.0	47.00	0.00193	403.5	0.15645
750	7.0	0.220	0.99993	0.0940	22.0	22.0	0.00194	503.5	0.09182
850	6.9	0.010	0.99993	0.0043	1.0	1.00	0.00194	603.5	0.00503
Totals					909.0	907.18			1.04642

$$\bar{\rho} = \frac{1}{V} \sum_{z_0}^{z_m} \rho_z A_z \, \Delta z = \frac{907.18}{909} = 0.99799 \text{ g/cm}^3$$

By interpolation, therefore, $z_{\bar\rho} = 246.5$ cm.

$$S = \sum_{z_0}^{z_m} (z - z_{\bar\rho})(\rho_z - \bar\rho)\frac{A_z}{A_0}\Delta z = 1.04642 \text{ g/cm}^2 \times 100 \text{ cm} = 104.6 \text{ g-cm/cm}^2$$

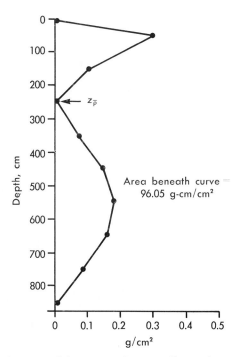

Fig. 8-5. Stability curve of Tom Wallace Lake, Kentucky, 26 June 1954. Area beneath curve represents about 96.05 g-cm/cm².

tion at that time. Fig. 8-5 is a plot of the calculations. Planimetric integration of the area under the curve, developed from the above formula, yields about 96.05 g-cm/cm². Table 8-2 includes results of summation rather than integration and gives 104.6 g-cm/cm². Note that the depth of the center of gravity is not needed in the procedures. Instead, the mean or final density, $\bar\rho$, is established by multiplying the density in each stratum by its volume (cm³) and by summing and dividing by total volume. The depth ($z_{\bar\rho}$) at which the mean density is present during the existing stratification is found by examining the data in column IV of the table and interpolating.

ANNUAL CIRCULATION PATTERNS AND LAKE CLASSIFICATION

The times when circulation occurs are, of course, periods of mixing. The noun *mixis* and its adjective *mictic* are used in compound words to categorize lakes according to annual circulation patterns. Such a classification is superimposed on older schemes; as a result some confusion exists. Moreover, it is not easy to classify many lakes, because their behavior varies from year to year.

Amixis

Some bodies of water never circulate. These are the *amictic* lakes, permanently ice covered and immune throughout to the stirring effects of wind. Hutchinson and Löffler (1956) diagrammed a theoretical scheme showing that amixis is improbable at sea level until latitudes of slightly more than 80° are reached, and at the equator, below 6,000 m elevation.

There is very little land above 80° in the Northern Hemisphere, but still there may be as many as 10 amictic lakes in northern Greenland and adjacent Ellesmere Island. One of these, Greenland's Angiussaq Lake, is 590 m above mean sea level at a latitude of slightly more than 77° N (Barnes 1960). The ice thickness varies from 1.8 to 4 m, capping water that attains a maximum depth of 187 m. Temperatures are very low and constant (0.1° to 0.7° C from surface to bottom), implying a lake quite isolated from outside influences.

Lake Hazen (81° 50′ N) on Ellesmere Island is a large lake at least 280 m deep. Although usually amictic, during some summers it is free of ice. For example in 1957 it was open for 54 days (McLaren 1964).

In Antarctica, perennially frozen lakes have been known since the time of the 1907-1909 British Antarctic Expedition. At least five of them were named on Ross Island's Cape Royds, almost 79° S lat, where the explorers wintered. A few protozoans, rotifers, tardigrads, and nematodes were observed, but no intensive work was done on Antarctic amictic lakes until much later when some of the Ross Island coastal ponds were revisited as part of a general limnologic reconnais-

sance of the McMurdo Sound region (Armitage and House 1962). Goldman's review of the history of Antarctic limnology (1970) has revealed that two lakes, Bonney and especially Vanda, have received most attention. A little more than 77° S lat, their basins lie in a strange dry valley system in Victoria Land.

Layering beneath the ice covers in these lakes is by no means simple. Saline stratification and unusual temperature profiles imply increments of heat from the bottom, from an inflow of saline thermal waters, or from the sun. Solar radiation is theorized to account for the temperature profiles of Lake Bonney; but in Lake Vanda, where temperatures attain 25.5° C more than 67 m below the ice, geothermal effects are important (Angino and associates 1965).

Other amictic lakes are found at high altitudes and relatively low latitudes. We owe much of our knowledge of these lakes to the Austrian limnologist Heinz Löffler (1964). His summary of tropical high-mountain limnology lists amictic lakes in the Peruvian Andes and at least one on Mount Kenya, Africa. The last, Curling Pond, is interesting because it is Africa's highest known lake (about 4,800 m elevation) and is located approximately on the equator. It lies below the theoretical 6,000 m limit proposed by Hutchinson and Löffler (1956) for equatorial amixis, and there is evidence that occasionally its ice cover partially melts.

It is obvious that permanent amixis can exist only in those rare cold climates where ice produced by unusual duration of subzero temperatures is not lost at another season. *Ablation,* the loss of ice through evaporation and melting, is largely a function of air temperature. Cold must prevail throughout the year to promote amixis.

Holomixis

Holomixis is a typical lake phenomenon whereby wind-driven circulation mixes the entire lake. Overturn periods involve the total water mass.

Oligomictic lakes. Originally Hutchinson and Löffler (1956) proposed the term oligomixis to describe conditions in certain equatorial lakes at low altitudes. These lakes have warm water at all depths and are subject to very little seasonal change. Rather effective stability is brought about by the warming of surface strata, thereby creating great density differences between them and the colder layers below (see Fig. 8-3). Occasional cooling of surface strata destroys density differences, reducing stability as a prelude to mixing. Circulation periods in these warm oligomictic lakes are unusual, irregular, and short in duration.

The geography of oligomictic lakes must be broadened when the behavior of some of the large subalpine European lakes are taken into account. For example, Maggiore, a large Italian lake formed by glacial corrasion, its surface 193 m above sea level and at 46° N lat, circulates for a few weeks during February and March. This occurs, however, only once every 5 to 7 years during unusually cold and windy winters (Vollenweider 1964). Nearby Lake Como (Italy) and, perhaps, Lake Geneva (France-Switzerland) behave similarly. Also, Hadžišče (1966), who studied Lake Ohrid for 24 years, found that this ancient Balkan lake circulates completely about once every 7 years, depending on climatic conditions.

This second type of oligomictic lake is characterized by comparatively cold water. Lake Maggiore, for example, circulates at about 6° C. It and the other members of the category are deep, voluminous bodies of water requiring tremendous work for holomixis; surface cooling and the resultant convection currents cannot bring about complete circulation in the absence of adequate wind. The climatic environment of these lakes is such that they experience seasonal contrasts. Thus, their periods of circulation are fixed but occur only with unusually low temperatures and high winds, unlike the equatorial or warm oligomictic lakes that experience a diel climate and circulate at irregular times throughout the year.

Monomictic lakes. Monomixis is defined as one regular period of circulation occurring sometime within the year. There are two main types, separated here on the basis of whether the overturn occurs during summer or in the cold season. Monomictic lakes usually exist in climates where seasonal changes are pronounced.

Cold monomixis. Cold monomictic lakes are frozen over during the winter months when the water is shielded from the mixing effect of wind. They are characterized by stagnation only during winter, when they are temporarily amictic. Ideally, these lakes exhibit inverse temperature stratification, with water ranging from 0° C below the ice to about 4° C in the deeps. With the melting of ice in spring, stability is extremely low and circulation commences. Throughout the summer they are essentially isothermal, warming but never stratifying to any extent.

Originally, cold monomixis was applied only to those lakes where surface waters do not rise above 4° C during the warm season. These were the "Polar Lakes" in a classification devised by Forel. Though not common, there are some of these that exist at high altitudes in lower latitudes far from the poles. Berg (1963) discussed the problem in detail, deemphasizing the 4° C threshold and broadening the definition of cold monomixis. He cited the case of windswept Oneida Lake, New York, that is at the most, poorly stratified during the ice-free season, sometimes being isothermal as high as 24° C.

Even the small, shallow Imikpuk at Point Barrow (71° 17′ N lat) on the Arctic coastal plain cannot be classified as a polar lake. It is open only about 60 days of the year, but during that short circulation period it warms 4 to 8 degrees above 4° C, depending on summer meteorologic conditions (Brewer 1958). Perhaps as much as 75% of the incoming vernal solar radiation serves to melt the ice blanket; after that, only a small amount is needed to raise the water temperature above 4° C in such a shallow lake.

The cold monomixis of deep New Quebec Crater Lake, although farther south (61° 17′), fits the definition of a polar lake. The thermal requirement to warm its great water mass above 4° C during the summer overturn period is much too great. Martin (1955) recorded summer surface temperatures of only 3° to 4° C in this lake.

Lake Hazen was free of ice during 54 days in August and September, 1957, and its open water did not exceed 3° C (McLaren 1964). That year it was a cold monomictic lake of the polar type rather than amictic.

Some shallow volcanic lakes on Anderson Mesa near Flagstaff, Arizona, freeze over during winter months and circulate much of the summer, warming to at least 22° C. Successive calm days result in warm upper strata and far more stability than would be found in Imikpuk, for example; but strong winds are the rule, and they soon spring up to destroy the transitory stratification. With some reservations, these lakes are classified as cold monomictic.

Also, according to Eddy (1963), Minnesota lakes such as Mille Lacs, Lake Winnibigoshish, and Leech Lake (all of which range from 15 to 32 km across) show little summertime temperature stratification. They are relatively shallow and exposed to the wind. Their winter stagnation, due to ice cover, and their typical mixing throughout the remainder of the year leave little choice but to designate them cold monomictic despite their departure from the 4-degree threshold of older classifications.

Bayly and Williams (1973) were aware of the two kinds of cold monomictic lakes. They termed the polar lake *cold thereimictic* and the cold monomictic lake with summer holomixis above 4° C *warm thereimictic.*

Warm monomixis. An old classification designated as subtropical those lakes that circulate during the winter months but are stratified during summer. The deficiency of this scheme is evident when regions such as the English Lake District and the Finger Lakes of New York are defined as subtropical. Warm monomictic is a better term to describe monomictic lakes that lack an ice cover and that circulate in winter. Direct stratification, arising during early summer, puts an end to complete circulation until the thermocline is destroyed sometime in autumn.

There are borderline regions where the classification breaks down at times. Cayuga Lake, New York, stratifies during the summer months but remains open and isothermal during the average winter when an effective wind plays upon its surface. Tremendous quantities of heat must be lost to bring the surface near freezing, and it is only during exceptionally cold winters, perhaps marked by periods of unusual calm, that a sheet of ice forms to stop circulation.

Warm monomixis is a usual occurrence south of about 40° latitude in North America where lakes are deep enough and sheltered enough to stratify during summer. The winters are mild, and the lakes circulate at comparatively high temperatures. Elephant Butte Reservoir, an impoundment on the Río Grande in New Mexico, circulates at about 8° C. Farther south and at lower altitudes, impoundments on the Salt River in central Arizona cool to about 11° or 12° C during the winter mixing period. Central American lakes such as Atitlán (Guatemala) and Güija (El Salvador) dip to about 20° C during their winter circulation periods. Obviously, the summer hypolimnia of these lakes can be no colder than the lowest temperature of the winter circulation and are far above 4° C (Deevey 1957).

Other warm monomictic lakes, however, are not so warm. Cayuga Lake circulates at temperatures below 4° C. Henson and co-workers (1961) reported isothermy at 2.8° C in March and cited earlier records of freely circulating water at only 1.3° C. The nearby Seneca Lake behaves similarly. Also, the Laurentian Great Lakes—Michigan, Superior, and Huron—although icebound marginally, are largely open during winter months and exhibit temperature stratification during summer. Their winter water temperatures commonly fall below 4° C.

The huge, relatively shallow Lake Victoria, although lying across the equator, behaves like a monomictic lake of temperate regions. One would expect it to exhibit almost continuous circulation, but through an unusual mechanism, it stratifies during the rainy season when its inflows introduce cool, dense water to the lake. Its direct stratification is brought about by cooling of bottom layers rather than by the familiar method of warming the surface. This phenomenon may be widespread in equatorial lakes.

Dimictic lakes. Dimictic lakes have two mixing periods, the vernal and autumnal overturns, each year. The idealized temperate-zone dimictic lake with an annual temperature cycle is commonly portrayed as a typical lake. However, there are important limnologic regions where dimictic lakes are wanting. Australian limnologists, for example, have no such bodies of water to study (Bayly and Williams 1973).

The typical dimictic lake stratifies directly during the warm months; if it were shallower and/or exposed to forceful wind, it might exhibit cold monomixis. The onset of cold weather starts the cooling of surface water that eventually destroys the stratification and initiates complete circulation. During the fall overturn, chilling of the entire water mass occurs until, ideally, the whole lake is uniform at about 4° C. On some cold, calm night the surface gives off enough heat to the atmosphere to cool to the freezing point, and a film of ice is formed. This inaugurates the winter stagnation period when wind-induced circulation is impossible. With the warming days of spring the ice melts, and a cold lake, with stability near zero, lies exposed to wind action. The result is the vernal overturn, a circulation period that continues until ended by the direct temperature stratification of summer. This is the dimictic cycle.

During the autumnal circulation period, loss of heat at the air-water interface creates dense water that streams downward, aiding the wind in the mixing process. After the entire water mass is 4° C, however, further cooling creates lighter water at the surface, and convection currents no longer move downward. In most instances, freezing soon follows. The stability of this stratification is so slight that wind can drive the cold stratum downward before freezing occurs. The result is a lake chilled well below 4° before an ice cover forms. Berg (1963) discussed this and pointed out that in some large, exposed dimictic lakes there is prolonged autumnal cooling resulting in isothermy at 1° or 2° C prior to winter stagnation.

Just as wind prolongs autumnal circulation, so it lengthens the vernal mixing period in warm monomictic and dimictic lakes. In years with stormy spring weather the circulation continues farther into the warming period; the whole water mass gains heat, and its temperature rises until it approaches ranges where slight differences in temperature are marked by significantly different densities. Then a calm day or two may initiate layering and summer stagnation. In years when calm weather prevails during spring, the heat gained in upper strata is not driven

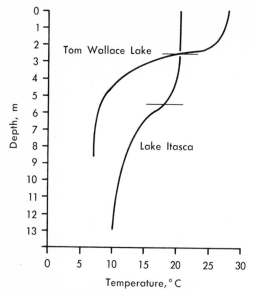

Fig. 8-6. Comparison of summer temperature profiles from Tom Wallace Lake, 26 June 1954, and Lake Itasca, 26 June 1970. Horizontal lines indicate planar thermoclines. Although Lake Itasca is 9° farther north, it has a warmer hypolimnion and a higher mean temperature because of a prolonged vernal circulation period.

downward, and the density differences between surface and lower waters may end circulation while bottom waters are still cold from conditions of the previous winter. Hypolimnion temperatures during early summer, therefore, reveal information about vernal weather conditions.

An excellent example of the vernal wind's effect on summer hypolimnion temperatures is seen by comparing the small Tom Wallace Lake, Kentucky, with Lake Itasca, Minnesota, more than 9° farther north. Tom Wallace is only 8.7 m deep and during mild winters does not freeze. Lake Itasca, with a maximum depth of 14 m, lies in a northern region where prolonged ice cover is the rule. The Kentucky lake has a small surface, a maximum length of 0.33 km, and is protected by steep, wooded hills that rise abruptly from its shores. Itasca, by contrast, is 4 km long and exposed to the wind. The differences in topography,

morphology and wind factors result in marked contrast in the temperatures of these two lakes. The June hypolimnion in the southern lake is no more than 7° or 8° C, whereas Lake Itasca's hypolimnion is 11° to 15° C (Fig. 8-6).

Polymictic lakes. Polymixis refers to many mixing periods or continuous circulation throughout the year. Polymictic lakes are influenced more by the changing diel fluctuations in temperature than by seasonal changes. The original examples described by Hutchinson and Löffler (1956) are close to the equator. In some small Andean ponds at fairly high altitudes the upper waters gain heat to stratify diurnally. Cold nights cool the upper layers to such an extent that downwelling convection currents destroy the stratification, and nocturnal circulation takes place until terminated by the following day's solar input.

A similar diel cycle was described by Foster (1973) in quite a different region. In small Arizona desert ponds, averaging about 1 m in depth, intense solar radiation in all seasons brings about pronounced diurnal density differences. At night the cooling of superficial layers sets up convection patterns that obliterate the stratification. In that arid region the nocturnal cooling is, to a great extent, a function of evaporation. Evaporation occurs, of course, throughout the 24-hour period and results in an annual loss of about 2.2 m; however, during daylight, its cooling effects are surpassed by solar heating.

The heat of vaporization for water at 30° C is about 580 cal/g. Thus the cooling effects derived from the evaporation of a film 1 mm thick beneath 1 cm² of pond surface would be 58 calories if it were distilled water. More heat exchange is involved in the evaporation of saline water and at lower temperatures (Table 8-3).

Although few data are available, it seems that large, shallow Lake Nicaragua represents another polymictic type. At night and during the morning hours

Table 8-3. Latent heat of vaporization for pure water at different temperatures

$^{\circ}C$	Calories per gram
0	597.3
10	591.7
20	586.0
30	580.4
40	574.7

some stratification occurs, although the lake has a mean depth of only 12.4 m. Temperature differences from 28° to 24° C, the range from surface to bottom at these times, imply density contrasts as great as those to be found, for example, in a range from 4° to 16° C. Each afternoon strong winds arise, reducing the morning stability to zero.

There are undoubtedly many shallow, unprotected bodies of water that circulate almost continuously in mild climates where ice blankets never exist. Unusual conditions account for lack of stratification in others. Pearse (1936) described some Yucatán cenotes that were unstratified, presumably because of water continuously entering and leaving somewhere below the surface. Montezuma Well, Arizona, resembles the cenotes in that it is usually isothermal although 17 m deep, remarkably protected from the wind, and has a relative depth of 17% (Cole and Barry 1973). Water amounting to about 10% of the Well's volume enters from deep subsurface crevices and leaves each day at a surface outlet, precluding all but the most transitory layering. Subject to a climate quite different from the Yucatan, Montezuma Well would freeze over during winter months but for the fact that its entering water supply averages about 24° C.

Polymixis seems to describe another condition, although quite different from the original use of the word. In regions near the boundary of warm monomixis and dimixis or cold monomixis (warm thereimixis in the sense of Bayly and Williams 1973), there may be unusual winters when ice lies across lakes that are usually open throughout the year. As a result lake categories change. On very rare occasions, for example, Cayuga Lake becomes ice covered and, therefore, falls into the dimictic class for that year. When there are multiple ice covers that come and go during a winter, the phenomenon must be termed a type of polymixis. One winter there were three separate freezings, punctuated by thawing and open water, at Tom Wallace Lake (Krumholz and Cole 1959). There were five distinct periods of circulation that year.

Meromixis

Meromictic lakes circulate at times, but incompletely. In contrast to holomixis, the entire water mass does not participate in the mixing. A dense stratum of bottom water remains stagnant and characteristically anaerobic. Findenegg (1935) coined the useful adjective meromictic to apply to some Austrian lakes he had investigated.

A unique terminology has evolved to describe the regions of a meromictic lake. First, there is a permanently stagnant layer containing a markedly greater concentration of dissolved substances than that found in the overlying water; this is the *monimolimnion,* a term we owe to Findenegg. The upper layer, being much more dilute, is mixed by the wind and shows seasonal changes; this is the *mixolimnion.* In a sense it is comparable to an entire holomictic water mass. Between the mixolimnion and monimolimnion there is a zone where salinity increases rapidly with depth, the *chemocline.*

The vertical density gradient in the chemocline is analogous to the thermocline in the sense of Birge, although the great stability of a meromictic lake is a function of materials in solution rather than of temperature. Any phenomenon that brings about loss of soluble material from the dense monimolimnion, or contributes significantly to the salinity of the mixolimnion, decreases the stability and may eventually terminate meromixis.

The words mixolimnion and chemocline came from Hutchinson (1937). They were derived from his study of Big Soda Lake, Nevada, a meromictic member of a group of lakes he investigated in the Lahontan Basin. His published report, cited above, contributed much to both arid-land limnology and our knowledge of meromixis.

Biogenic meromixis. There is a classification of meromictic lakes based on the manner by which solutes accumulate in the monimolimnion. The first type to be observed in North America was the biogenic meromictic lake. In this kind there is an accumulation of substances derived from bacterial decay, diffusion from the sediment, and from photosynthetic precipitation of carbonate. There is no striking accumulation of salts such as NaCl. The waters are typically the calcium bicarbonate type, and the dissolved materials in the monimolimnion are much like those found in the hypolimnion of a eutrophic lake toward the end of summer stagnation.

Eggleton (1931) described unusual summer temperature profiles and deep anoxic water, foul with H_2S and devoid of metazoan life, in Fayetteville Green Lake, New York. At that time meromixis lacked a terminology and backlog of published research that would begin later with Findenegg (1935). Eggleton did not expand on the unusual features he had discovered until later (Eggleton 1956).

The plunge-basin Green Lake and its neighbor Round Lake, of similar origin, illustrate some of the unusual requisites for biogenic meromixis. Morphologic, topographic, and meteorologic conditions that hinder overturn are necessary, either singly or working in chorus, for the accumulation of the substances of

biogenic origin that impart density to the bottom waters. In the case of Eggleton's lake, steep, wooded slopes rise abruptly from the shores for 120 m, serving to protect the surface from air currents in three directions. Moreover, the depth (59 m) of Fayetteville Green Lake is great in relation to its area, about 27 ha. Its relative depth, z_r, is a surprising 10%; this is typical when meromixis is due to biogenesis.

An instructive comparison can be made between Sodon Lake, Michigan (Newcombe and Slater 1950), and Tom Wallace Lake (Cole 1954). The former, a pit lake in thick glacial drift, is meromictic; Tom Wallace was formed by artificial impoundment and is holomictic. Both are surrounded and protected by wooded hills, and they have nearly identical areas, about 2.31 and 2.34 ha, respectively. Sodon Lake is more nearly circular and has a maximum length of 192 m, compared with the Kentucky lake's wind-effective length of 328 m. The most striking difference between the two, however, is their maximum depths: Sodon Lake is 17.7 m deep; Tom Wallace is 8.7 m deep. Their respective relative depths are 10.3% and 5.0%. Sheltered Tom Wallace Lake shows several effects of insulation from wind, but it lacks the morphologic extremes that established meromixis in Sodon Lake. Table 8-4 further emphasizes the high relative depths found in most biogenic meromictic lakes.

One of the most celebrated of the biogenic meromictic lakes is the Austrian Längsee, one of the Carinthian lakes that Findenegg studied in his early investigations of meromixis. It is a fairly shallow lake with an unusually low (for meromixis) relative depth of only 2.13% and is shielded to some extent by hills. The key factor, however, in its meromixis is meteorologic. In that part of Austria calm weather with low wind velocities characterizes the autumn when the fall overturn is expected. The American Frey (1955)

Table 8-4. Relative depths (z_m) of types of meromictic lakes in North America

Type of meromictic lake	Relative depth (percent)
Ectogenic and crenogenic lakes	
Big Soda, Nevada	1.17
Blue, Washington	2.90
Hot, Washington	2.70
Long (northern tip), Alaska	2.00 (?)
Lower Goose, Washington	3.76
Nitnat, British Columbia	3.37
Ogac, Baffin Island	4.40
Pingo, Alaska	5.50
Powell, British Columbia	3.60
Sakinaw, British Columbia	4.38
Soap, Grant Co., Washington	1.16
Soap, Okanogan Co., Washington	1.29
Tessiarsuk, Labrador	2.05
Vee, Alaska	0.70
Wannacutt, Washington	2.77
Partial meromixis, ectogenic	
Cinder Cone Pool in Zuñi Salt Maar, New Mexico	4.49
Green Pond, Arizona	6.54
Red Pond, Arizona	4.27
Biogenic meromictic lakes	
Arco, Minnesota	7.67
Budd, Minnesota	6.77
Canyon, Michigan	9.89
Demming, Minnesota	7.92
Fayetteville Green, New York	10.03
Hall, Washington	8.46
Josephine, Minnesota	5.27
Mary, Wisconsin	20.36
Sodon, Michigan	10.03
Squaw (protected bay only), Minnesota	22.80
Stewart's Dark, Wisconsin	9.03

studied the sediments, pollen grains, and animal relics in a 9.1-m core taken near the center of the lake and arrived at a theory to account for the start of meromixis in Längsee. The uppermost 1.5 m of sediment is sapropel, a shiny black material formed under intense anaerobic conditions. This chemically reduced ooze is confined to the monimolimnion and represents an estimated 2,000 years of continuous meromixis. A transition zone below the sapropel contains bands of clay, pollen from cultivated plants and agricultural weeds, and a smaller number of beech pollen grains than are found at lower levels in the core. Below this lies gyttja, the typical organic sediment found in the profundal zone of a eutrophic, holomictic lake. This structured material, only partially oxidized and semireduced, may be a forerunner of sapropel if subjected to strongly reducing conditions. Frey concluded that clearing land by cutting the beech forest and breaking the soil for agricultural purposes led to increased erosion and importation of clay to the Längsee hypolimnion. The slowly settling particles, lingering in the bottom water, increased its density to such an extent that, with accumulation of the normal summer metabolic products from the sediments and the epilimnion above and a comparatively windless autumn, no overturn occurred. Thus, meromixis was triggered by man's activities two millennia ago. The annual contribution from lake organisms more or less mineralized by bacteria has served to increase stability, and today the lake is considered a model of biogenic meromixis.

It has been established that some protected lakes in the Minnesota forests are good examples of partially meromictic lakes (Eddy 1963; Baker and Brook 1971). One of these is Demming Lake (Fig. 8-7), where the meromixis is biogenic and generally persists for years; occasionally there is a complete overturn. Findenegg (1937) discussed at length this intermediate type of lake, lying somewhere.

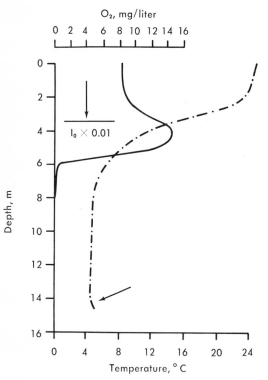

Fig. 8-7. Demming Lake, Minnesota, 3 July 1963. Arrow points to slight dichothermic temperature curve. A positive heterograde oxygen curve is present with a metalimnetic peak, and the lower level of the euphotic zone ($I_0 \times 0.01$) is indicated.

between holomixis and complete meromixis. Difficulty arises in classifying partially meromictic bodies of water because oligomictic is an adjective that also describes them.

Certain deep African Rift Valley lakes, lying near the equator and experiencing little seasonal temperature change, are extremely stable and meromictic. Lake Tanganyika (about 5° to 7° S lat) is the most striking of these, with nine tenths of the lake permanently stratified and deoxygenated from 200 m to the bottom at 1,430m (Beauchamp 1964). Lake Nyasa (11° S lat) is shallower, having a maximum depth of 760 m. It is said to mix completely every decade or two, although usually water below 300 m is anaerobic for years.

Ectogenic meromixis. Effective contrasts in density can be brought about by delivery of water to a lake from outside sources. This leads to what is termed ectogenic meromixis. The water can be delivered in two forms: first, as a dilute superficial layer that comes to lie above a preexisting saline body of water; or, second, the outside source can be saline water that finds its way to the bottom of a freshwater lake. The topographic, morphologic, and meteorologic requirements for biogenic meromixis are needed to a far lesser degree for ectogenic meromixis (Table 8-4).

The stability of ectogenic meromixis is a function of salinity differences. Ectogenic meromictic lakes are much more saline, containing relative proportions of ions that differ from the ratios typical of biogenic meromictic lakes. These lakes are usually found in arid regions, where water is concentrated by evaporation, or in coastal areas, where sea water contributes to density extremes.

An artificial and relatively recent condition is causing ectogenesis in unexpected geographic locations. Judd (1970) has studied the effects of the runoff of winter salt from city streets. The salt used to deice winter roads is flowing to the bottom of freshwater lakes in the northern United States, creating a temporary layer of dense, saline water. Incipient meromixis is the result.

The small Hot Lake, Washington, lies in an artificial basin rich in $MgSO_4$ that accounts for dense saline water. Runoff from snow melt each spring adds a dilute mixolimnion and serves to maintain perennial stability (Anderson 1958b).

Ectogenic meromixis tends to diminish through time when there is no rejuvenating event to compensate for the slow mixing of saline and fresh water. In Hot Lake the rejuvenating event is the arrival of melt water each spring; in Judd's lakes it is the winter salt from nearby highways that restores a fleeting meromixis. Two other examples come to mind. The pool in the cinder cone rising from the Zuñi Salt Maar, New Mexico, contains very saline water derived from springs within the maar. At irregular intervals rainfall added directly to the pool creates meromixis that lasts for months. Without the addition of more dilute water, the pool eventually becomes isohaline and holomictic (Bradbury 1971). Twenty-four kilometers to the west, the twin salt ponds at the Long-H Ranch, Arizona, show a temporary meromixis that seems to have a seasonal pattern (Cole and associates 1967). The monimolimnion in each lake is formed by concentration of ectogenic fresh water by evaporation in a closed basin. During cool seasons the same dilute water reaches the basins and adds a mixolimnion. The meromixis lasts only a few months; during the intense summer heat, evaporation interrupts the arrival of fresh water from springs in the banks above, increases the salinity of the mixolimnion, and reduces pond volume. At the same time monimolimnion salts are diffusing upward into the chemocline until the pond becomes isohaline-isothermal in late summer. The regularity of this cycle suggests a type of monomixis.

Some fjord lakes, of which at least five have been described from North America, are meromictic because of occasional invasion by sea water that sinks to the deepest part of the basin to establish a monimolimnion. In some instances, as in Tessiarsuk in Labrador, the introduction of marine water occurs almost daily (Carter 1965). Williams and associates (1961) believe that sea water was introduced in Powell Lake, British Columbia, about 13,000 years ago. Similar ancient monimolimnia had been described earlier from Norwegian fjord lakes.

Crenogenic meromixis. Subsurface flows of saline, dense water into a basin bring about the crenogenesis of meromixis. The continuous import from one or more deep springs contrasts with a superficial freshwater influent. If equilibrium between the two types of water is established, the water becomes persistently stable; an outflowing stream makes this possible in some instances.

The African Lake Kivu is similar to some of its rift neighbors: it is meromictic and contains anoxic water below 60 m. It differs from Nyasa and Tanganyika by having about 4.5 times more salinity in its deep water than in its mixolimnion. It is believed that the saline water is introduced by deep sublacustrine springs.

Dussart (1966) laments the loss of two excellent examples of crenogenic meromictic lakes to further scientific study because of modification and utilization for hydroelectric power. These are Lake Girrotte (France) and the Swiss Lake, Ritom. The saline subsurface inflows became visible in each lake when it was partially drained in preparation for construction of the power facilities.

Likens (1965) described an unusual pond in Alaska that may be the world's shallowest meromictic lake. Vee Pond has a maximum depth of but 1.6 m and a relative depth of 0.7%. Its monimolimnion, with an upper boundary between

0.5 and 1.0 m, is maintained by saline springs marked by light bottom areas here and there in the pond's dense carpet of benthic vegetation.

Distinctions are not always clear-cut when the origin of meromixis is sought. Hot Lake, Washington, for example, may be considered ectogenic because dilute water comes from external sources to float above heavy magnesium sulfate water in the basin. The edaphic factors account for the presence of MgSO₄ because the lake occupies old epsomite (MgSO$_4$ • H$_2$O) diggings. If springlike seepage of ground water into the concavity is a phenomenon at Hot Lake, the meromixis is due to crenogenic as well as ectogenic agents.

Other phenomena establishing meromixis. Goldman and co-workers (1967) studied Antarctic lakes and proposed cryogenesis as a method of delivering salts to a monimolimnion and reducing the salinity of upper waters. This is a simple freezing-out process that may be very effective at times. Cole and associates (1967) concluded that temporary meromixis during winter in two Arizona saline ponds was, in part, based on such a phenomenon. Freezing occurred each night, followed by daytime melting. Melted ice from the ponds contained a mean of 11.6 g/liter of filtrable residue, whereas immediately beneath the ice there were 41 g/liter. The diurnal ice melt left a layer of dilute water over the lower saline strata.

A similar phenomenon in saline waters during winter is the precipitation of Na$_2$SO$_4$ even without freezing. This compound's solubility is decreased with lowered temperature, and many examples are known where large crystals of mirabilite (Na$_2$SO$_4$ • 10 H$_2$O) are precipitated during cold weather. The surface waters become diluted as material is sent to the bottom, where it may go into solution again at higher temperatures. Increased stability and meromixis, thus, may be brought about through low temperatures at the lake surface.

UNUSUAL TEMPERATURE PROFILES

In earlier pages isothermy and direct and inverse stratification were explained. Also, an unusual inverse stratification brought about by salt layering was presented. A specific vocabulary has grown up around some bizarre curves found in meromictic lakes. We are indebted to the Japanese limnologist Yoshimura (1936 and 1937) for the terms pertaining to these curves.

Dichothermy

Eggleton (1931) graphed unusual summer temperature profiles for Fayetteville Green Lake, making little comment about them. A year later Juday and Birge (1932) called attention to the unusual character of a similar temperature curve in Lake Mary. Their words describe what we know now as a dichothermic curve, "The coldest stratum . . . was found at an intermediate depth and not at the bottom in summer."

Dichothermy is illustrated by a vertical temperature curve with an inflection within it; there is a low point bounded above and below by warmer water (Figs. 8-7 and 8-8,*D*).

Dichothermy is characteristic of meromictic lakes so that, if a slight temperature elevation is detected in the bottom waters in summer, at least partial meromixis is implied. (Such a rise near the bottom in winter might signify nothing more than the slow cooling of sediments that had been warmed the preceding summer.)

The origin of heat in the monimolimnion is complex, but in many meromictic lakes it is biogenic, bacterial metabolism being the major source. Zobell and co-workers (1953) estimated that in holomictic Lake Mead the heat produced by microorganisms amounted to 30 × 10^{-12} cal per cell per hour. Pamatmat and

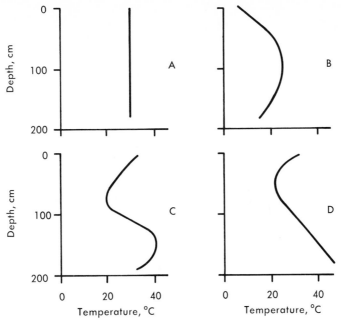

Fig. 8-8. Idealized vertical temperature curves shown at different seasons at Red Pond, Arizona. *A*, Isothermal curve in late summer; *B*, mesothermal curve in late winter; *C*, poikilothermal curve in late spring; and *D*, dichothermal curve in early summer. (Modified from Cole and co-workers 1967.)

Bhagwat (1973) estimated that a gram of sediment from the deeps of Lake Washington released from 0.003 to 0.017 cal/hour, and much of this was through anaerobic activity. With the monimolimnion not participating in circulation, any heat accumulating there can be lost only by slow conduction.

Geothermal sources in relatively deep basins, such as Lake Vanda, and direct solar radiation in shallow saline meromictic lakes account for the rise at the lower extreme in dichothermic temperature curves.

Mesothermy

In waters with unusual salt stratification it sometimes happens that a vertical temperature profile shows a high point within the curve. The temperature increases with depth, momentarily suggesting inverse stratification, but decreases before the bottom is reached. The result is a mesothermal contour indicating a warm stratum sandwiched between upper and lower colder layers (Fig. 8-8, *B*).

In some instances mesothermy is transitory. For example, in the twin salt ponds at the Long-H Ranch, Arizona (Cole and co-workers 1967), an annual cycle includes a time in early winter when dilute water is extruded onto an isothermal, dense, saline pool. Solar radiation penetrates the clear layer and is absorbed rapidly by the upper part of the saline stratum, effecting a mesothermal profile. This may be a prelude to the establishment of inverse stratification brought about by the slow diffusion of heat downward. Before a complete inverse profile is achieved, however, vernal warming of the surface layers of these ponds proceeds to such an extent that dichothermy is produced.

The amictic Antarctic Lake Bonney shows a mesothermal curve that may persist throughout the year. Interestingly, it increases from 0° C to a maximum of 7.9° C and then decreases to −2.8° C, the effect of high salinity depressing the temperature of maximum density. Vertical water motions in the lake are very small, and the ice is so transparent that direct solar heating is responsible for the warm inflection in the curve 14 m beneath the ice (Ragotzkie and Likens 1964).

Poikilothermy

Complex temperature curves, marked by the inclusion of at least one low point and one high point, have been described from saline-layered waters (Fig. 8-8, *C*). In the Long-H ponds, poikilothermic curves represent the transition from late-winter mesothermy to dichothermy. Before heat has diffused downward from the warm midpond layer to raise the temperature of the lowest level, the days of early summer heighten surface temperatures. The result is, from top to bottom, the following sequence: a warmed upper layer, perhaps mixed downward to some extent; a layer where temperature diminishes, representing some of winter's cold; a region where temperature rises to a high point, signifying the accumulation of solar heat during winter when mesothermy ruled; and a cooling trend to a bottom sheet not yet warmed by conduction of heat from above.

Data from Hot Lake (Anderson 1958b) indicate dichothermy, mesothermy, poikilothermy, and a hot inverse stratification beneath the winter ice. Such an array of seasonal curves probably is displayed only by saline meromictic lakes and small briny pools.

9
Heat energy and water movements

HEAT VERSUS TEMPERATURE

The distinction between temperature and heat is commonly obscured, the words often being interchanged erroneously. In 1798 Count Rumford published his observations, which led to the eventual overthrow of the theory that heat is some sort of mysterious juice. Since then heat has been considered the energy of interatomic forces and the kinetic energy of moving molecules in a substance. The speedier the chaotic motions of these molecules, the more energy present, and the higher the temperature of the substance. Temperature is a measurable manifestation, a kind of translation of the kinetic energy in molecules of a substance. It reveals the intensity of the molecular agitation, which could be the same for boiling water in either a tea cup or an enormous vat. The quantities of energy, however, in the two containers are vastly different. Temperature reveals intensity but does not clarify capacity.

At present, the word heat implies a further meaning: the dynamic concept of energy being transferred to or from an object or system and its surroundings. The reason for such fluxes, always from the higher to the lower energy concentration, is explained by the second law of thermodynamics and is revealed by temperature differences. One might say that energy flows because a temperature gradient exists, showing how intertwined the two words have become. Actually, temperature reveals that there is an energy contrast or gradient that causes heat transfer. The energy tends to become equalized by proceeding toward entropy or randomness.

An older concept defines heat as energy contained in some sample of matter. From this idea have come terms such as heat content, specific heat, and internal energy; the quantity is expressed in calories. When heat is expressed in this manner, a conversion factor changing the units to mechanical equivalents is necessary in order to employ the data in modern thermodynamic calculations. The common dynamic units of energy are joules or ergs. One calorie equals about 4.184 absolute joules, but at present the common denominator in ecologic literature is the calorie.

In most physiologic discussions, temperature is considered more significant than heat. A fish swimming through 5° C water is little influenced by the total energy content of its habitat; it does not matter whether the water fills a small pond or a large lake. The intensity factor —temperature—is the same and controls the fish's metabolism, even though the heat contents of the two habitats would differ markedly. There is a tremendous literature dealing with effects of temperature on metabolism, feeding, reproduction, and other aspects of life cycles. Typical is the case, recently reported, of *Diaptomus pallidus,* a common planktonic grazer in midwestern ponds and lakes, which develops more than 4.5 times faster at 25° C than at 10° C (Geiling and Campbell 1972).

Interrelations between total lake heat content and organisms are less direct. A great body of water yields so much heat to the atmosphere during autumnal cooling that the surrounding land is affected, and the first frosts of winter are postponed. Conversely, in spring such a body of water absorbs so much heat that the onset of the terrestrial growing season is delayed. Likewise, temperature fluctuations within the lake itself are modulated by these exchanges. These phenomena are a function of the unusually high specific thermal capacity of water, defined as the ratio of heat capacity to the mass or volume of water. Expressed as calories per gram per degree, it tells the number of calories required to raise 1 g of water 1° C. Conversely, it tells how many calories must be taken from a gram to cool it 1°. Today the gram-calorie (g-cal) is taken to mean the 15-degree calorie: the heat needed to elevate the temperature from 14.5° to 15.5° C at 1 atmosphere pressure.

The thermal capacity of pure water is remarkably high, about 1.0 or 4.187 joules/gram-degree at 14.5° C. Sea water, containing 35 g of salts per kg of water, has a lower specific thermal capacity, 0.93 or 3.902 joules/gram-degree. The ordinary fresh water of lakes and streams, then, has a thermal capacity a bit smaller than 1.0 because of contained solutes. This means that fewer calories are needed to warm lake water than an equal amount of distilled water. This difference can be overlooked in most instances, but in desert limnology it might assume significance because of the marked concentration of minerals in closed basins. Mason (1967) used a factor of 0.924 for Mono Lake waters because they contain more than 70 g of salts per liter.

MEAN TEMPERATURE AND HEAT CONTENT

A series of temperatures in a vertical profile taken from a lake tells much about conditions there; but without knowledge

Table 9-1. Some thermal data from Tom Wallace Lake, Kentucky, 3 August 1951

I	II	III	IV	V	VI	VII	VIII
Depth (m)	Temperature (°C)	Strata (m)	Volume (m³)	Relative volume	Mean temperature of strata (°C)	Heat content (IV × VI)	(V × VI)
0	28.9						
		0-1	21,460	0.237	28.1	603,026	6.66
1	27.2						
		1-2	17,990	0.198	26.9	483,931	5.33
2	26.7						
		2-3	14,980	0.165	25.6	383,488	4.22
3	24.4						
		3-4	12,280	0.135	20.3	249,284	2.74
4	16.1						
		4-5	9,775	0.108	13.3	130,007	1.44
5	10.6						
		5-6	7,195	0.079	10.3	74,108	0.81
6	10.0						
		6-7	4,645	0.051	9.4	43,663	0.48
7	8.9						
		7-8	2,090	0.023	8.9	18,601	0.20
8	8.8						
		8-8.75	230	0.003	8.8	2,041	0.03
8.75	8.8						
Totals	170.4		90,647	1.000		1,988,140	21.91

of morphology, little thermal information can be gained. If the lake is 8° C from top to bottom, one can state that the mean temperature is 8° C, but one cannot set down the total heat content in calories or relate it to unit surface area for comparative purposes.

In general we can assume that a gram of water occupies a volume of 1 cm³ or 1 ml and that its heat content is ml × C°. The absolute Kelvin scale is not taken into account, and only the heat above 0° C is considered. Thus, 1 ml or 1 g of water with a temperature of 8° C equals 8 cal, the product of volume and temperature being heat.

Table 9-1 shows some data taken in August 1951 from Tom Wallace Lake. Ten temperatures were measured from top to bottom in the deepest part of the lake. The mean of these is 17.0° C, but this is no more than the average temperature of a sampled vertical column in the lake. It is not the lake's mean temperature. Obviously there is a much smaller volume of water in the deeps at 8.8° C than there

is in the upper 1-m stratum between 28.9° and 27.2° C. The temperatures are not weighted properly for determining the mean lake temperature, and the average of the 10 profile readings does not apply.

Fortunately, morphologic details of Tom Wallace Lake permit further treatment of the data. The volume is 90,647 m³, and the area is 2.34 ha or 23,400 m². From these data we get the mean depth, volume divided by area, or 3.87 m.

In Table 9-1 the volume of every stratum of Tom Wallace is shown and summed in column IV. In addition, the volume of each stratum relative to the total is given as a decimal fraction in column V. In column VI, the temperature for each 1-m stratum is shown; this was found by averaging the upper and lower temperatures of each layer.

Multiplying the items in column IV by those in column VI gives us heat content, the product of volume and temperature. The sum of these products divided by lake volume yields the average or mean temperature, 21.9° C, almost five degrees higher than the results derived from averaging the vertical profile without taking volume into account.

Had we simply multiplied column V by the temperatures in column VI and summed the products as shown in column VIII, the lake's mean temperature would have been revealed immediately. By the same method, the mean temperature on 26 June 1954 can be calculated easily from data in Table 8-2. It was 19.5° C.

The products of water volumes and temperatures, shown in Table 9-1, column VII, are heat. If the lake volumes had been converted to cm³, the total heat content in calories would have been found as the sum of column VII. Remembering that 1 m³ equals 10^6 cm³, we can state that the total heat content of Tom Wallace Lake on 3 August 1951 was 1,988,140 × 10^6 cal. This is of some interest but of little value for comparative purposes. It would be possible to find a larger lake with, let us say, 5° C water throughout that would have a heat content identical to that of summertime Tom Wallace.

For comparative purposes, heat content is referred to unit surface area. Tom Wallace Lake's surface is 2.34 ha, or 2.34 × 10^8 cm². The calories beneath the average cm² of lake surface, then, amounts to the quotient of total heat and area:

$$\frac{1,988,140 \times 10^6 \text{ cal}}{234 \times 10^6 \text{ cm}^2} = 8,496 \text{ cal/cm}^2$$

Another way of approximating the heat beneath the average cm² of lake surface is by multiplying mean depth by mean temperature. In Tom Wallace, $\bar{z}$ is 387 cm, meaning there are 387 cm³ on the average beneath each cm² of lake surface. This could be expressed as 387 cm³ per cm², or 387 g/cm². When multiplied by mean temperature, the results are 387 g/cm² × 21.9° C = 8,475 cal/cm², a discrepancy of less than 1%. Similarly, on 26 June 1954 (see Table 8-2) the product of mean temperature and mean depth was 7,545 cal/cm².

HEAT DISTRIBUTION: WORK OF THE WIND

The August temperature curve from Tom Wallace Lake was translated to vertical distribution of heat when volumetric data were taken into account. The dispersion of calories contrasts sharply with the condition during the spring overturn when uniformity prevailed and also with the pattern of heat supplied by solar radiation during the warming period, as reflected by a typical vertical light curve (see Fig. 8-1). Work, in addition to energy supplied by the sun, must have been invoked to explain this unusual pattern of heat. After the vernal overturn when isothermy and uniform density prevailed, solar radiation heated the surface; work must then have been required to push the lighter layers of water downward as they were formed. This process is analogous to forcing down sheets of floating cork.

Birge (1916) developed the concept of the wind work (B) necessary to accomplish this downward distribution of heated water (through water of uniform density) to a particular level of stratification. In a sense, this wind work is the opposite of stability, for it is an expression of the stress necessary to create rather than destroy stratification. The work unit, B, as is true for S, is the dyne-cm or erg per unit area with the acceleration due to gravity omitted. This leaves Birge's work of the wind expressed as g-cm/cm²:

$$B = \frac{1}{A_0} \int_{z_0}^{z_m} z(\rho_i - \rho_z) A_z \, dz$$

Where

A_0 = A, the surface in cm²
A_z = the area (cm²) at some depth z
z = depth, considered positive and in cm
ρ_i = the initial density, constant at all depths
ρ_z = observed density at depth z, created by the work of the wind

Table 9-2. Data and calculations for establishing work of the wind, Tom Wallace Lake, Kentucky, 26 June 1954

I	II	III	IV	V	VI	VII
z	T_z	A_z/A_0	ρ_z	$\rho_i - \rho_z$	$A_z/A_0 \times z$	$(V \times VI)$
cm	$C°$		g/cm^3	g/cm^3	cm	g/cm^2
50	27.7	0.9188	0.99634	0.00366	45.9	0.16799
150	26.7	0.7692	0.99662	0.00338	115.4	0.38998
250	20.9	0.6410	0.99804	0.00196	160.2	0.31409
350	14.0	0.5278	0.99927	0.00073	184.7	0.13485
450	10.3	0.4188	0.99970	0.00030	188.5	0.05654
550	8.1	0.3098	0.99987	0.00013	170.4	0.02215
650	7.3	0.2009	0.99992	0.00008	130.6	0.01045
750	7.0	0.0940	0.99993	0.00007	70.5	0.00493
850	6.9	0.0043	0.99993	0.00007	3.7	0.00026
Total						1.10355

$$B = \sum_{z_0}^{z_m} z\,(\rho_i - \rho_z)\,\frac{A_z}{A_0}\,\Delta z = 1.10355 \text{ g/cm}^2 \times 100 \text{ cm} = 110.4 \text{ g-cm/cm}^2$$

Table 9-2 includes some Tom Wallace Lake data from which the work of the wind can be calculated and serves for the ordination of points used in Fig. 9-1, a so-called direct work curve, representing the work spent on each layer by the wind in pushing buoyant water down to that depth. These data are for the same day that stability was calculated (see Table 8-2).

The distribution of the summer heat is not necessarily or entirely a result of the wind's work. Factors other than solar heating and its distribution by air currents at the lake surface account for the summer heat content. As surface temperatures heighten, back radiation and evaporation dissipate heat. Also, direct solar warming of shallow, littoral sediments creates unstable inverse temperature gradients resulting in upward transfer of heat to the water. This could be relatively important in small lakes. Ricker (1937) put forth as possible a further factor: the daily vertical migration of enormous numbers of zooplankters. Having warmed in the epilimnion during night hours, they transfer heat, amounting to 0.07 cal/cm² per day,

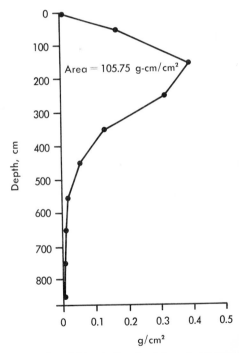

Fig. 9-1. Plot of Birge's "work of the wind." Direct work curve for Tom Wallace Lake, Kentucky, 26 June 1954. Based on data in Table 9-2.

while moving downward to the hypolimnion toward dawn. The plankton predator *Chaoborus* may also be responsible for such heat exchanges.

The summer heat income, then, as evidenced by the difference between the highest mean temperature and the temperature at the spring overturn, is accomplished and modified by Birge's work of the wind as well as other factors.

The direct stability curve (see Fig. 8-5) can be combined with the direct wind-work curve (Fig. 9-1) to yield a direct total work curve (Fig. 9-2). This has been symbolized G. Expressed in g-cm, the temperature stratification of Tom Wallace Lake, 26 June 1954, implies that work in the amount of 105.75 g-cm for every cm² of the lake surface had been performed to change the density stratification since the time of uniformity at 4° C. Similarly, the stability shows that 96.05 g-cm/cm² are

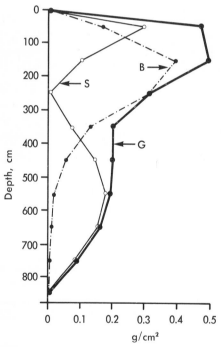

Fig. 9-2. Total direct work curve *(G)* for Tom Wallace Lake, Kentucky, 26 June 1954. *S,* Stability, from data in Table 8-2 and Fig. 8-5; *B,* work of the wind, from data in Table 9-2 and Fig. 9-1; *G,* the sum of *S* and *B,* 201.8 g-cm/cm².

needed to mix the water to a new uniform temperature and density, about 21° C and 0.99799 g/cm³. The total work involved in the stratification is, therefore, 201.8 g-cm/cm² (Fig. 9-2). This is the total work that would have been needed to distribute heat from the time of the vernal overturn in order to keep the lake unstratified and isothermal at the mean temperature observed on 26 June.

HEAT BUDGETS

Heat budgets refer to the heat absorbed by a body of water during some period of time. Of these, the *annual heat budget* is the major category and is the sum of other types. It is the total amount of heat that enters a lake from its lowest mean temperature of the year to its highest. Certain symbols have become useful in designating the heat budget. Θ refers to the total heat content in calories; *a,* in this case, refers to the annual gain, and *b,* according to the standard set by Birge, refers heat to unit surface area. Thus Θ_{ba} is the symbol for the annual heat budget: total heat gained during the year expressed as cal/cm².

If the peak summer heat content in Tom Wallace Lake were represented by the 3 August 1951 datum of 8,490 cal/cm², and if that year the coldest mean winter temperature had been 4° C, as is sometimes the case, Θ_{ba} could be computed. The lowest heat content of the year would be:

$$\frac{V, cm^3 \times 4.0° C}{A, cm^2} = \frac{90,670 \times 10^6 \times 4.0° C}{234 \times 10^6 cm^2} = 1,548 \ \ cal/cm^2$$

The difference between highest and lowest heat contents is:

$$\Theta_{ba} = 8,490 - 1,548 = 6,942 \ cal/cm^2$$

Hutchinson (1957) suggested a method of calculating Θ_{ba} by planimetry or any other way of determining area beneath a curve. Using observations over several years at Tom Wallace Lake, this is demonstrated in Table 9-3. It shows the greatest temperature differences ever recorded

Table 9-3. Areas and temperature extremes observed at various depths in Tom Wallace Lake, Kentucky, used for calculating heat budget, Θ_{ba}*

| Depth (m) | $cm^2 \times 10^6$ | Temperatures (°C) | | | Product |
		Lowest	Highest	Range	Range × area × 10^6
0	234	0	30.7	30.7	7,183.8
1	196	3.6	29.2	25.6	5,017.6
2	164	3.6	28.0	24.4	4,001.6
3	136	3.6	23.3	19.7	2,679.2
4	111	3.8	22.2	18.4	2,042.4
5	85	4.0	19.4	15.4	1,309.0
6	60	4.0	17.8	13.8	828.0
7	34	4.0	10.5	6.5	221.0
8	10	4.0	10.0	6.0	60.0
8.5	1	4.0	10.0	6.0	6.0

*Also see Fig. 9-3.

at each meter depth, and these data are used in plotting Fig. 9-3. It represents a theoretical extreme, not a mean annual heat budget for Tom Wallace, because the temperature difference at each level was based on more than one year's observation. The area beneath the curve (Fig. 9-3) roughly equals $1,971 \times 10^9$ cal. Dividing by A, in this case 234×10^6 cm², gives 8,423 cal/cm² as some sort of extreme yearly budget.

In some lakes the annual heat budget is clearly composed of two portions. With w standing for winter, the symbol Θ_{bw} is translated as the birgean *winter heat income*. It is defined as the difference between the lowest heat content and that found at the vernal overturn when the lake is isothermal at 4° C. In dimictic and cold monomictic bodies of water much of the winter heat income is used to melt the ice. In those that fit the definition of a polar lake, never warming above 4° C, the annual heat budget is composed of only the winter income; it is fairly small because the annual range in temperature is not great. Recalling the heat exchange when pure water freezes or when ice thaws to the aqueous phase, about 80 cal/g, we see that a mantle of ice 1.0 m thick would absorb about 8,000 cal/cm² in the final conversion to water.

A monomictic lake such as Cayuga, although not often freezing, cools below 4° C during winter circulation; its Θ_{bw} is considerable, being about 24% of Θ_{ba}, yet involving no ice melt.

Warm monomictic Lake Tahoe usually circulates at a temperature very near 4°

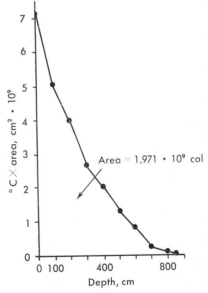

Fig. 9-3. Extreme heat budget for Tom Wallace Lake, Kentucky, based on data in Table 9-3. Product of extreme temperature ranges and area plotted on vertical axis; depth plotted on horizontal axis. Therefore, area beneath curve is (° C × cm²) × cm = ° C × cm³ = calories.

C. It has, therefore, a winter income of zero. Problems arise in quantifying the winter heat income of warm monomictic lakes circulating well above 4° C. Hutchinson (1957) resolved this by suggesting a negative winter income based on the circulating temperature above 4° C. On the Rio Grande the monomictic impoundment called Elephant Butte mixes at 8° C; from this value and its mean depth of 18 m, a negative winter heat budget is calculated to be −7,200 cal/cm². Farther south, the Guatemalan Atitlán, with a $\bar{z}$ of 183 m, circulates near 20° C during the winter; its negative Θ_{bw} is −288,300 cal/cm².

The summer heat budget (Θ_{bs}) is that part of the annual income extending from the coldest isothermal condition to the maximum summer heat content. In a warm monomictic lake circulating at 4° C or above, Θ_{bs} equals Θ_{ba}. In dimictic and cold monomictic lakes the summer heat budget is one segment of the annual heat budget. The summer income is mostly wind-distributed heat, although other factors are operative, as pointed out earlier.

The discussion above refers to apparent heat budgets that are calculated from changes in water-mass temperature alone. Any careful, analytical study considers all avenues by which heat is gained or lost from the lake to arrive at an annual balance sheet. Heat is gained from the internal energy content of influent waters, from freezing, and from the sediments. Evaporation, amounting to considerable loss of heat (see Table 8-3), back-radiation to the atmosphere, and loss through outflow, melting ice, and conduction to the sediments are some of the ways by which heat, gained and distributed by the wind, is dissipated.

In a small lake apparent annual heat budgets are founded on underestimation of calories taken up by the lake, since there is considerable heat exchange between water and sediments. Krumholz

and Cole (1959) found that during winter there was a decreasing temperature gradient from the profundal ooze to the overlying water in Tom Wallace Lake. They concluded that the sediments were a source of heat that had been gained during summer and the fall overturn. The classical picture of such a phenomenon was presented by Birge and associates (1928), who inserted temperature probes into the bottom deposits of Lake Mendota. Seasonal temperature changes 5 m deep in the bottom deposits were marked by undulations with an amplitude of 1.6° C. These were compared with a variation of 21.5° C from summer to January at the lake-bottom interface, which was 8 m below the lake surface. In addition, the seasons were out of phase deep in the deposits; the high point, for example, was reached in January when the heat gained in summer finally reached that depth. Beneath 23.5 m of water, the annual variation 5 m deep in the bottom deposits was only 0.7° C. The rate at which heat was conducted through the sediments was very similar to what might occur in still water unstirred by currents.

Analytic energy budgets

Analytic energy budgets approaching completeness are relatively rare; they are, perhaps, unattractive to biologists, who comprise a large percentage of the world's limnologists. Nevertheless, a few published accounts from Lake Mead (Anderson and Pritchard 1951), some lakes of Israel (Neumann 1953), and Lake Ontario (Rodgers and Anderson 1961) are evidence of some researchers' interest in physical problems of lakes.

The data from research at Lake Mead and the lakes of Israel demonstrate an important effect of evaporation in desert waters. Mean temperatures begin to decline before the heating season has come to a close in Lakes Mead and Kinneret (formerly Lake Tiberias or the Sea of Galilee). The cooling effect of intense evaporation is greater than the effect of solar warming. This may be much less pronounced in Lake Mead today than it was at the time of Anderson and Pritchard's investigation because Lake Mead receives colder water from the deeps of Lake Powell.

Analytic energy budgets take into consideration every factor contributing to gain or loss of heat, expressing them uniformly as cal/cm². The underlying goal is to balance the various positive and negative agents of heat transfer. The following serves as a general equation:

$$Q_S + Q_H - Q_R - Q_U - Q_E + Q_V - Q_B - Q_s - Q_T = 0$$

The gains, marked by positive signs, are:

Q_S = incoming solar radiation
Q_H = diffuse radiation from the sky
Q_V = net advected energy, such as that entering via an influent surpassing effluent loss

Q_R and Q_U are always negative, representing reflectance and backscattering from beneath the surface, respectively; Q_E is the energy in evaporation and condensation, usually a loss; Q_B is the net transfer of long-wave energy between water surface and air, depending on their temperature differences, and is not necessarily negative; Q_s is the conduction of sensible heat from the water to the atmosphere, or vice versa, when it would be positive;and Q_T is the heat stored in the water mass. The last term could represent the gain in energy, revealed by rising water temperature, and the equation could be set down in terms of this.

Lakes in tropical and polar regions have low heat budgets because annual temperature contrasts are not great. Low budgets are especially obvious in equatorial zones. Deevey (1957) found a remarkable exception: Atitlán, 14° 40′ N lat, has a budget as high as those of some lakes at latitudes much farther north. The strong daily winds on Lake Atitlán mix a tremendous volume of water, distributing a quantity of heat comparable, for example, to Θ_{bs} of Cayuga Lake in New York, 28° lat to the north.

Gorham (1964) studied heat budgets in temperate lakes for their possible relationship to the effects of morphology. He found good positive correlation between volume and budget. As lake volume increases, there is a rise in heat uptake. The greater the water column, the more heat taken up each year.

The largest annual budgets calculated to date are for Lake Baikal and Lake Michigan; they amount to 65,500 and 52,400 cal/cm², respectively.

Meromixis tends to lower heat budgets because part of the lake does not participate in overturns when heat is gained or lost. The monimolimnion also stores significant quantities of heat so that mean winter temperatures remain unusually high. Anderson's (1958a) comparison of meromictic Soap Lake, Washington, 27 m deep with Θ_{ba} 14,902 cal/cm², with its shallower, holomictic neighbor, Lake Lenore, 11 m deep with Θ_{ba} 16,100 cal/cm², illustrates this tendency. The partially meromictic Long-H ponds in Arizona have apparent annual heat budgets of about 1,000 cal/cm² (Cole and coworkers 1967). Heat stored in the temporary monimolimnia works against a summer-winter differential; in early February their mean temperatures are over 20° C, although they lie in a region where the mean ambient temperature is only about 2.8° C for that time. A hypothetical dilute-water holomictic pond, having the same dimensions as the Long-H ponds (z_m, 2.0 to 2.5 m) and ranging from 4° to 25° C annually, would have an apparent annual income of 2500 cal/cm².

In small ponds there is a relatively significant sediment heat budget, and in arid regions, especially, evaporation is a factor to be taken into account. In addition, the marked effects of their salinity on evaporation should be considered. The lowering of the surface levels of the Long-H ponds by some 30 cm during the summer required about 300 cal/cm² per day; in a dilute freshwater pond, 250 cal/cm² would have sufficed.

LANGMUIR CIRCULATION

In 1938 the American physical chemist Langmuir wrote of observations he had made at sea and the subsequent experiments they inspired in a New York lake. His work is an excellent example of the close relationships that exist between oceanography and limnology. During an Atlantic crossing, he noticed parallel, elongate lines of seaweeds where the water seemed to be converging. Upon his return, he carried out experiments in Lake George to explain the streaks and brought to light an important mechanism whereby wind distributes surface heat and materials downward.

Elongate, spinning spirals of water, oriented with the wind, are now called Langmuir cells. They rotate about horizontal axes (parallel to the water surface and the wind's direction). These cylindrical helices of water alternate in direction of roll from clockwise to counterclockwise where they adjoin. Surface streaks mark parallel lines of convergence and downwelling. Upwelling areas lie between the streaks but are less conspicuous because water diverges there, and floating materials do not accumulate. In many instances oily material gathers in the converging, downwelling lines, accounting for the name "surface slicks." Langmuir spread oil on the surface of oligotrophic Lake George and observed its subsequent convergence and accumulation as elongate slicks, moving downwind with a velocity greater than the adjacent interstreak water. The streaks are sometimes marked by floating debris—autumn leaves in Lake George and windrows of *Sargassum* in the Atlantic.

The streaks mark downwelling lines of great vertical velocity, up to more than 9 cm/sec in Lake Ontario, according to Harris and Lott (1973). Langmuir ob-served that autumn leaves converged in the streaks, and the less buoyant leaves moved downward at rates far in excess of natural sinking, the vertical velocity decreasing with depth. The mechanisms of streak formation are complex, but the downwelling velocities correlate well with wind speed.

Langmuir cells are less obvious in small bodies of water, but they also permit the generalization that action of wind on the lake surface is not uniform and has a nonrandom pattern. Langmuir found that the helices descended 10 to 15 m in Lake George, mixing the summer epilimnion to those depths. At the autumnal overturn the helices were diffuse but reached the bottom.

Wind forces, then, account in part for patchiness in the distribution of plankton and surface nutrients. So, care must be taken in sampling. For example, samples from upwelling areas might contain considerably more phosphate than the average upper layers. In sampling near-surface organisms, more representative information will be obtained from plankton-net tows across the wind (crossing upwelling and downwelling, as well as intermediate waters) than from tows aligned with wind direction.

The active role played by the animals in their spotty distribution was demonstrated by Stavn (1971), who induced miniature Langmuir circulations in small tanks containing *Daphnia* and studied the reactions of these cladocerans. During daylight they clumped in low-velocity downwellings, swimming upward against the current. At higher velocities the *Daphnia* assembled in the upwelling side of the Langmuir spiral, swimming downward. They clumped at the bottom of the spirals, swimming horizontally against currents of intermediate velocities.

In the sea, the accumulation of *Sargassum* and an associated, specialized marine fauna is well known; but congregations of thousands of the poisonous sea snake *Pelamis platurus* in surface streaks of the Pacific are more spectacular (Dunson and Ehlert 1971).

AUSTAUSCH COEFFICIENTS

The symbol A comes from the German *Austausch,* meaning exchange. It pertains to various types of turbulent transport by eddy systems, including heat conductivity, diffusivity of dissolved materials, and mass-momentum transfer in various directions. A clarification of two important concepts is necessary in any discussion of Austausch coefficients. First is the understanding of turbulence, which is irregular, unsteady motion, in contrast to the smooth, regular laminar flow of fluids or gases. Turbulence is induced when the velocity of laminar flow is increased to a point where friction assumes prominence as fluids rub solid substrates or against each other. It is the result of shearing stress. The velocity of turbulence at any point fluctuates in direction and magnitude in a random and chaotic manner. Second, the concept of an eddy must be understood; it applies to currents moving in directions different from the main flow. They are circular and swirling motions that may be vertical as well as horizontal.

Early descriptions of turbulent eddy flows emphasized their analogy to molecular diffusions, and molecular diffusivities were simply replaced by the greater eddy coefficients. This kind of comparison with molecules is useful but imperfect. One example will suffice to show the contrast: a continuous supply of energy is necessary to maintain eddy turbulence.

Coefficient of eddy viscosity

The mass-momentum transport refers to the coefficient of eddy viscosity, the excess over normal molecular viscosity, the degree to which water resists flow when some force, including friction, is applied. The viscosity of a fluid is usually tested by timing the flow through standard tubes, pure water having a coefficient of 0.01 (dyne-sec/cm^2) at 20° C. In the desert waters of Mono Lake, viscosity is 20% greater than distilled water and must be taken into account in the study of physical limnology of that lake (Mason 1967). But normally viscosity can be ignored in limnologic studies.

Turbulence acts to give the effect of greater internal friction by slowing the descent of sestonic particles and speeding the transfer of momentum. The latter effect is seen in some data from physical oceanography (von Arx 1962). If only molecular viscosity of water were taken into account, it would take centuries for a wind velocity of 20 m/sec to generate a current of 1 m/sec to a depth of 100 m. In the oceans such a current can be developed within a few days because eddy viscosity can surpass the molecular viscosity of sea water (about 0.0107 at 20° C) by factors ranging from 100 to 10^{10}.

Coefficient of eddy conductivity

More effort in limnology has been devoted to the study of coefficients of eddy conductivity—those gentle turbulent currents involved in heat transfer that are mostly inferred from temperature changes—than to coefficients of eddy viscosity.

Limnology owes an important theoretical consideration and treatment of heat transport to the oceanographer McEwen (1929), whose article stimulated further work by Hutchinson (1941). Since then, a pertinent literature on the subject has slowly grown.

The data for calculating coefficients of eddy conductivity are provided by a series of vertical temperature measurements, preferably made at close intervals of time during the heating season. The total temperature change, θ, at a depth, z, divided by the number of days (or some other unit of time) since the start of observations, gives a value $d\theta/dt$, which can be plotted on semilog paper against depth (the latter on the arithmetic axis). From the ordination of points for every depth, a curve may result in which there is a straight segment, showing that the rate of heating falls exponentially with depth (Fig. 9-4). Hutchinson (1941) called the layer of the lake represented by this straight line the *clinolimnion.* In the epilimnion above, the points show effects of direct solar heating, wind-induced mixing, and other losses and gains by atmospheric exchange. The results lead to irregularity in the plot, although the points often show somewhat similar heating rates at different depths.

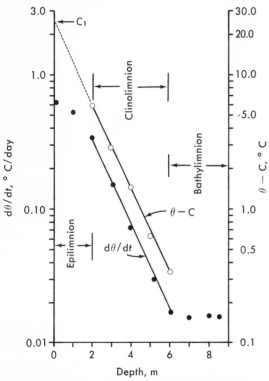

Fig. 9-4. Semilog plot of heating rates $(d\theta/dt)$, solid circles, and temperature increments $(\theta - C)$, open circles, plotted against depth. Heating season of 1951, Tom Wallace Lake, Kentucky. Epilimnion from 0 to 2 m; clinolimnion from 2 to 6 m; bathylimnion from 6 to 8.75 m. C_1 at 25° C indicated by arrow at top left.

Below the clinolimnion is the deepest part of the lake, which Hutchinson termed the *bathylimnion.* The $d\theta/dt$ plot in this region is usually puzzling because it suggests a turbulent region, the reasons for which are obscure. The rates of heating for bathylimnion depths are fairly uniform. Since the bathylimnion is far removed from direct wind action, several other factors—density currents of chemical origin, turbulence induced by internal waves, and heat gained from the sediments—must influence this divergence from the clinolimnion curve.

The main feature of interest is the clinolimnion, however. It resembles a completely undisturbed stratum of water through which heat is moving; the heat flux would be due to molecular motion alone. For pure water, this molecular thermal conductivity is usually taken to be 0.12×10^{-2} g/cm per sec. Over a span of time, then, temperature changes in quiet water would suggest heat progressing at that rate due to molecular thermal conductivity. The difference between this rate of flux and a higher one would be caused by eddy currents and is symbolized A, the *coefficient of eddy conductivity.* In a sense, this conductivity is analogous to the conductivity of some metal alloy: downwelling water distributes heat exponentially in the same manner as a solid conductor. The value A (in excess of 0.12×10^{-2} g/cm per sec) is the effective thermal conductivity of the eddy current. It is also a *coefficient of turbulence,* carrying gases and other substances downward in excess of the normal diffusion rate. Therefore, *coefficient of diffusivity* is another name for this type of exponentially decreasing eddy.

The method Hutchinson used for solving A is permissible only in the clinolimnion. Furthermore, the constancy of A is suspect if a semilog plot of $(\theta - C)$ versus z is not parallel to the $d\theta/dt$-depth line in the clinolimnion (Fig. 9-4). C was the temperature at the start of the experiment, preferably the vernal overturn, and $(\theta - C)$ is, therefore, the temperature increment.

Mortimer (1959) questioned whether clinolimnetic conductivity coefficients are always representative of a heat transport mechanism acting steadily. He pointed out that in order to produce two good parallel lines, a great many temperature measurements are required at each depth. He therefore suggested that the conductivity coefficients may be the statistical results of enormous numbers of observations of intermittent and even localized heat transfers brought about by winds and the oscillations of standing waves. However, Idso and Cole (1973) found that very few data were necessary to achieve good results in the sheltered Tom Wallace Lake, and concluded that the mean eddy conductivity there (0.94 $\times$ 10^{-2} g/cm per sec) may very well be a real heat transport mechanism. Such may also be true for other small lakes not exposed to strong winds. In any event, the strange eddy currents operating below the epilimnion are probably ultimately wind induced, owing much to the energy of standing waves.

Theory and methodology of eddy conductivity were discussed in detail by Hutchinson (1957), and most subsequent literature on computing coefficients of eddy conductivity was cited by Idso and Cole (1973). The value for A can be solved if, within the clinolimnion, the points showing rate of heating $(d\theta/dt)$ and those designating the temperature gain since spring overturn $(\theta - C)$ lie on straight and parallel lines, decreasing exponentially with depth. This indicates that A is practically constant throughout the clinolimnion and validates the use of the following:

$$\frac{d\theta_z}{dt} = A\, a^2\, (\theta_z - C)$$

C, the temperature observed at spring overturn, is a constant, as is a^2, derived

from:

$$\frac{1}{z} \ln \frac{\theta_z - C}{C_1} = -a$$

In the above, z is depth in centimeters for each point, and C_1 is a constant found by extending the $(\theta - C)$ versus z line to zero depth where it intersects the log axis. This intersection gives what Hutchinson called the "virtual surface temperature" (Fig. 9-4).

Because clinolimnetic turbulence is inferred from temperature changes, direct solar heating could invalidate some A values. However, few authors have made corrections for this possibility. For example, the eddy conductivity coefficient 85.6 $\times$ 10^{-2} g/cm per sec for Cultus Lake, British Columbia, is high (Ricker 1937; Hutchinson 1957). The relatively large surface area of this lake may be responsible for this high value, since clinolimnetic eddies may ultimately be a function of wind and area. On the other hand, Cultus is a very transparent lake, and direct solar heating could be a factor at times.

CURRENTS DURING STAGNATION

The word stagnation is used to describe conditions beneath an ice cover or thermocline. It does not refer to pollution, anaerobiosis, or saprobic situations; it applies to the absence—or the supposed absence—of water movements.

Bryson is one of the important names in the investigation of water currents in American lakes. He, his students, and other co-workers applied meteorologic methods to lacustrine situations, summarizing some results that show that seemingly steady currents exist in the quiet hypolimnion (Lathbury and others, 1960). Currents averaging 7.7 cm/sec move above the profundal floor during summer stagnation in Lake Mendota. The cause of these currents is varied and not well understood. Bicarbonate and other ions and compounds diffusing from sediments could impart density to adjacent water, which then streams down the basin slope. Internal standing waves and turbulence set up by Langmuir cells may also transmit some energy necessary for currents, but they seem to be an insufficient explanation for all of the observed motions in the deeps of Lake Mendota.

Beneath the ice, where the wind is ineffective, there are, surprisingly enough, movements of water and isotherms that refute the concept of a uniform inverse stratification. Samples taken through a single hole in the ice over the deepest part of a lake have yielded most of our knowledge about winter limnology. Krumholz and Cole (1959) at Tom Wallace Lake drilled hundreds of holes along various transects to study events beneath the ice one cold winter. The results of a series of measurements made during a period of 49 days showed that most water was warmer than 4° C, and bizarre temperature profiles existed that could not be explained by temperature-density relations. The arrangement of water masses beneath the ice must have been unstable, however, for temperature data indicated water movement and especially horizontal currents. Heat gains from the sediments in deeper parts of the basin and from solar radiation through the ice were inferred from abrupt temperature gradients. The evidence was indirect, but the concept of winter stagnation was contradicted by the changing temperature conditions from day to day.

Likens and Hasler (1962), going a step further, placed ^{24}Na, a radioisotope of sodium, beneath the ice of a Wisconsin lake and followed its movements. Within the first day there were rapid lateral movements from 15 to 20 m, and by 3 days radioactivity was demonstrable 30 m from the source. This was a direct manifestation of water motion. More recently, Stewart (1972) published results of studying temperature beneath ice-covered lakes in New York and Wisconsin; he ex-

pressed the opinion that there is no absolute stagnation with respect to water motion at any time of year.

There are several ways by which currents are induced beneath the ice. Chemical density currents can form so that water masses stream down the basin slope, reaching equal or slightly greater density layers, where they are deflected horizontally. Small volumes of water beneath littoral ice may become anaerobic or at least rich in carbonic acid. This acid dissolves sedimentary marl, which flows toward deeper levels as calcium bicarbonate in solution. In Tom Wallace Lake a yellowish red mass of ferric iron, precipitated and lying on the bottom downslope from a subsurface seep, marks the course of a density current carrying invisibile, soluble ferrous iron from anaerobic subterranean stores.

Warming of water beneath the ice by the greenhouse effect increases its density and initiates a downward flow. This is accented in the shallows where solar heat can be absorbed and stored by the sediments, thus warming overlying water even more.

In addition, water just below the ice may cool enough to freeze. As the ice cover thickens and the newly frozen stratum at the bottom gives up many electrolytes, the freezing-out effect increases density of the top water. Subsequent solar warming of this layer would have more consequence than raising the temperature of dilute water.

SEICHES
The external seiche

The Latin word *siccus* is still with us, accounting for the modern word desiccation (and perhaps difficulties in spelling it). From siccus the word *seiche* (pronounced sāsh) may have been derived. This term was used by lakeshore dwellers at Le Léman since at least the sixteenth century and was brought to prominence by Forel (1895). Wilson's review article (1972) is recommended as an introduction to the subject of seiches.

If a shallow area that was covered by water a few hours earlier is suddenly dry, or at least laid bare and exposed, and sometime later floods again, a seiche has been observed. Usually where the shallows have an almost imperceptible slope, a slight fall in water level exposes conspicuous areas of littoral bottom; yet one of the most obvious seiches occurs in the narrows of Lake Geneva (Le Léman) and has long been known. There, near the city of Geneva, a funneling effect accents ebb and flow.

In simplest terms the seiche is a free oscillation of water, reestablishing equilibrium after having been displaced. The least complicated seiche would be a standing wave oscillating on a single node. Such an oscillation could have been energized by several mechanisms. Actually any force that can pile water up at one side of the lake and cause an instability may lead to creation of a seiche. The high water eventually streams back to restore equilibrium. It overshoots the mark and returns, the surface rocking with an ever-decreasing amplitude until no free energy remains.

Forel explained the elementary seiche as the result of two long waves traveling simultaneously in opposite directions through each other. In a uninodal seiche, each wave has a distance between crests equal to twice the length of the lake, or at least two times the distance between shores located at right angles to the wave (Fig. 9-5). Sometimes harmonic binodal, trinodal, or polynodal waves make up a seiche, and it may be complicated further by the coexistence of multiple seiches.

In all such instances the wave length (λ) would show the following relation to lake length (L):

Uninodal $\lambda = 2L$
Binodal $\lambda = L$
Trinodal $\lambda = \frac{2}{3} L$
n-nodal $\lambda = \frac{2}{n} L$

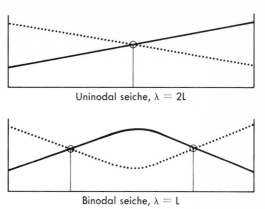

Uninodal seiche, $\lambda = 2L$

Binodal seiche, $\lambda = L$

Fig. 9-5. Diagram of uninodal and binodal seiches.

The periodicity of a seiche is a function of lake-basin morphology. In a simple rectangular pan or aquarium the period could be demonstrated by generating a wave at one end of the tank. It arrives at the other end in time equal to $L/(gh)^{1/2}$, where L is the length, g is the acceleration due to gravity, and h is the uniform depth. The velocity is $(gh)^{1/2}$. Reflection sends the wave back to the original point after the same period of time. The total periodicity (T), therefore, is $2L/(gh)^{1/2}$, twice the length divided by velocity. Using this formula, we can learn something about a wave generated by tipping an ordinary rectangular cake pan 28 cm long and holding 3.5 cm of water. If we assume that the acceleration due to gravity is 980 cm/sec per sec, the velocity of the wave is 58.566 cm/sec, and the periodicity is 0.956 sec:

$$T = \frac{2L}{\sqrt{g\,h}} = \frac{56 \text{ cm}}{\sqrt{980 \text{ cm/sec}^2 \times 3.5 \text{ cm}}} = \frac{56 \text{ cm}}{58.566 \text{ cm/sec}} = 0.956 \text{ sec}$$

This example demonstrates the largest possible free oscillation, a wave rocking on one node. The periodicity of such a system with n nodes would be $1/n$ times that of an uninodal wave. It is far more complex in natural bodies of water because they are not contained in vertical-sided pans of uniform depth. In water contained by a bowl parabolic in dimensions, the periodicity of a binodal seiche would be somewhat greater than half the uninodal time. The data from most lakes indicate that the concavities they occupy are more like parabolas than rectangular depressions of uniform depth.

Energy for the seiche

A common agent supplying the energy for a seiche and working at the lake surface is the wind—a lapsing wind. Strong air currents pile up water at leeward shores and then cease; the pent-up water surges back toward the windward shore as a returning current. A restoring force is acting to reestablish equilibrium following displacement.

A seiche is strengthened by the passage of small barometric fluctuations over the lake, fluctuations of a period matching that of the seiche. Closely associated with this prevalent phenomenon would be the rapid changes in air pressure as a squall blows across the water or as gusts of wind varying in velocity and pressure pound at the surface.

An unusual event brought about by strengthening of a seiche occurred at about 9:30 AM on 26 June 1954 along the southwestern shore of Lake Michigan at Chicago. The water rose rapidly, attaining heights 3 m above normal in some places. Several people lost their lives as a result. A seiche, reflected from the shore near the southeastern border of the lake, had sped at velocities in excess of 100 km/hr, traveling to the scene of the Chicago tragedy in 80 minutes. An explanation for the spectacular wave was pieced together from meteorologic reports by Ewing and associates (1954). A squall line from the northwest, moving with the same speed and in the same direction as the seiche, had energized it. A pressure jump (best described as a high-pressure zone at the squall front) accompanying the high winds had transferred energy to the wave. If the seiche velocity had been less, the squall would have passed over it without such a remarkable effect.

Sudden heavy and localized precipitation—hail, snow, or rain—on a portion of a body of water and the flooding in of a swollen stream at one end of the lake represent other forces that create the gradients and inequalities that power a seiche.

The most spectacular of seiche energizers, although rare, is the earthquake. Seismic tilting in bayous and rivers along the northern coast of the Gulf of Mexico followed the far-distant Alaskan earthquake of 27 March 1964.

One might consider adding the pull of the moon to the list of agents supplying energy to the seiche, but even in the largest of lakes the greatest tidal amplitudes observed are usually no more than 10 mm; and there is evidence that they often are damped out by seiches.

Seiches of noteworthy amplitude might occur if many powering agents are working in harmony, but amplitudes are most unusual if they attain 2.0 m.

Internal or temperature seiches (internal waves)

Mortimer (1952) published results of a study of vertical temperature profiles in Windermere, including some interesting data from a day in late May. At 11:20 AM the 10° C isotherm was about 4 m below the surface; by 4:30 PM it was 4 m deeper, or about 8 m below the surface, and warmer water lay at the 4-m depth. This could mean either marked absorption of heat in 5 hours or vertical eddy currents distributing warm water downward at a remarkable rate. Neither explanation was adequate. The temperature-time data had revealed tilting of the thermocline. A particular type of movement, the internal seiche, had been observed. Pioneer studies on internal rocking in lakes had been detailed 45 years earlier by Wedderburn (1907), who concentrated especially on phenomena in Loch Ness. Because there is no drying, the term internal seiche should probably be replaced by internal wave.

In thermally stratified lakes oscillations of different layers occur.The standing wave generated by wind may not have a great amplitude (measured by surface deviations from equilibrium), but its effect on the stratum of dense water below, marked by the top of the thermocline, is great. The thermocline, or metalimnion, is depressed by piled-up water and is released to bound back when surface waters surge toward the opposite shore. Thus, the rocking thermocline starts out of phase with the standing wave above as it is forced downward by the wave crest over it. The resulting amplitudes and periods are much greater than the oscillations of an external seiche although not readily observable except by measurements of temperatures or, in some instances, by the rise and fall of plankton aggregations. The explanation for the magnified amplitude lies in the very small density differences between waters at the boundary of the epilimnion and metalimnion, compared with the great contrast at the air-water interface. This is demonstrated by a generalized formula for the energy *(E)* in the amplitude of an oscillating two-layered system:

$$E = \frac{1}{2}(\rho - \rho')\, g \text{ (amplitude)}$$

In the above equation, ρ is the density of the lower layer and ρ' is that of the upper layer; g is the acceleration due to gravity. If the temperature of a metalimnion is 10° C and that of an epilimnion is 20° C, $(\rho - \rho') = 0.0015$, and the difference between the densities of the epilimnion and of the overlying air is about 0.9970. This shows that for identical amplitudes, the surface wave has about 665 times more energy than the internal wave.

The depression of the lower interface affected by the amplitude of the surface wave is:

$$\text{amplitude} \times \frac{\rho}{\rho - \rho'}$$

This would be 666.4 for the two temperatures of 10° and 20° C. Thus, a surface seiche of 10 mm could depress the thermocline 6.66 m. A most remarkable internal wave, observed in Lake Baikal, had a period of 38 days and an amplitude of 75 m. Theoretically, a surface seiche amplitude of about 10 cm could have energized this wave.

The above discussion of internal waves has pertained to a two-layered system, but a stratified body of water is roughly three layered. In some studies there has been evidence of two internal oscillations in addition to an external seiche. The lower interface of the metalimnion was displaced so that a second internal wave was generated.

The seiche with all its complexities (harmonic and otherwise) is important to limnology. It is believed that turbulence generated by the free oscillations of the seiche and resultant internal waves create eddies and currents of fundamental importance in mixing and transporting heat, dissolved gases, and nutrients.

SURFACE WAVES

All standing waves, like simple seiches, are characterized by a trough and a crest fixed in space but alternating in time. The water particles move along different paths, although in phase. Vertical movements are pronounced at the crest and trough. At the node only horizontal oscillations prevail. At a time half way in the period of such a wave all water particles are briefly at rest.

Another type is the progressive wave, crest following crest in such a manner that the water mass within each crest seems to be moving in a given direction with the wind. Actually all the water particles in such a wave are moved up and down and back and forth so they follow identical paths during a wave period. The water movements describe orbits that are usually ellipses. Such waves have been of great interest to oceanographers, who have developed much of the theory pertaining to them and other forms of water motion. They have not attracted the attention of limnologists and are cursorily dealt with here.

Surface waves start with gentle air currents that form the familiar ripples called capillary waves. Ideally, these tiny swells have a length no more than 1.72 cm between crests, with heights of about 0.022 cm from trough to crest; their maximal amplitude, therefore, is 0.011 cm. Once established, they travel forward and persist until dampened by surface tension. Uneven water surface adds to the effectiveness of the wind.

As wind velocity increases, ordinary gravity waves replace capillary ripples, and the relative importance of surface tension is reduced as gravity assumes importance in restoring the wind-induced waves. As winds mount, the waves may reach critical steepness, theoretically when the wave length is seven times the height. In oceans and large lakes where winds are strong, wave length increases faster than height, and eventually this brings about the long swells that escape the influence of the wind that raised them.

The above is probably of less limnologic import than what occurs in the shallows where vertical movements in the wave are restricted and the predominant movements are backward and forward. When a wave enters shallow water, it slows down and its leading slope steepens. Its crest suddenly heightens as it overtakes the trough in front of it and then breaks. The breaking of the crest occurs at a place where water depth beneath the trough is about 77% of the height. Theoretically, a wave traveling at 6 m/sec would have a height of 55 cm and would, as a result, break when its trough is 43 cm above the bottom. The surf zone formed where the crests break adds a forward component to the waves, which crash against the shore with erosive effectiveness. If the waves are large, a considerable amount of water is thrown up on the beach and flows back to the lake as a return current.

It is in the littoral region that surface waves have the most effect in lakes. Return currents carry eroded shore material lakeward to create subsurface banks that have abrupt drop-offs. Swells approaching the shore obliquely tend to form longshore currents parallel to the shoreline. In this manner spits are formed that may isolate bays to form shoreline pools. Debris is swept from the bottom, and in windswept shore regions there may be a paucity of aquatic macrophytes compared with the stands in protected bays. Drift lines of debris may be concentrated to provide habitats for various aquatic invertebrates. These are just a small sample of the wave effects in the shallows and at the lake bank.

CORIOLIS EFFECTS

Oscillations such as seiches and the currents in large bodies of water seem to have their directions altered by more than wind, density differences, and gravity. The deflecting effect of the planet's rotation comes into play from the earth-bound observer's reference point. If we were able to stand upwind and watch a mass of water move away from us or if we tracked a cannon ball rolling across an immense level plane, we would be aware of curving in each path. If there were space enough, the cycloidal nature of the tracks would become apparent, and during the course of several days successive loops might appear. It is as though a force were acting at right angles to the horizontal path of particles in motion, causing them to swerve. To account for the apparent deviations from the straight line that inertia would dictate, the concept of the Coriolis force is employed. Its name is derived from the French scientist who published an influential paper on accelerations in rotating systems, emphasizing fluid motions on earth (Coriolis 1835).

In the Northern Hemisphere an observer would see a current veer to the right as it flowed from him. In the Southern Hemisphere the apparent deflection is to the left. These phenomena are the result of the earth's rotation and its shape.

Where the circumference of the earth is greatest, at the equator, a particle at rest is traveling at a tangential velocity of about 1,000 mph as the globe makes 1 revolution per day. As the earth's circumference diminishes along a line from the equator to either pole, the tangential velocity also decreases. Therefore, a particle moving toward the North Pole will seem to move eastward progressively faster than stationary particles it encounters because its initial velocity in that direction was greater. A particle moving toward the equator from higher latitudes will seem to lag farther to the west of stationary particles in its path because they have a greater eastward velocity.

For east-west movements other factors bring about the deflection. Two forces act upon particles at rest on the earth's surface: one is centrifugal force acting at right angles to the axis of rotation and tending to move the particles toward the equator; a second force prevents this. The equatorial buldge makes the slope toward the pole steeper than the surface of a sphere. Gravity acts on a particle resting on this slope, pulling it poleward and thus balancing the centrifugal force. The equilibrium is disturbed when the particle is set in motion. Motion to the east increases its tangential velocity, thereby augmenting the centrifugal component, and the particle swerves toward the equator. Westward motion decreases the tangential velocity, and gravity pulls the particle toward the pole.

The horizontal Coriolis force varies with latitude, being a function of the sine of latitude. The apparent deflection from a straight path is maximal at the poles and decreases to zero at the equator. There are vertical components to Coriolis force, but they are not treated here.

The angular velocity of the earth is:

$$\Omega = 2\pi/86{,}164 \text{ sec} = 7.29 \ 10^{-5} \text{ radians/sec}$$

This corresponds to a complete rotation of the earth in one sidereal day. The magnitude of the Coriolis force on a fluid parcel traveling horizontally in any direction at a speed of v (cm/sec) is tentatively $2\Omega \times v$. There is a characteristic value for 2Ω at each latitude (ϕ) so that the complete equation for the Coriolis parameter must be set down as $2\Omega \sin\phi$, and the force of the acceleration is $2\Omega \sin \phi \ v$. Thus, for a current moving 10 cm/sec at a geographic latitude of 40° N the Coriolis force necessary to account for the observed drift would amount to:

$$\frac{14.58 \times 10^5}{\text{sec}} \times 0.6428 \times \frac{10 \text{ cm}}{\text{sec}} = 9.37 \times 10^{-4} \text{ cm/sec}^2$$

Although the effect of the planet's rotation on atmospheric motions and sea currents is marked, Coriolis forces in lakes are less pronounced, and few limnologists have been concerned with the subject. Mortimer (1955) discussed the effect of the earth's rotation on internal waves in stratified lakes, and a few other authors have published their results from large lakes. Most lake surfaces are so small that shoreline influences preclude much of the Coriolis effect except possibly an initial drift to the right or left, depending on the hemisphere.

Recently, Emery and Csanady (1972) published the result of examining data collected on surface currents in many large lakes north of the equator. In general, the major circulations are counterclockwise, the opposite of what would be inferred from Coriolis forces working without horizontal constraint in deep water. The explanation put forth by those authors is that a water-air temperature differential suppresses turbulence and that surface water, cooler than the atmosphere, reduces wind stress. This is illustrated when bands of cold surface water are glassy compared with adjacent warm areas rippling with capillary waves, a sign of wind stress. Water, especially less dense or warmer water, moving down-wind is deflected to the right shore. There in the shallows it is warmed further, even as cold water wells up at the left; and a marked horizontal temperature differential is created. Now the warm water at the right is dragged along more effectively than the cold water, which is subjected to far less wind stress. Thus, the Coriolis force effects the temperature differences, and those are sufficient for the wind to set up counterclockwise circulation.

10
Oxygen and other dissolved gases

ATMOSPHERIC SOURCE OF GASES

Although we may be inclined to associate gases with the atmosphere rather than with water, it must be noted that there are at least five or six important gases dissolved in lakes, streams, and the seas. They all have biologic and physicochemical functions, but they differ from one another in behavior and origin.

Surface waters in contact with the mixture of gases and water vapor called air absorb some of its components. Nitrogen, oxygen, and carbon dioxide are especially important because of their essential biologic roles. The first two, in addition, are the most abundant constituents of the atmosphere, about 78% and 21%, respectively, at sea level (Table 10-1). Carbon dioxide is surpassed some 28 times in aerial abundance by argon, for example, but it is at least 15 times more soluble in water (Table 10-2). For that reason, carbon dioxide, dissolved in the gaseous state, by absorption at the lake surface, occupies about the same percentage of volume as argon, despite the greater atmospheric store of the latter.

Among the atmospheric gases found in

Table 10-1. Gaseous composition of atmosphere in percent by volume

Gas	Percent
Nitrogen (N_2)	78.084
Oxygen (O_2)	20.946
Argon (A)	0.934
Carbon dioxide (CO_2)	0.033*

*Estimates vary, but this is close to 1973 value.

Table 10-2. Solubility of the common atmospheric gases in pure water at 10°C and at (I) a theoretical 1-atmosphere pressure of the gases and at (II) their normal partial pressures*

Gas	I	II
Nitrogen (N_2)	18.61	14.53
Oxygen (O_2)	38.46	8.06
Argon (A)	41.82	0.39
Carbon dioxide (CO_2)	1,194.00	0.39

*All values are in ml per liter.

trace quantities are molecular hydrogen, carbon monoxide, nitrous oxide, ozone, methane, ammonia, sulfur dioxide, and such inert gases as krypton and neon. Water vapor is present in varying amounts, ranging up to 3% by volume.

HENRY'S LAW AND GAS SOLUBILITY

To understand the physics of gases in natural waters certain fundamentals must be kept in mind. The first of these is the notion of gas solubility in a liquid. This is a function of the characteristics of the individual gas itself, modified by pressure, temperature, and salinity. Here we must recall Henry's law, which states that at a constant temperature the amount of gas absorbed by a given volume of liquid is proportional to the pressure in atmospheres that the gas exerts. The following formula shows this and will be useful in later pages:

$$c = K \times p$$

Here c is the concentration of gas that is absorbed; it may be expressed in moles, mg per liter, or ml per liter. The partial pressure that the gas exerts is p. K is a solubility factor, differing from gas to gas.

Most gases obey Henry's law fairly well, and one can predict the amount of an atmospheric component to be found dissolved in lake water. Carbon dioxide, however, may combine with various cations upon entering natural waters to become more abundant than the precepts of Henry's law would dictate. It is found both free and in combined states.

Effect of altitude

With an increase in altitude to a more rarefied atmosphere, the value p in the formula decreases. Therefore, solubility, expressed as the amount of gas dissolved at equilibrium with the air, lessens. Table 10-3 shows that with each 100-m rise above sea level the mean atmospheric pressure decreases by 8 to 9 mm Hg, the amount of gas dissolved at saturation levels decreasing roughly about 1.4% with each 100-m ascent. Thus, solubility of a gas is clearly a function of its partial pressure, p, in the solubility formula.

The pressure reduction with increasing altitude is not so simple as stated above. Actually from sea level to the first 600 m, the reduction is about 4% for every 300 m; from 600 to 1,500 m, the rate is less, about 3% for each 300 m; and from that elevation to 3,050 m, the decrease is 2.5% on the average for each 300 m. Moreover, it should be pointed out that the International Standard unit of pressure measurement is the bar, not shown in Table 10-3. This is 0.98692 atmospheres, or 750.06 mm Hg, very close to the mean sea level pressure of 760 mm Hg.

Effect of temperature

With p held constant in the solubility formula as temperature is altered, a

Table 10-3. Factors for correcting partial pressure *(p)* and relative saturation of gases at different altitudes

Altitude		Pressure		
Feet	Meters	mm Hg	Partial (p) factor	Solubility factor
0	0	760	1.00	1.00
330	100	750	0.99	1.01
655	200	741	0.97	1.03
980	300	732	0.96	1.04
1310	400	723	0.95	1.05
1640	500	714	0.94	1.06
1970	600	705	0.93	1.08
2300	700	696	0.92	1.09
2630	800	687	0.90	1.11
2950	900	679	0.89	1.12
3280	1000	671	0.88	1.13
3610	1100	663	0.87	1.15
3940	1200	655	0.86	1.16
4270	1300	647	0.85	1.17
4600	1400	639	0.84	1.19
4930	1500	631	0.83	1.20
5250	1600	623	0.82	1.22
5580	1700	615	0.81	1.24
5910	1800	608	0.80	1.25
6240	1900	601	0.79	1.26
6560	2000	594	0.78	1.28
6900	2100	587	0.77	1.30
7220	2200	580	0.76	1.31
7550	2300	573	0.75	1.33
7880	2400	566	0.74	1.34
8200	2500	560	0.73	1.36

typical feature of gas solubility is observed. The solubility decreases as the temperature rises. This inverse relationship permits the generalization that cold water can hold more gas in solution than warm water. Here it might be well to point out that water is surpassed by some other liquids in its capacity to dissolve gases. Furthermore, anomalous behavior, typical of water, is evidenced by the presence of low points in gas solubility curves plotted against temperatures. The resultant, somewhat parabolic, curves are of little concern to the limnologist, however, because within normal temperature ranges of natural waters the inverse relationship is nearly linear.

Effect of salinity

The occurrence of various minerals in solution lowers the solubility of gas, but it has been customary in limnologic theory to overlook this. Usually, when saturations are defined, inland waters are considered to be pure with zero percent salinity. The reduction of saturation values of gases in seawater, when compared with distilled water, is on the order of 20%. Seawater is about 3.5% salinity, and this converted to ppm or mg per liter is 35,000, far above most natural inland waters. The limnologist working in arid regions, however, is advised to keep this in mind, because he may work with saline pools and lakes containing 5 or 6 times the dissolved minerals that seawater holds.

Relative saturation

Gas saturation is quantified on the basis of equilibria at the boundary of water surface and the atmosphere. The usual definition of gas solubility is presented as the ratio of its concentration in the solution to its concentration above the solution. Even lake gases at subsurface levels are referred to the existing temperature at that depth and to the atmospheric pressure above the lake, ignoring the effects of hydrostatic pressure. The ideal physical saturation that could be calculated at greater pressures beneath the surface would occur more than briefly only in some improbable body of water with neither vertical nor horizontal currents and with no other exchange processes. Although a pressure increment of about 1 atmosphere or bar accompanies an increase in water depth of 10 m, this does not enter into conventional discussions of saturation.

Relative saturation is the relation of existing solubility (amount of gas present) to the equilibrium content expected at the same temperature and partial pressure. It is expressed as a percentage. From Table 10-3 it can be seen that a concentration of gas at sea level, representing 100% saturation, would signify 125% of saturation at 1,800 m, other factors being equal. Similarly, a saturated situation at 1,800 m would amount to only 80% of sea-level saturation.

OTHER SOURCES OF GAS

The important gases entering water at the air-water interface may have additional origins within the lake. Obviously CO_2 is produced through respiration and decay, while oxygen appears as a by-product of photosynthesis. The other gases common in some aquatic habitats are formed almost wholly within the lake itself. For example methane, CH_4, is a prominent constituent of some waters but owes its origin to anaerobic decomposition of plant and animal material rather than to atmospheric exchange.

Another consequential gas in some aquatic situations is hydrogen sulfide. It is formed within the lake by chemical and bacterial transformations. Although extremely soluble in water, it occurs only rarely in ordinary atmosphere. Therefore, it does not enter via the lake surface.

An important nitrogenous end product of heterotrophic bacterial breakdown of organic substances is ammonia. Aquatic invertebrates also produce this gas as a major excretory result. Being extremely soluble, it is swept away from the organisms before toxic effects develop. Ammonia is prominent in the summer hypolimnion of eutrophic lakes, where it may occur as the gas NH_3, the ion NH_4^+, or in undissociated states such as NH_4OH. Its atmospheric store is minute, although it is believed that it was abundantly represented in the earth's early atmosphere.

OXYGEN: INTRODUCTION AND METHODOLOGY

For most organisms, oxygen in the environment is a requisite for life. It is represented abundantly in the atmosphere (Table 10-1) and dissolves readily in water. There is a wealth of data on its occurrence in the seas, lakes, and streams, and a knowledge of the oxygen content and dispersion within a body of water reveals much of the nature of that habitat.

A technique for assaying the dissolved oxygen in aqueous solutions was introduced many decades ago by Winkler. Modified through ensuing years, the method has proved relatively easy. Because of efficient methodology and the importance of oxygen, analysis of this gas is one of the first measurements made in lake and stream surveys.

Recent introductions of various oxygen probes permitting electrometric oxygen analysis may signal the end of the

Winkler titrametric method. At this time, however, it stands as the most precise procedure to arrive at exact oxygen values.

The theoretical basis for oxygen determination by the Winkler method is not well known, even to workers who know the procedure well. There is an alkaline phase and an acidic phase in the methodology. The important reactions depend on two facts: first, manganous hydroxide is easily oxidized to manganic hydroxide; and, second, manganic salts are unstable in acid solutions with an iodide and revert to manganous salts, the acid radical combining with the iodide and freeing iodine. The sequence is: (1) production of manganous hydroxide in the water sample to which manganous sulfate was introduced when KOH plus KI are added; (2) oxidation of manganous hydroxide to manganic hydroxide by the dissolved oxygen in the sample; (3) conversion of manganic hydroxide to manganic sulfate when concentrated sulfuric acid is added; (4) replacement of iodine in an iodide (KI) by sulfate, releasing free iodine; and (5) titration of the iodine solution with sodium thiosulfate until all free iodine has combined into sodium iodide. The end point, marked by the disappearance of the brown iodine color, is made sharper by addition of a starch indicator. The equations follow (reactions 3 and 4 proceed simultaneously):

(1) $MnSO_4 + 2KOH \rightarrow Mn(OH)_2 + K_2SO_4$
(2) $2Mn(OH)_2 + O_2 + 2H_2O \rightarrow 2Mn(OH)_4$
(3) $2Mn(OH)_4 + 4H_2SO_4 \rightarrow 2Mn(SO_4)_2 + 8H_2O$
(4) $2Mn(SO_4)_2 + 4KI \rightarrow 2MnSO_4 + 2K_2SO_4 + 2I_2$
(5) $4Na_2S_2O_3 + 2I_2 \rightarrow 2Na_2S_4O_6 + 4NaI$

SOURCES OF OXYGEN
Atmosphere and solubility

When the atmospheric mixture of gases is in contact with water, some oxygen goes into solution. It is almost 4 times less abundant in the air than nitrogen but is more than twice as soluble. The amount of oxygen absorbed depends on temperature, salinity, and pressure. Briefly, cold water absorbs more oxygen than does warm water, salinity decreases solubility, and pressure increases it.

It has not been easy to determine the solubility of oxygen. Early values established experimentally with dry air-water interfaces were replaced about 50 years later by those of Truesdale and others (1955), who based their work on what occurs when a water-saturated atmosphere contacts pure water at different temperatures; this is more realistic than dry air-water exchanges. In 1958 Steen performed careful experiments that brought results much like those of workers decades earlier, although he allowed equilibrium to become established between moist air and water. Despite this, tables based on the data of Truesdale have been used almost exclusively, and for almost 20 years, in calculating oxygen solubilities. More recently, however, Montgomery and associates (1964) presented convincing evidence that suggests that most previous estimates were slightly low because iodine vapor was lost during Winkler analyses. Therefore, the results of their work are presented in Table 10-4. Those authors also presented a simple formula for sea-level solubility at any Celsius temperature, t, applying within ± 0.04 mg/liter between 4° and 33° C.

$$\text{Solubility in mg per liter} = \frac{468}{31.6 + t}$$

At mean sea level beneath 1 atmosphere of pressure, pure water containing 10 mg O_2 per liter would be only 78% saturated, if the temperature were 5° C. At 20° C this amount of oxygen would represent about 110% of saturation. In pure water at 15.2° C, allowed to come into equilibrium with sea-level atmosphere, 10 mg O_2 per liter would represent saturation.

From Henry's law it is evident that saturation, a function of pressure, would decrease with ascent above sea level. Thus,

Table 10-4. Solubility of oxygen in pure water at equilibrium with moist air at sea level

°C	mg/liter	°C	mg/liter
0	14.63	21	8.91
1	14.23	22	8.74
2	13.84	23	8.57
3	13.46	24	8.42
4	13.11	25	8.26
5	12.77	26	8.12
6	12.45	27	7.97
7	12.13	28	7.84
8	11.84	29	7.70
9	11.55	30	7.57
10	11.28	31	7.45
11	11.02	32	7.33
12	10.77	33	7.21
13	10.53	34	7.09
14	10.29	35	6.98
15	10.07	36	6.88
16	9.86	37	6.77
17	9.65	38	6.67
18	9.46	39	6.57
19	9.27	40	6.47
20	9.08		

Data from Montgomery and others, 1964.

a dissolved oxygen value at 1 atmosphere might be substantially less than saturation but would indicate a much closer approach to equilibrium at a higher altitude. Factors to correct for this phenomenon take into account the fact that saturation equilibria decrease with altitude. An example illustrates this. Assume there is a pond lying 1,500 m above sea level with water at 14° C and containing 5.45 mg O_2 per liter. Table 10-4 shows that 10.29 mg/liter is the saturation value for pure water at 1 atmosphere and 14° C. The amount 5.45 is about 53% of 10.29; this calculation neglects a correction for reduced pressure, which according to Table 10-3 requires a factor of 1.2 for an altitude of 1,500 m. Thus, the product of 5.45 and 1.2 gives a relative saturation of 6.54 mg/liter, and it shows to what sea-level oxygen content 5.45 mg/liter at 1,500 m is comparable. Compared with 10.29, then, 6.45 mg/liter is 63.55%. A

simpler step to show that oxygen in the pond water is closer to equilibrium than might be inferred at first glance is 53% × 1.2 = 63.6%.

The various minerals dissolved in water lower its ability to absorb and hold oxygen. Therefore, saturation-equilibrium values are greatest in dilute water. Limnologists rarely take this into account, and, indeed, it is usually insignificant. Compared with distilled water, seawater has its oxygen-dissolving capacity reduced about 18% because of the 35 g of salts dissolved in every kilogram.

Despite the gaseous nature of oxygen, it is rarely expressed as cubic centimeters; commonly the data are set down as milligrams of oxygen per liter, greater by a factor of 1.4.

The addition of atmospheric oxygen to a lake surface and its spread throughout the water require agitation and turbulence to be effective. In an anaerobic body of water, if oxygen were distributed by molecular diffusion alone (an unlikely situation), it would require years for traces to reach a level 5 m below the surface. Wind-driven waves and spray increase absorptive surfaces at the air-water interface and promote eddies and currents that move the absorbed oxygen to lower levels. Conversely, agitation can bring about a loss of gas from the water; this depends of course on the saturation gradient. It is not unusual for people to think of a cold, cascading brook as containing the largest amount of oxygen of all aquatic habitats. This has some basis because of the increased solubility of oxygen in cold water and the aerating effect of tumbling waters. On the other hand, extreme agitation promotes gaseous loss, and no values above saturation could be expected despite the input from photoautrophic organisms. The highest oxygen tensions are found in algal-rich ponds during sunny windless weather or, less commonly, in relatively undisturbed lake strata below the surface where oxygen produced by photosynthesizing algae accumulates.

Oxygen from photosynthesis

Most lacustrine oxygen originates as a by-product of photosynthesis. The general and much simplified equation showing the process in green plants is the familiar

$$6CO_2 + 6H_2O \rightarrow C_6H_{12}O_6 + 6O_2$$

This reaction is powered by light, requiring 674 kcal per mole of hexose produced, as CO_2 is reduced to CH_2O and water is oxidized to O_2 by dehydrogenation. The oxygen resulting from photosynthesis comes, therefore, from the water rather than from the CO_2.

If only simple carbohydrate were produced, each mole of CO_2 absorbed would account for the release of one mole of oxygen. The photosynthetic quotient, PQ (the ratio $+\Delta O_2/ -\Delta CO_2$), would be 1.0. Many observations have shown that this is rarely the case, and limnologists assume that a PQ of 1.2 is a realistic average figure.

In most lakes the phytoplankton contributes the bulk of the oxygen supply because tremendous amounts of chlorophyll are present in epilimnion algal populations. In shallow waters the limnetic phototrophs may be overshadowed by littoral species—the macrophytes, the attached algae, and benthic algal mats being the chief producers. In small brooks the periphyton algae account for most autochthonous production, although organic detritus imported from outside may be more important in the economy of the stream.

LOSS OF OXYGEN

Decreases in oxygen can be attributed mostly to the respiration of plants, animals, and the aerobic bacteria of decay. Purely chemical oxidation can occur, but many oxidative processes in aquatic habitats are probably mediated through bacterial action.

There is considerable loss of O_2 at the interface of organic lake sediment and the overlying water. In this microzone the oxygen content may be much less than it is a few centimeters above. For this reason the morphology of a lake can influence the vertical oxygen curve. A certain stratum of water may have an unusually great area of sediment in contact with it compared with similar strata that overlie bottom regions where slopes are precipitous.

Gas bubbles rising from the sediments remove oxygen from the water. This brings to mind a method of producing anaerobic water by bubbling nitrogen through it. Many years ago Lindeman (1942a) needed anaerobic lake water for some experiments on the tolerance of benthic organisms to anoxic conditions beneath the ice in Cedar Bog Lake. He toyed with the idea of using nitrogen bubbles but finally settled on shaking the organic, semireduced sediment (including bacteria) in bottles of lake water and allowing it to settle. When tested a day later, the supernatant water was found to be anaerobic and, therefore, sufficed for his experiments. Bacterial uptake may have been most important, but purely chemical oxidation, unmediated by microorganisms, can occur, especially in the sediments of dystrophic lakes.

On a purely physical basis, the warming of a summer epilimnion could account for oxygen decrease. This is, of course, a function of lowered solubility of gas as water temperature rises.

The massive fish kills that occur sometimes in shallow, ice-covered lakes are the result of several factors. There is no gaseous exchange with the atmosphere, and if enough snow is present to prohibit light penetration, photosynthesis ceases. Respiration predominates, and in a shallow dimictic or cold monomictic lake with a small initial oxygen content, the level of this gas may fall to lethal thresholds for fish.

In some instances, attempts to alleviate

low oxygen tensions by pumping air through holes in the ice have proved disastrous, for the organic sediments were stirred up, creating a situation reminiscent of Lindeman's bottles. An article by Greenbank (1945) is still a valuable reference for the effects of snow and ice cover on aquatic fauna.

The amount of oxygen required by fishes is to a great extent a function of temperature. Moore (1942) found that during summer months when water temperatures range above 20°C, northern fishes usually die if confined to waters containing no more than 3.5 mg O_2 per liter, but this level is not lethal during winter when metabolism is low. Extreme and unusual adaptations are seen in some fish of desert thermal springs. Hubbs and Hettler (1964) reported that *Crenichthys* from a Nevada hot spring could survive less than 1.0 mg O_2 per liter at 30° C.

Catastrophic drops in summertime oxygen have been reported on several occasions despite the absence of an ice cover. These have been brought about by the concurrence of calm, hot weather with the decomposition of a massive organic aggregate derived from the death of an immense algal bloom.

The enrichment and pollution of the western arm of Lake Erie that had been going on for decades was brought suddenly to light in the summer of 1953, when a period of windless days permitted thermal stratification (Britt 1955). The lower waters became anaerobic and destroyed the mayfly naiads (Ephemeroptera) that comprised an important element of the bottom fauna. They have not recovered since then, and the sediments of the lake are now occupied by groups of organisms more tolerant to lowered oxygen levels (Carr and Hiltunen 1965; Beeton 1969).

VERTICAL DISTRIBUTION OF OXYGEN AND LAKE TYPOLOGY

The sources of dissolved oxygen in a lake are the biologic dehydrogenation of water during photosynthesis and exchanges with the atmosphere at the surface. A deep stratum is removed from both these sources if light does not penetrate to it. As a result, respiration and decomposition prevail there; oxygen is consumed rather than produced.

At times of circulation—during the spring and autumnal overturns in dimictic lakes, for example—oxygen is distributed more or less uniformly from top to bottom. If one should plot a curve based on oxygen values in relation to depth, the line would be nearly straight. This is an *orthograde* curve.

When thermal stratification occurs during summer months and the lake is no longer homogeneous throughout, the tropholytic zone becomes isolated from the upper waters. Now oxygen begins to be consumed there. In lakes with large hypolimnion volumes and relatively little production of organic matter in the epilimnion above, the demands on the oxygen in the tropholytic zone are so slight that it shows no appreciable decline. The summertime oxygen profile, therefore, is orthograde despite thermal stratification. This is characteristic of oligotrophy (Fig. 10-1, *A*). The biomass, the ratio of epilimnion volume to hypolimnion volume, and the hypolimnion temperature interact to produce vertical oxygen curves.

If environmental factors favor the production of a large epilimnion biomass, the situation will be quite different during summer stratification. Great quantities of dead and dying organic matter effect a severe drain on the oxygen in hypolimnion waters. A diminution of oxygen occurs with a conspicuous departure from the orthograde distribution seen during periods of circulation. The vertical curve is now termed *clinograde* (Fig. 10-1, *B*). Clinograde oxygen distribution characterizes stratified eutrophic lakes.

In some lakes unusual oxygen profiles are observed. One of these shows a maximum in the thermocline. The maximum may be well above saturation, in some

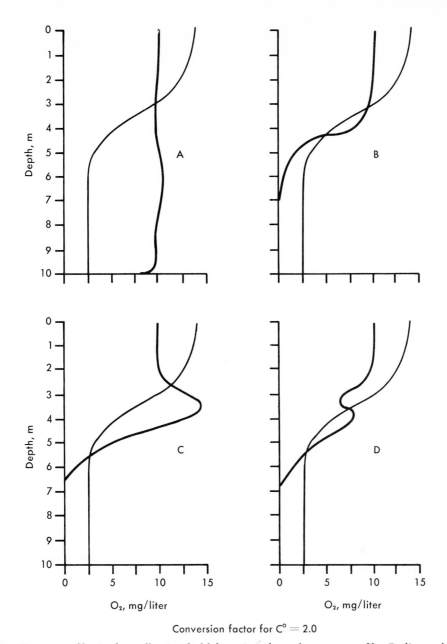

Fig. 10-1. Oxygen profiles in thermally stratified lakes. *A,* Orthograde oxygen profile; *B,* clinograde oxygen profile; *C,* positive heterograde oxygen profile; *D,* negative heterograde oxygen profile. Oxygen plotted with thicker lines; temperature plotted uniformly and with thinner lines; figures on x axis times 2.0 = °C.

instances over 400%. This is *positive heterograde* distribution (Fig. 10-1, *C*). More than 50 lakes are known where such a condition persists throughout the summer. In many instances a dense layer of *Oscillatoria agardhii* is responsible for

unusual oxygen profiles. These blue-green algae thrive in the dim light of the metalimnion; much of the oxygen they produce accumulates because photosynthesis exceeds respiration and turbulence is low at that lake level. Eberly

(1964) summarized what is known about these lakes. It is difficult to assign one causal factor for positive heterograde distribution, but in all cases light must penetrate the thermocline, and some of the lakes have remarkably high relative depths (z_r).

Persistent oxygen minima within vertical profiles are harder to explain. Such distribution is *negative heterograde* (Fig. 10-1, *D*). Some metalimnion oxygen minima are explained by respiration of a marked concentration of nonmigrating animals. Other possible causes were summarized by Shapiro (1960): oxygen consumption by decaying seston, having been slowed in its descent by colder, denser water; unusual morphologic features of the lake basin and horizontal movement of water from regions where organic sediments have lowered oxygen levels; and the phenomenon occasionally seen in artificial lakes where density currents result in water masses with low concentrations of dissolved oxygen becoming interpositioned between well-oxygenated layers.

It is not unusual for a lake to show at least three types of oxygen curves during the year. Little Tom Wallace Lake is orthograde from late October to early April; then a positive heterograde distribution persists a while, but by midsummer there is a definite clinograde profile that remains until the autumnal overturn.

PRIMARY PRODUCTION MEASURED BY THE OXYGEN METHOD
The light-dark bottle technique

The estimation of total photosynthesis beneath a unit of water surface can be approached from more than one angle. Although preceded by workers in the late nineteenth and early twentieth centuries, Gaarder and Gran (1927) are often credited with early attempts that led to development of one technique known as the light-dark bottle method. It depends on the facts that oxygen is produced as a by-product of photosynthesis and is consumed during respiration.

The procedure begins by making a subsurface collection with an appropriate water sampler. After the sample is thoroughly mixed, three glass-stoppered reagent or BOD (biochemical oxygen demand) bottles are filled with what should be exactly equal quantities of water and its contained phytoplankton. One of the bottles is light-tight; this is the dark bottle, wrapped and blackened with electrician's tape or some other material that allows no light to strike the algae within. The dark bottle and a clear bottle are stoppered, immediately returned to the level from which the sample was taken, and suspended for a period of time. The third portion of the sample is analyzed quickly for dissolved oxygen. It is called the initial bottle, and its oxygen content represents the oxygen at the beginning of the experiment. IB, which equals the amount of oxygen in the initial bottle, is the base from which production will be calculated.

Later the subsurface bottles are brought up, and the oxygen they contain is assayed. The oxygen in the clear, light bottle is designated LB. Ideally, it has increased since it was first collected. LB − IB = net gain in oxygen, or net primary production expressed in terms of oxygen released. Now it is obvious that some oxygen could have been produced and subsequently consumed by respiratory activities in the bottle and, therefore, would not be available for testing. Events in the dark bottle are assumed to be purely respiratory, and DB represents the oxygen remaining in the dark bottle after a period of total respiration. Theoretically, respiration (R) would have been similar in both the light and dark bottles and is shown by the decrease in oxygen content in the latter, so that IB − DB = R, the amount of oxygen that was respired in both bottles.

Net production plus respiration equals

gross production, GP, the total amount of oxygen produced by photosynthesis during the time in question. Because the net gain plus respiration, yielding GP, is (LB − IB) + (IB − DB), cancellation leads to LB − DB = GP. Thus, gross primary production could be ascertained with only the light and dark bottle oxygen contents after a given time, but without the initial bottle test neither respiration nor net production can be learned.

In eutrophic waters a test running from dawn to noon or from noon to dusk is adequate. Doubling the results approximates diurnal production and respiration. Dividing by the number of hours of incubation gives mean hourly rates. In oligotrophic waters with low phytoplankton densities, longer periods of time are needed for detectable oxygen changes to occur. But this is not satisfactory because the sampled plankton community should be kept as short a time as possible in the unnatural confinement of bottles.

In polluted ponds where, perhaps, the phytoplankton cells are so numerous that they make a green, soupy suspension, care must be taken not to incubate too long. Photosynthesis may proceed so rapidly that the water will become more than saturated and bubbles of oxygen will accumulate, or respiration may be so intense that the dark bottle becomes anaerobic. In each instance the mark was overshot, so rate cannot be determined; one does not know when the light bottle first became saturated, nor when oxygen reached the zero level in the dark bottle.

In eutrophic waters the oxygen method is probably more reliable than other procedures, but it also has faults. In an often-quoted article, Pratt and Berkson (1959) reported on their experiments that underlined sources of error in the light-dark bottle method. In addition to showing that much of the respiration attributed to the phytoplankton was actually bacterial, they demonstrated that phytoplankton

and bacterial populations in the two bottles changed differentially after 2 days of confinement and that conditions inside the bottles did not mirror the situation outside.

The net production concept is based on the notion that respiration is due to plants metabolizing their own photosynthates and tissues. This is a somewhat idealized approach. Some of the new primary production could have been passed on to herbivorous animals during the incubation of light-dark bottles. In a sense, the problems are like those inherent in estimating net production by harvesting a crop at some given time and comparing its mass and energy content with what it had been earlier. The part nibbled away by herbivores in the meantime is not evident, and, therefore, the estimate of net production is too low. For this reason some limnologists filter out the larger zooplankters before incubating.

About the time Pratt and Berkson were experimenting with opaque and clear bottles, a few plant physiologists were commencing work on a new area of research, the phenomenon of *photorespiration.* Most work has been done on angiosperms, and although there are many gaps in our knowledge of the subject even now, the research has shown that respiration in the dark bottle may be quite different from that in the light one.

Photorespiration, occurring only in the light, may be used to designate two categories of plants. There are those whose rate of photosynthesis diminishes rapidly as CO_2 is used until at a certain level the uptake of CO_2 is balanced by a respiratory output. The substrate oxidized is glycollate, a photosynthate. Oxygen serves as the electron acceptor, and the process is sensitive to oxygen tension. Other plants may remove practically all the CO_2 from the environment without marked photorespiration occurring. At least some freshwater algae, such as *Chlorella,* are the latter type. They may excrete glycollate rather than oxidize it. The phytoplankton is complex, however, and there may be many limnetic phototrophs that begin to oxidize glycollate when CO_2 tension falls to some crucial level.

Dark respiration differs. Its rate is more or less insensitive to ambient oxygen but levels off when the gas concentration is very low. It is centered in the mitochondria, coupled to ATP (adenosine triphosphate) generation, and the speed at which ATP is utilized governs the rate—the uptake of oxygen and evolution of CO_2 in the dark. In addition, there have been reports of dark respiration being surpassed threefold by light respiration. Therefore, there has been serious undermining of the assumption that the value R derived from decrease of oxygen in the dark bottle is always the same as that in the light bottle. This has led to the technique of incubating the experimental bottles for 24 hours, lessening errors caused by difference in night and daytime respiration.

Closer to the point, was Golterman's limnologic study (1971) using organic inhibitors* such as those employed by plant physiologists. He found that oxygen consumption in the light was usually greater than respiration in the dark. This means that gross primary production might surpass that calculated from the usual light-dark bottle studies.

Diel oxygen changes in natural waters

Estimates of diel production can be made in natural waters by considering night as the dark bottle and day as the clear bottle. The increase in oxygen from dawn to dusk reflects net primary productivity. The decrease from dusk until

---

*DNP (2, 4-dinitrophenol) inhibits bacterial action without killing the microflora, and DCMU (dichlorophenyl-dimethyl-urea) stops photosynthesis. The latter does not interfere with respiration in the dark, but typical photorespiration seems to be inhibited by it.

dawn represents one-half the diel respiration. Adding the oxygen that disappeared at night to the daytime gain gives a sum that is daily gross photosynthesis.

An error that is inherent in any such consideration of unconfined water results from the diffusion of oxygen across the air-water boundary, both in and out of lake or stream. Ideally, a study of daily photosynthetic rates would be carried on when wind-induced turbulence is at a minimum. Should an afternoon gale spring up, the data for that day must be discarded.

Odum (1956) described a second way of estimating primary production from oxygen variations in lotic environments. When water is flowing down a stream, its oxygen increases when photosynthesis prevails and diminishes at night. Benthic plants and phytoplankton release oxygen into the water during the lighted hours. Benthic and planktonic organisms take up oxygen continuously. Perhaps chemical oxidation, especially in the sediments, is also a constant depleter of oxygen. Furthermore, there is an exchange of oxygen with the air, the direction depending on the saturation gradient. Ideally, this would be outgoing in daylight and incoming at night, when oxygen tensions are lowest.

Between two stations marking a stretch of stream there is, of course, an area in square meters, and a flow of water amounting to a certain number of m^3 or liters during a period of time. If, to this information, are added the data on increase in oxygen from the upstream station to the downstream site, a rate of production in terms of oxygen per m^2 per hour can be estimated.

The following is a very simple example of production rate, uncorrected for diffusion and respiration. One June day starting at about noon, there was a gain of 1.17 mg O_2 per liter in a stretch of the stream leaving Montezuma Well, Arizona (Cole and Batchelder 1969). The gain occurred

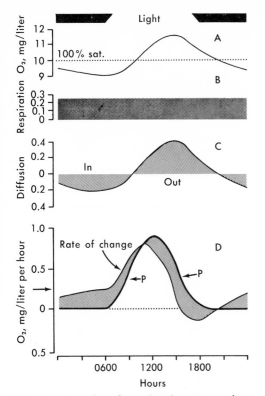

Fig. 10-2. Procedure for estimating gross primary production on the basis of oxygen changes in flowing water. *A,* Diel values in mg O_2 per liter; *B,* respiration in mg O_2 per liter, its rate assumed to be constant throughout the 24-hour period; *C,* diffusion in mg O_2 per liter, *in* (left hatching) and *out* (right hatching), following the saturation gradients shown in *A; D,* gross primary production, *P,* shown by thick-lined curve. This is the sum of hourly changes in oxygen and respiration (thin-lined curve) from which oxygen diffusing in from the atmosphere has been subtracted and to which the outgoing oxygen has been added. Multiplication by mean depth quantifies the production on an areal basis. (Modified from Odum 1956.)

during a flow of 40 minutes in a section of the stream with a total area of 1,053 m². The outflow from the Well was 256.8 m³/hr, or 171.2 m³/40 min. The net production rate for 40 minutes was, then:

$$171.2 \text{ m}^3 \times 1.17 \text{ g O}_2 \text{ per m}^3 \times 1/1{,}053 \text{ m}^2 =$$
$$0.190 \text{ g O}_2 \text{ per m}^2$$

The hourly production rate was 0.285 g O_2 per m² in that segment of the Arizona stream. As will be shown later, this rep-

resented the fixation of about 0.09 g C per m² hour or the net production of organic substances equaling 1.0 kcal/m². There were no data on respiration, so gross production for the 40-minute flow cannot be stated.

Similarly, the changes occurring at one spot in the stream could be used to approximate production if establishment of two stations were not feasible. Much of the procedure, shown in Fig. 10-2, applies also to the two-station technique, including details not brought out in the example above.

Profiles of production rates

Water can be taken from and returned to several depths in light and dark bottles for incubation. From such experiments vertical profiles of photosynthetic rates can be plotted. The results give at least four types of curves (Fig. 10-3).

Findenegg (1964) clearly showed three of these curves, which he termed classes, in lakes of the European Alps, and in all three of his classes the rate of production is low at the surface. Within the upper meter the inhibitory effects of intense light, and perhaps specifically UV, are evident.

The first class is a production-depth curve in which there is a maximum rate in the upper epilimnion and a rapid decline deeper. This class is typical of lakes rich in phytoplankton and with a resultant low light penetration. This type of curve characterizes, for example, Lake Minnetonka, Minnesota, a very rich lake with blue-green algae common in the phytoplankton. An article concerning photosynthesis in this lake (Megard 1972) is a valuable reference to the interaction of factors contributing to planktonic productivity.

The second class contains no distinct maximum within the depth-production curve. It is more or less orthograde, although production is low in the surface stratum. Light penetrates deeply, and its lack is not an immediate limiting factor, as in the first class. Nutrients are relatively low, and phytoplankton populations are impoverished. Photosynthesis occurs at a low rate throughout the euphotic zone.

The third class shows two peaks, one epilimnetic, the other metalimnetic. This brings to mind the heterograde positive oxygen curve, either temporary or prolonged. Perhaps the upper peak is due to optimum light conditions; the lower, to favorable nutrient accumulation in addition to light penetration. In such cases,

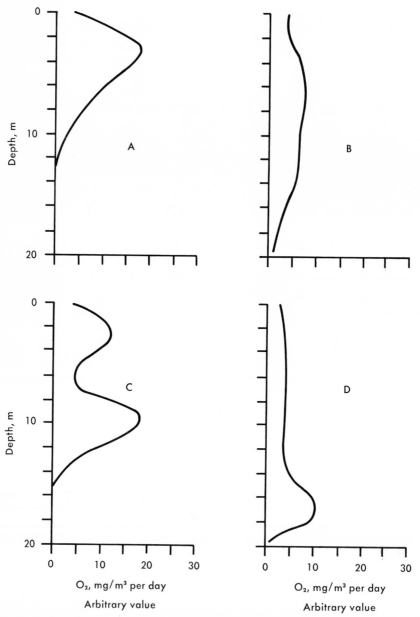

Fig. 10-3. Vertical profiles of photosynthetic rates discussed in text. (Classes A, B, and C modified from Findenegg 1964; Class D from Rodhe and others 1966.)

the euphotic zone extends into the meta-limnion or even into the upper hypolimnion, rich in nutrients.

Another type of curve exists in some extremely oligotrophic high mountain lakes containing very clear water with great light penetration. Rodhe and co-workers (1966) explained that the trophogenic zone is far removed from the surface as a result of the inhibiting effects of ultraviolet light penetrating farther than in most lakes. Below the influence of ultraviolet, in a deep layer where visible light is still adequate, the phototrophic algae thrive.

An integrated curve of production

If one plots the rate of oxygen increase against depth (Fig. 10-3), a curve is produced that may represent either net or gross production in terms of some unit of time—an hour or a day, for example. The titrations were probably done in terms of mg O_2 per liter, which could be expressed as g per m^3 with no change. The area beneath the curve represents, then, g O_2 per $m^3 \times$ m (Fig. 10-4). By cancellation this becomes g O_2 per m^2 in terms of some unit of time. The area of the curve can be established with a planimeter or by

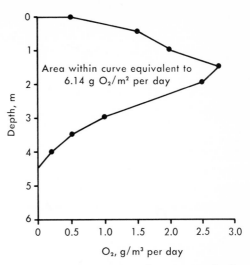

Fig. 10-4. Integrated curve of oxygen production beneath 1 m^2 and uncorrected for morphologic factors. (Data from Table 10-5.)

some other method, and the primary productivity (expressed as oxygen) under 1 m^2 of lake surface can be found. If, however, you are a stickler for details, you will not accept this as a measure of productivity for the entire lake. Morphologic details were not taken into account. When the volume of each stratum is multiplied by the grams of O_2 per m^3 produced within it and the products for all strata are

Table 10-5. Data from Tom Wallace Lake, Kentucky, used to compute primary production in two ways*

I Depth (m)	II Oxygen (g/m³ per day)	III Area$_z$ (ha)	IV A$_z$/A$_0$	V Product Column II × column IV
0	0.50	2.34	1.0	0.50 g O_2/m³ per day
0.5	1.50	2.14	0.914	1.37
1.0	2.00	1.96	0.837	1.67
1.5	2.75	1.80	0.769	2.11
2.0	2.50	1.64	0.701	1.75
2.5	2.00	1.49	0.637	1.27
3.0	1.00	1.36	0.581	0.58
3.5	0.50	1.22	0.521	0.26
4.0	0.20	1.11	0.474	0.09
4.5	0.00	0.85	0.460	0.00

*Column II plotted against depth gives unweighted production per m^2 as in Fig. 10-4. Column V plotted against depth gives primary production for the entire lake referred to unit area, m^2, as shown in Fig. 10-5.

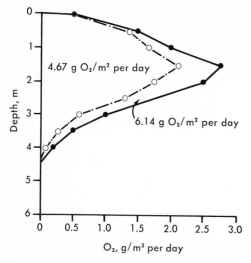

Fig. 10-5. Two integrated curves of oxygen production: the solid-line curve (from Fig. 10-4) shows production beneath a square meter of the lake, uncorrected for morphologic details; the dotted-line curve, which shows production beneath same area, corrected for morphology, is only 0.76 the rate derived from the uncorrected curve. (Data from Table 10-5.)

to convert oxygen evolved to CO_2 consumed. Similarly, carbon, with an atomic weight of 12 compared with oxygen's molecular weight of 32, allows the factor $12/32 = 0.375$ to be used for conversions.

The photosynthetic quotient (PQ), however, is not always unity. If only hexose were being synthesized, as implied by the simple formula, the ratio O_2/CO_2 would yield a PQ of 1.0, but photosynthetic quotients vary. For example, if fats are being synthesized to a significant extent, the ratio becomes greater than one. At present it is customary to use a factor of 1.2 in converting oxygen released by photosynthesis to carbon simultaneously fixed. On the average, oxygen is 1.2 times greater on a molar basis. For example, if one assumes that the annual production established by Winkler analyses is 1.0 kg O_2 per m_2 and that PQ is unity, 0.375 kg C per m^2 is the equivalent. If, however, a PQ of 1.2 is employed, the calculations become:

$$1.0 \text{ kg } O_2 \times 0.375 \times 1/1.2 = 0.313 \text{ kg C}$$

It is conventional to phrase primary productivity in terms of the area on which radiant energy falls. The photosynthesis occurring beneath a square meter of a shallow, eutrophic pond may be intense, but the water column is short. For this reason the production per m^2 in such a pond may be surpassed by that in a deep oligotrophic lake with marked light penetration. In volumetric terms of carbon fixed or oxygen released per m^3, however, the eutrophic pond's photosynthetic activity may be far greater.

An example of this is shown by a comparison of some data from transparent Lake Baikal with that of an imaginary small pond. The average Secchi disc transparency is 13 m, although 41 m has been recorded from Baikal (Kozhov 1963), and photosynthesis occurs in the upper 50 m. Data from Winberg (1963), Kozhov (1963), and Moskalenko (1972) suggest that 2.0 g O_2 per m^2 could represent a

summed, the total production is revealed. Dividing the total oxygen by the surface area gives a depth-productivity figure for the entire lake that differs from that below the square meter where the oxygen production was determined. A modification of this procedure is shown in Table 10-5, where oxygen, relative areas, and their products are shown. When plotted against depth (Fig. 10-5), the curve encompasses total production per m^2 of lake surface.

Conversion of oxygen data to carbon

It is becoming popular to express primary production in terms of carbon fixed rather than oxygen evolved. Oxygen values, therefore, are often converted to carbon. One method would assume that one mole of oxygen is released for each mole of carbon dioxide that is fixed, as implied in the simple photosynthetic formula. The molecular weights, 44 for CO_2 and 32 for O_2, permit use of the factor $44/32 = 1.375$

typical summer day's production. This means that the average production per m^3 in the 0- to 50-m stratum would be 0.04 g O_2. A pond with a mean depth of 2 m and with an identical intensity of photosynthesis (0.04 g O_2 per m^3 per day) would have a daily production, on an areal basis, of only 0.08 g O_2 per m^2. To match Baikal's production of 2.0 g/m^2, the pond's volumetric daily rate would have to increase 25 times to 1.0 g/m^3.

The production of a transparent oliotrophic lake can be compared with that of a eutrophic pond in another manner. If the maximum volumetric rate is divided by the integrated production per m^2, the result is oxygen per meter, with no reference to the shape of the production curve or to the depth of the trophogenic zone.

Conversion of oxygen data to calories

The conversion of all units of production to calories is recommended in an energy approach to what Winberg (1963) termed biotic circulation. The simple photosynthetic formula for the manufacture of glucose from CO_2 and H_2O with an attendant release of oxygen tells us that for every mole (180 g) of glucose, 6 moles (192 g) of oxygen are released. In calorific terms, about 674 kcal are released when a mole of glucose is burned. This means that every mole of oxygen evolved represents one sixth of 674 kcal, or 112.3 kcal.

Oxycaloric coefficients established by experimentation on mixtures of plant and animal proteins, fats, and carbohydrates indicate an average composition of plant and animal tissue of 3.5 cal/mg O_2. If 112.3 kcal is divided by a mole of oxygen, 32 g, the result is 3.5 kcal/g O_2, which is identical to 3.5 cal/mg O_2. Thus, the oxygen released in primary production tells much of the calorific value of newly produced organic molecules. Rates of production, biomass, and respiration can all be unified and reduced to caloric energy units, or perhaps, in time, to the International System unit, the joule.

AN INDEX OF PRODUCTIVITY

A comparative index of lake productivity and an aid in categorization (lake typology) come from knowing the distribution of oxygen in the hypolimnion. The rationale has been presented before (p. 11). Organic material produced in the trophogenic zone sinks to lower strata, decaying as it descends to tropholytic waters. Decay mirrors epilimnion productivity, the oxygen decline associated with it serving to indicate some order of the magnitude of production. Oxygen deficits that indicate some intensities of decomposition can be determined, and eventually a rate can be established for comparative purposes.

Apparent oxygen deficits

If a stratified lake is visited on a summer day and data are collected on the vertical temperature profile and dissolved oxygen at various levels, important information can be inferred. The oxygen present at any depth can be compared with the amount that would be present at the existing temperature and pressure if it were saturated. This comparison gives the *actual deficit.* The *relative deficit* can be computed if we compare the summertime oxygen content with the amount of oxygen at the very end of the spring overturn when the lake was still uniform throughout. The *absolute deficit* compares the summertime oxygen content with the amount that would be present at 4° C.

Examples of these terms are presented for a hypothetical lake 500 m above sea level, with a certain hypolimnetic stratum at 7.0° C and containing 4.70 mg O^2 per liter. The saturation would be 12.13 mg/liter for that temperature at sea level (Table 10-4) and 11.44 when corrected with a factor of 1.06 for the reduced partial pressure at that altitude (Table 10-3). The actual deficit is 11.44 − 4.70 = 6.74 mg/liter. At the close of the spring overturn the water at the level was known to have contained 11.03 mg/liter; the relative deficit is $11.03 - 4.70 = 6.33$ mg/liter. The absolute deficit, based on saturation at 4° C at 500 m, is $12.37 - 4.70 = 7.67$ mg/liter.

The real oxygen deficit

These *apparent deficits* may be close to reality, but if oxygen were very scarce or absent, one would have to go beyond calculating the difference between 100% saturation and zero. Anoxic water implies more than just lack of oxygen, for there are substances present that occur only in the absence of oxygen and that were involved in its decline. For example, every milliliter of methane (CH_4) in anaerobic water represents the consumption of about 2.87 mg O_2. To determine the *real deficit,* therefore, one must take such substances and relationships into account when calculating actual, relative, or absolute deficits.

The hypolimnetic areal deficit and its rate

The next step unifies the various deficits by relating them to the area of the hypolimnion. Visualizing organic material raining through the plane that is the roof of the hypolimnion and imagining some amount that passes through the average cm^2 of this plane leads to the concept of the hypolimnetic areal deficit. This concept involves the difference between total amount of oxygen beneath each cm^2 of the hypolimnetic area on the summer day when it was sampled and what could have been there at the observed temperature (saturation), at the temperature of the vernal overturn, or in 4° C water.

A knowledge of the lake's morphology is needed to find the total amount of oxygen present in the hypolimnion as well as the hypolimnion area. Samples must be taken from various depths, and the concentration of oxygen (mg/liter) for each stratum of the hypolimnion must be multiplied by volume (liter) of that stra-

tum. For example, if oxygen amounts to 5 mg/liter in a certain stratum that is composed of a billion liters, the total oxygen present is 5 mg/liter $\times 10^9$ liters $= 5 \times 10^9$ mg O_2. Summing the amounts of oxygen concentrated in the various strata yields the total oxygen content of the hypolimnion.

Using volume data and theoretical saturation amounts, one can then find the total oxygen that might be there, that was present during spring circulation, or that would represent saturation at 4° C. The difference between these amounts and the actual summertime total divided by the area of the hypolimnion in cm^2 gives the *hypolimnetic areal deficits* in terms of mg O_2 per cm^2.

The discussion shows that the summertime hypolimnetic oxygen per unit area allows the designation of actual, relative, or absolute hypolimnetic areal deficits (either real or apparent) and permits comparison of different lakes. It does not indicate, however, what oxygen totals had been a week before or predict what they will be a week hence. A further dimension is needed: the *rate* at which the hypolimnetic oxygen disappeared per unit area of the hypolimnion. Oxygen assays must be made at intervals, preferably from the spring overturn well into the summer, but even incomplete data are instructive. Thus, if on 25 May the hypolimnion contains 0.83 mg O_2 per cm^2 of its surface and 10 days later on 4 June there is 0.33 mg/cm^2, calculations show that oxygen disappeared at the rate of 0.05 mg/cm^2 per day during that period.

The rate of the hypolimnetic areal oxygen deficit is an index of the intensity of decomposition in waters lying below the trophogenic zone. Hutchinson (1957) suggested figures that define the limits and allow interpretation of deficit rate as an index. A broad boundary between oligotrophic and eutrophic lakes is 0.025 to 0.055 mg O_2 per cm^2 per day. A lake exhibiting a deficit rate within this range might be termed mesotrophic.

Factors vitiating the index

Unfortunately, there are factors that can render data on oxygen deficits useless for comparative purposes. Lakes shallower than 20 m may give spurious results. Thus, summer data from productive Lake Itasca falsely suggest oligotrophy because light penetrates the shallow hypolimnion, bringing about some photosynthesis and oxygen production. There is more going on, then, than just the day to day disappearance of oxygen that would prevail in deeper lakes with dark, undisturbed hypolimnia.

The value of the hypolimnetic deficit as an index depends on the assumption that the decay of autochthonous organic material is involved in the dwindling oxygen supply. Two lakes with identical productivity could show quite different deficits if the hypolimnion of one were receiving significant quantities of organic matter from without. The natural input of leaves and pollen and man's introduction of cannery effluent and raw sewage place a burden on the hypolimnion's oxygen supply that is unrelated to epilimnetic production.

Moreover, morphologic relations may modify the oxygen picture. The ratio of the epilimnion volume to that of the hypolimnion is important here. Two lakes of identical surface area and productivity might show quite different rates of hypolimnetic oxygen depletion if their ratios of epilimnion to hypolimnion volume differed significantly. A relatively large hypolimnion commences with a greater store of oxygen to be used in bacterial decomposition than does a smaller hypolimnion. In the former instance, the demands are easily met without depleting the oxygen supply; the oxygen in a small hypolimnion, however, might diminish rapidly with the same organic input from the epilimnion.

The principle of van't Hoff, that metabolism roughly doubles with each 10° C rise in temperature, introduces another factor in hypolimnion oxygen deficit. If hypolimnetic temperatures are relatively low, at 10° C, for example, bacterial metabolism is somewhat depressed, and the quantity of decaying organic matter governs the distribution and diminution of oxygen. There is a pitfall in comparing the dynamics of oxygen consumption in this lake with consumption in a lake having summer hypolimnetic temperatures of 20° C. Microbial metabolism is accelerated to such an extent in the warmer hypolimnion that it assumes the primary position in determining the rate at which oxygen disappears. This bacterial factor precludes making comparisons of the hypolimnetic oxygen deficit as an index to productivity in a tropical lake and in a similar body of water from the temperate zone. Although they might have identical epilimnetic productivities, the oxygen would disappear more rapidly in the warm hypolimnion of the tropical lake.

In addition, to avoid oversimplification, one must realize that the disappearance of oxygen in the deeps is not always brought about by the decay of newly formed organic matter. Researchers have shown that, in some lakes, the sediments consume this gas to a significant degree; this means that the production of previous years can be involved in oxygen's hypolimnetic decrease. Moreover, much of the epilimnetic organic production can be mineralized before it reaches the hypolimnion. Despite these phenomena, comparing rates of hypolimnetic oxygen diminution is a good way of estimating the relative trophic status of lakes.

In a meromictic lake the real oxygen deficit in monimolimnetic water is great. Time is the major factor here. Many decades of anoxic stagnation contribute to accumulation of reduced substances. The annual production need not have been high through the years.

Under certain conditions, on a regional basis, comparisons can be made of lakes of varied depths and sizes by studying winter deficits without considering maximum depths and hypolimnetic disturbances. Schindler (1971a) compared a cluster of Canadian lakes, sharing climatic and edaphic environments but differing morphologically, by finding the rate at which oxygen was depleted beneath the ice. In early winter, supersaturation of oxygen was found in the upper water because of the freezing-out effect and because of the transparency of new, clear ice. Soon, however, snow lay on the ice of all the lakes, effectively blocking light penetration. It was possible to calculate total oxygen content in each lake at different times during the winter and to compute rates of depletion in terms of mg O_2 per m^3 per day.

THE ISOTOPES OF OXYGEN

There are two stable isotopes of oxygen in addition to the common ^{16}O. The relative abundances of the three in ocean water are: ^{16}O, 99.763%; ^{17}O, 0.0372%; and ^{18}O, 0.1995%. The $^{18}O/^{16}O$ ratio in materials is usually compared with a seawater standard, SMOW, the acronym for Standard Mean Ocean Water. The oxygen isotope composition of a substance reflects, among other things, the temperature at which it was formed or deposited. This has proved useful in studying oceanic ecosystems and in gaining information about past world climates. The temperatures at which marine sediments were laid down and at which $CaCO_3$ was formed in mollusc and foraminiferan shells is interesting, particularly to oceanographers. The analysis of ^{18}O in lake environments is just beginning to assume importance, despite the example set by marine investigators. Recently, for example, Stuiver (1970) demonstrated thermal effects in the isotope ratios of freshwater carbonates and discussed their value as indicators of past climates.

Covich and Stuiver (1974) made use of another phenomenon of the oxygen isotopes to infer past hydrologic conditions in Laguna Chichancanab, a large closed basin in northern Yucatán. Because the common ^{16}O isotope has a lighter mass, it evaporates faster than ^{18}O, and the vapor from evaporating water contains relatively more ^{16}O than the water source. As evaporation proceeds, therefore, the remaining water becomes enriched with ^{18}O. Covich and Stuiver assumed that, because of the lake's tropical setting, mean annual temperatures had remained stable in comparison with evaporation and inflow rates. They studied the oxygen isotope ratios in the shells of an aquatic snail taken from cores of lake sediment. Changes in the relative abundance of ^{18}O in the shells were correlated with other evidence and pointed to major fluctuations in the lake level during the past 28,000 years.

11

Carbon dioxide, alkalinity, and pH

ATMOSPHERIC STORES AND SOLUBILITY OF GASEOUS CO_2

The earth's atmosphere contains relatively small amounts of carbon dioxide, although recent evidence points to significant annual increments. Estimates of the proportion of this gas in the atmosphere have ranged from 0.027% to 0.044%. Careful studies using infrared gas analyzers in regions not subjected to local industrial contamination revealed a mean of about 0.03145% during January 1960 and an annual increase leading to a fair estimate of about 0.0324% for 1973; this is not far from 0.033%, a figure that has been used in many calculations (see Table 10-1).

The yearly increase in atmospheric CO_2 seems to be the result of burning fossil fuels such as peat, oil, and coal. The amount of CO_2 added to the atmosphere by the oxidation of these geologic reserves was calculated to be 10 billion metric tons for 1960. A little more than half of this amount remains in the atmosphere; the rest disappears, probably being utilized in photosynthesis, with planktonic diatoms

Table 11-1. Factors (K) for calculating solubilities of carbon dioxide in water at different temperatures according to Henry's Law $(c = Kp)$*

°C	mg/liter	millimoles/liter	ml/liter
0	3347	76.07	1713
5	2782	63.24	1424
10	2319	52.70	1194
15	1979	44.98	1019
20	1689	38.39	878
25	1430	32.50	759
30	1250	28.41	665
35	1106	25.14	592
40	970	22.05	519

*Factors should be multiplied by partial pressure (p) to give solubility (c) in units indicated.

of the open seas playing a paramount role. (According to Small [1972] 88% of the earth's annual photosynthetic production is in the oceans.)

Despite the small proportion of CO_2 among the gases of the air, it is relatively abundant in natural waters. A major reason for this abundance is its high coefficient of solubility. Carbon dioxide is far more soluble than the two most abundant atmospheric gases, nitrogen and oxygen (see Table 10-2).

Table 11-1 shows some solubility factors for CO_2 at different temperatures. If we consider these figures as Henry's law constants (K in the formula $c = Kp$), we can determine the amount of CO_2 that would be dissolved when in equilibrium with the atmosphere. By substituting the partial pressure, p, of the gas and solving the formula, we get the following at 20° C:

If $p = 0.03\%$
  $c = 1689 \times 0.0003 = 0.507$ mg CO_2 per liter
  $c = 38.39 \times 0.0003 = 0.12$ millimoles CO_2 per liter
  $c = 878 \times 0.0003 = 0.263$ ml CO_2 per liter
If $p = 0.044\%$
  $c = 1689 \times 0.00044 = 0.743$ mg CO_2 per liter

SOURCES OF CO_2 IN INLAND WATERS

Rainwater is charged with CO_2 as it falls toward earth. Theoretically, 0.55 to 0.60 mg/liter should be present and could be introduced directly at the water surface. Water trickling through organic soil may become further charged with products of decomposition and later enter a stream or lake from a subterranean source, introducing gaseous CO_2 in solution.

Subterranean water rich in CO_2, and hence (as will be shown) containing some carbonic acid, may dissolve carbonates and bring them into solution as bicarbonates. The bicarbonates are later introduced into the aquatic environment and made available to most aquatic autotrophic plants as a source of carbon for photosynthesis.

The respiration of plants, animals, and aerobic bacteria of decay add CO_2 to the environment; anaerobic decomposition of carbohydrates in bottom sediments is another important source of CO_2 gas. Such free CO_2 produced within a body of water can cause the dissolution of $CaCO_3$ lying within the sediments and put it in solution as $Ca(HCO_3)_2$.

ISOTOPES OF CARBON FOUND IN CO_2
Carbon-13

The common stable carbon is ^{12}C, and the overwhelming majority (about 98.9%) of CO_2 molecules contain this isotope. Another nonradioactive isotope of carbon is the heavier ^{13}C. Photosynthetic organisms show a marked preference for ^{12}C and fractionate the two isotopes to produce organic material enriched in that common lighter isotope. The carbon of plant tissue is predominantly ^{12}C.

The value of isotopes for working out lacustrine carbon budgets was demonstrated in the 1960's in some Connecticut and New York lakes (Oana and Deevey 1960; Deevey and Stuiver 1964). The accumulation of metabolic CO_2 in the summer hypolimnion includes both free (gaseous) and half-bound (bicarbonate) portions. Some of it is produced aerobically by the oxidizing of organic seston particles in the water; another part is a result of anaerobic events, formed along with CH_4 and revealing another fractionation process. The sediments and the seston sinking to augment them are relatively enriched in ^{12}C through the action of green autotrophs in the epilimnion, as would be expected. Microorganisms responsible for the anaerobic metabolism utilize the parent material, low in heavy carbon, to produce CO_2 and CH_4, which are high in heavy carbon. The summer increase of ^{13}C, then, reflects the intensity of fermentation processes in the profundal ooze—the *pelometabolism*. The carbon accumulating during stagnation is of diverse origins; analysis of its isotopic composition permits estimation of the quantity derived from each source.

Carbon-14

Radioactive carbon, ^{14}C, is formed at high altitudes where primary cosmic radiation enters the atmosphere and produces neutrons. Some neutrons bombard atmospheric nitrogen to form ^{14}C and hydrogen, as shown by the notation:

$$^{14}N + n \rightarrow {}^{14}C + H$$

The newly formed ^{14}C atoms combine with oxygen to produce carbon dioxide that reaches the earth's surface via turbulent mixing and convection. Here it makes up a tiny fraction of the atmospheric CO_2. The gas containing the stable ^{12}C is about 10^{12} times more abundant than the CO_2, made up of the heavier, radioactive isotope.

THE FATE OF CO_2 IN WATER
The two dissociations of carbonic acid

When CO_2 enters pure water, a small proportion of it (well below 1%) is hydrated to form carbonic acid, as shown:

$$CO_2 + H_2O \;\rightleftharpoons\; H_2CO_3 \qquad (1)$$
$$\text{carbonic acid}$$

Some of this carbonic acid dissociates into bicarbonate and hydrogen ions, bringing about a lowering of the pH, a typical occurrence when CO_2 is dissolved in water.

$$H_2CO_3 \;\rightleftharpoons\; HCO_3^- + H^+ \qquad (2)$$

Compared with the total amount of CO_2 in the water, including both H_2CO_3 and CO_2, only a very small amount ionizes. The so-called first dissociation constant of carbonic acid is K_1', in contrast to the less satisfactory true constant derived from the ratio of the ionized form to H_2CO_3 alone.

$$K_1' = \frac{[HCO_3^-]\,[H^+]}{[CO_2 + H_2CO_3]}$$

Each bracket, you will recall, serves as a symbol of molecular concentration. Thus, the ionization constant, K_1' above, is the product of the concentration of the ions divided by the concentration of the unionized molecules, when they are at equilibrium. Table 11-2 shows the effect of temperature on the dissociation of carbonic acid, and Fig. 11-1 shows it as a function of pH. The relationships are valid in dilute waters but must be viewed

Table 11-2. First (K_1') and second (K_2') dissociation constants of carbonic acid in relation to temperature, with cologarithms pK_1' and pK_2'

°C	$K_1' \times 10^7$	pK_1'	$K_2' \times 10^{11}$	pK_2'
0	2.65	6.587	2.36	10.625
5	3.04	6.517	2.77	10.557
10	3.43	6.464	3.24	10.490
15	3.80	6.419	3.71	10.430
20	4.15	6.381	4.20	10.377
25	4.45	6.352	4.69	10.329
30	4.85	6.327	5.13	10.290
35	4.91	6.309	5.62	10.250
40	5.06	6.298	6.03	10.220

Data from Harned and Davis (1943) and Harned and Scholes (1941).

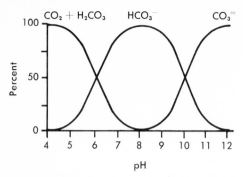

Fig. 11-1. Relative proportions of the forms of CO_2 in relation to pH.

with caution in concentrated, mineral waters.

From the curves in Fig. 11-1 it is obvious that by the time pH has dropped to about 4.5, nearing pH 4.3, reaction 2 has proceeded to the left, and almost no bicarbonate ion is present. For this reason, a common method of measuring bicarbonate ion concentration is based on titrating the unknown with a strong acid until the pH is lowered to about 4.3. Certain liquid indicators show a distinct color change near this pH, where CO_2 and H_2CO_3 are present, but the bicarbonate ion is nearly absent. Thus, the ionization of H_2CO_3 is completely reversed at about pH 4.3.

As pH rises, reaction 2 goes to the right, and dissociation of carbonic acid begins to assume importance at about pH 6.4. Gaseous CO_2 and H_2CO_3 decrease until they are no longer analytically present at approximately pH 8.3, the turning point of the indicator phenolphthalein. Below pH 8.3 phenolphthalein is colorless; it is pink at pH 8.3 and above.

From the curves in Fig. 11-1, we perceive that relative HCO_3^- begins to decline above pH 8.3. The decline results from the following reaction (3) proceeding to the right:

$$HCO_3^- \rightleftharpoons CO_3^{--} + H^+ \qquad (3)$$

Reaction 3 is the second dissociation of carbonic acid; its dissociation constant

(Table 11-2) is based on the following ratio:

$$K_2' = \frac{[H^+][CO_3^{--}]}{[HCO_3^-]}$$

From the preceeding discussion it is obvious that carbonic acid dissociates twice, depending on pH. Similarly, it could be said that it is neutralized at two points on the pH scale. Above pH 8.3 the second dissociation prevails, resulting in the ions CO_3^{--} and H^+, which are neutralized to HCO_3^- as pH is lowered to 8.3, the phenolphthalein end point. Below this pH, HCO_3^- and H^+ are the only dissociated ion pairs in the carbonic acid system. They persist until about pH 4.4, the turning point of methyl orange, where most of these ions are neutralized to undissociated H_2CO_3.

The constants K_1' and K_2' are modified by both temperature and ionic strength (p. 198). Despite this fact, it is customary for workers to make the following deductions after placing a few drops of phenolphthalein in a container of sampled water. With the appearance of a pink hue, the pH is 8.3 or above; there are probably carbonates present, and there is no carbonic acid or free CO_2 that can be analyzed, although theoretically it occurs in minute amounts up to a pH of 9.1. If colorless, the pH is below 8.3; free CO_2 and carbonic acid are present, and carbonate is virtually absent. Bicarbonate ions occur in both cases if the water is normal and lies somewhere within the pH range 4.3 to 12.6. Within limits, then, a few drops of phenolphthalein can reveal much about the nature of a water sample and the forms of CO_2 it contains.

Further examination of the symmetry of the three curves in Fig. 11-1 shows that pH 8.3 corresponds to the maximum in the HCO_3^- curve and is halfway between the points where concentrations of H_2CO_3 and free CO_2 nearly equal HCO_3^- (about 6.4) and where bicarbonate concentration approximates that of carbonate, about

10.2. These relationships permit the calculation of free CO_2 in some natural waters and are discussed again in later treatments of alkalinity and cations (such as calcium and sodium).

THE FORMS OF CO_2 IN WATER AND TOTAL CO_2

In most natural waters gaseous CO_2 occurs in the presence of alkali metals or alkaline earth metals and combines with them to form the bicarbonates and carbonates discussed above. If calcium is used as an example, it is possible to describe an equilibrium relationship for its salts:

$$Ca(HCO_3)_2 \rightleftharpoons CaCO_3 + CO_2 + H_2O \quad (4)$$
calcium bicarbonate   calcium   free CO_2
(mono) carbonate

This reaction indicates that carbon dioxide has 3 important forms in water: the *half-bound* state, represented by the bicarbonate ion; the *bound* form, represented by monocarbonate; and the *free* dissolved gas. To these should be added the *hydrated* state, carbonic acid.

In another sense, it could have been stated that the equilibrium reaction (4) shows that carbonic acid is present in the water as an acid salt, as a neutral (or normal) salt, and as its anhydride, gaseous CO_2.

In a natural water very low in alkaline earth metals or in alkali metals, there would be relatively little bicarbonate formed. By contrast, when the metals are abundant, there is opportunity for the formation of much bicarbonate. In either case, after CO_2 is absorbed, it abandons the precepts of Henry's law and enters into chemical reactions that result in its total content, in one form or another, being far above the saturation value for the gas.

Any equilibrium equation using certain calcium salts as examples should show a small amount of free CO_2 in the system with the bicarbonate; this gas is the *CO_2*

Table 11-3. Equilibrium CO_2 in relation to total alkalinity

Total alkalinity (mEq/liter)	Equilibrium CO_2 (mg/liter)	Total alkalinity as $CaCO_3$ (mg/liter)
0.5	0.15	25
1.0	0.6	50
1.5	1.2	75
2.0	2.5	100
2.5	4.0	125
3.0	6.5	150
3.5	10.1	175
4.0	15.9	200
4.5	24.3	225
5.0	35.0	250
5.5	48.3	275
6.0	64.1	300

of equilibrium, sometimes called attached CO_2 (not to be confused with bound or half-bound CO_2). The CO_2 of equilibrium is necessary for maintaining $Ca(HCO_3)_2$ in solution, but it will dissolve no more $CaCO_3$. If more gaseous CO_2 were added to the system, it would begin to dissolve $CaCO_3$, and reaction 4 would proceed to the left until an equilibrium were again attained. The gas in excess of the equilibrium level is termed *aggressive CO_2*. It would also be in excess as gas in relation to the equilibrium between atmosphere and water. Total free CO_2 includes the aggressive and the equilibrium CO_2. The amounts of equilibrium CO_2 calculated as necessary to keep various amounts of $CaCO_3$ dissolved as $Ca(HCO_3)_2$ are shown in Table 11-3.

ALKALINITY

Very closely associated with the forms of CO_2 is the so-called alkalinity of the water. The name is not a happy choice, for it actually has little to do with pH terminology; waters on the acid side of the pH scale can rank high in alkalinity. Alkalinity is customarily expressed in terms of equivalent bicarbonate or carbonate, although other ions could contribute to it. Additional names for alkalinity are: titrable base, buffer capacity, excess base, acid-combining strength, and SBV *(Säuerbindungsvermögen),* as the Germans call it, loosely translated as acid capacity, or power to combine with acid.

Ordinarily, alkalinity is an index to the nature of the rocks within a drainage basin and to the degree to which they are weathered. Alkalinity commonly results from carbon dioxide and water attacking sedimentary carbonate rocks and dissolving out some of the carbonate to form bicarbonate solutions. If Me denotes an alkaline earth metal, such as calcium or magnesium, it is permissible to write:

$$MeCO_3 + CO_2 + H_2O \longrightarrow Me^{++} + HCO_3^-$$

An assay of alkalinity is the common method for determining carbonate content. A given sample is titrated with a standard acid to the end point of methyl orange or bromcresol green, or with an electrode to about pH 4.5 or 4.4.* In North America, 0.02N H_2SO_4 is frequently employed for this titration: 1 ml of this acid corresponds to 1 mg of $CaCO_3$. Therefore, if the water sample is 100 ml, the milliliters of acid titrant used to attain the end point are multiplied by 10 to arrive at total alkalinity expressed as mg $CaCO_3$ per liter. Multiplying the total alkalinity by 0.599 then yields CO_3^{--} in mg per liter; the factor 1.219 converts total alkalinity to the HCO_3^- ion; and 0.02 times the alkalinity gives the alkalinity as mEq per liter.

The rationale for the above carbonate and bicarbonate evaluations hinges upon the assumption that the titrations deal with salts of carbonic acid only. This

---

*The exact end point depends on the total quantity of the three forms of CO_2. If total CO_2 is about 130 mg/liter, the end point is between 4.4 and 4.5. It is higher in more dilute concentrations and lower when greater amounts of CO_2 are present. For example, pH 5.2 is the end point for 4.4 mg/liter, and pH 4.2 applies for waters with 440 mg total CO_2 per liter.

leads to a reexamination of the curves in Fig. 11-1 to clarify the alkalinity procedure. Ideally, the aliquot to be assayed is tested first with phenolphthalein. If a pink color shows, one assumes the presence of carbonate, probably bicarbonate, and possibly OH^-. (Bicarbonates of alkali metals, such as $NaHCO_3$, cause the pink reaction even in the absence of carbonate.) The titration continues until the pink fades away, somewhere below but very near pH 8.3. This implies that the following steps could have taken place:

$$H_2SO_4 + Ca(OH)_2 \longrightarrow CaSO_4 + 2H_2O$$
$$H_2SO_4 + 2CaCO_3 \longrightarrow CaSO_4 + Ca(HCO_3)_2$$

Any hydroxide present, as in the first reaction above, is counted as an equivalent of normal carbonate. The second reaction shows that each carbonate ion in solution takes up 1 hydrogen ion to become a bicarbonate ion. When most of the carbonate ions have been converted, a small addition of acid produces a rapid lowering of pH, marked by the disappearance of the pink. This *phenolphthalein alkalinity* is only a fraction of the so-called carbonate alkalinity, including CO_3^{--} and HCO_3^-, and is part of the total alkalinity. Continuing with the acid titration: in the presence of an indicator, such as methyl orange, that turns color near pH 4.4, the step, simplified, is:

$$H_2SO_4 + Ca(HCO_3)_2 \longrightarrow CaSO_4 + 2H_2CO_3$$

The titration leads to the point where carbonic acid no longer dissociates and alkalinity is zero (Fig. 11-1). Each bicarbonate ion took up one hydrogen ion to form a molecule of undissociated carbonic acid. The sum of the milliliters of acid titrant used to convert carbonate to carbonic acid by two steps is used in computing the total alkalinity.

It may be obvious now that alkalinity measures the buffering capacity of the water. If the assumption stands that only the carbonate-bicarbonate-carbonic acid buffering system is involved in the titration, then the total CO_2 content in its various forms can be stated with confidence.

Factors contributing to alkalinity

Unfortunately, natural waters contain additional negative ions that react with hydrogen ions; therefore, an alkalinity titration may deal with buffer systems other than the salts of carbonic acid. For example, about 5% of the alkalinity in seawater comes from borate ($H_4BO_4^-$), and this anion could assume importance in inland waters of certain arid regions. Some saline desert lakes of California, such as Little Borax and Mono Lake, contain great quantities of boron.

In some dystrophic bogs and other waters rich in humic acids, the occurrence of humates precludes the valid conversion of alkalinity titrations to carbonate (Berg 1962). In polluted lakes and rivers, organic anions may become a part of the total alkalinity.

Phosphate alkalinity must be reckoned with in some situations. The ions PO_4^{---}, HPO_4^{--}, and $H_2PO_4^-$ may all combine with H^+ to increase the titer. Silicates and, to a lesser extent, arsenates and aluminates could also be involved as buffers in alkalinity titrations.

Water specialists in the U. S. Geological Survey convert total alkalinity to the bicarbonate ion and list it specifically as such in their reports. In some German and Austrian journals, however, it is common to find the major cations and anions reported in mg per liter, while the alkalinity titration is expressed in mEq per liter, with no mention of carbonate or bicarbonate. This is a safe way to express alkalinity because a mixture of buffer systems might prevail. Accuracy is sacrificed by converting the results to carbonate or bicarbonate.

The International Association of Physical Oceanography in 1939 defined alkalinity as the number of milliequivalents of hydrogen ions neutralized by 1 liter of

Table 11-4. Conversions of pH values to hydrogen ion concentrations

pH	Molarity (M) of hydrogen ions (moles/liter)
6.0	1.0×10^{-6}
6.05	8.913×10^{-7}
6.10	7.943×10^{-7}
6.15	7.079×10^{-7}
6.20	6.310×10^{-7}
6.25	5.623×10^{-7}
6.30	5.012×10^{-7}
6.35	4.467×10^{-7}
6.40	3.981×10^{-7}
6.45	3.548×10^{-7}
6.50	3.162×10^{-7}
6.55	2.818×10^{-7}
6.60	2.512×10^{-7}
6.65	2.239×10^{-7}
6.70	1.995×10^{-7}
6.75	1.778×10^{-7}
6.80	1.585×10^{-7}
6.85	1.413×10^{-7}
6.90	1.259×10^{-7}
6.95	1.122×10^{-7}

The same basic values, with different exponents, apply in other ranges of pH; for example:
pH 5.8 is equivalent to 1.585×10^{-6} M
pH 7.8 is equivalent to 1.585×10^{-8} M

seawater. This somewhat unspecific approach recognizes that, depsite the major influence of HCO_3^- and CO_3^{--}, borates account for about 5% of the alkalinity in marine samples.

Carbonate alkalinity can be calculated from determinations of pH, temperature, and total inorganic carbon dioxide. The following formula applies:

$$\text{Carbonate alkalinity (mEq/liter)} = \frac{[(H^+) + 2K_2'] \times K_1'}{(H^+)^2 + (H^+)K_1' + K_1'K_2'} \sum C \text{ in mM}$$

The hydrogen ion concentration in the formula is derived from the pH in Table 11-4. The first and second dissociation constants of carbonic acid at different temperatures can be found in Table 11-2. The total inorganic CO_2, designated as ΣC, is:

$$(CO_2) + (H_2CO_3) + (HCO_3^-) + (CO_3^{--})$$

A method described as "simple gas chromatography," which takes no more than 5 minutes per sample, can be employed to find the total CO_2 (Park and co-workers 1964).

An excess in the titration (above the calculated carbonate alkalinity) reveals the presence of other buffers in the system that would have invalidated the use of acid titration for precisely assaying carbonate ion and other forms of carbon dioxide. For example, a detailed study of waters from the Columbia River and some of its tributaries disclosed that, on the average, only 94% of the total alkalinity is due to carbonate alkalinity (Park and co-workers, 1969).

Diel changes in alkalinity

Usually, daily fluctuations in alkalinity are negligible. In dilute waters the effects of photosynthesis and respiration on the carbonic acid system are marked mostly by pH changes; despite changes in the proportion of bicarbonate to carbonate, alkalinity titrations yield about the same result throughout the day and from day to day. The addition of CO_2 lowers pH without much change in alkalinity. Carpelan (1967) reported an exception to this where impressive diel fluctuations occurred in small pools within a desert canyon in California. Photosynthetic precipitation of $CaCO_3$ took place during the daylight hours, diminishing total alkalinity. This was accented by rising water temperatures that lowered the solubility of $CaCO_3$. The following night, aggressive CO_2 from excess respiration redissolved the calcite to raise the alkalinity to a high dawn level. One sunny day in late May during the first 189 minutes after dawn, the pH rose from 7.1 to 7.6, and the loss of free CO_2 was matched by an increase in dissolved oxygen. During the next 40 minutes, however, the pH soared to 8.4 while alkalinity simultaneously decreased from 4.6 to 3.28 mEq/liter.

Often in hard carbonate lakes there is a decrease in epilimnion alkalinity during the growing season as photosynthetic uptake of CO_2 results in the precipitation of $CaCO_3$. The sinking carbonate is redissolved in the hypolimnion by the carbonic acid formed from hydration of the CO_2 of decay and is returned to the epilimnion at the next overturn. Seasonal heightening and ebbing of alkalinity values occur in such cases.

pH AND THE HYDROGEN ION
Definitions

A review of the concept of pH is inserted here, although it may be of little use to the advanced student. On the other hand, it might serve as a valuable refresher. An abbreviation of *potentia hydrogenii,* pH indicates the concentration of hydrogen ions. It expresses the intensity of an acid, depending upon its dissociation as well as the total amount that is present.

Water is a weak electrolyte; hence, by definition a small fraction of it dissociates into the ions that compose its molecule. The obvious ions in pure water would be H^+ and OH^-, the former making for acidity and the latter typical of a base. The following dissociation equilibrium applies:

$$H_2O \rightleftharpoons H^+ + OH^-$$

The prevailing practice treats the dissociation of water as a function of the hydrogen ions and hydroxyl ions alone, although the hydronium ion (H_3O^+) far surpasses the former in abundance. It forms when a hydrogen ion is hydrated with at least one molecule of water.

$$H_2O + H^+ + OH^- \longrightarrow H_3O^+ + OH^-$$

The dissociation constant of pure water at a given temperature is expressed as:

$$K_w = \frac{[H^+]\,[OH^-]}{H_2O} \text{ or } \frac{[H_3O^+]\,[OH^-]}{H_2O}$$

The ionizing fraction is so small that the

Table 11-5. Effect of temperature on K_w, pK_w (negative logarithm of K_w), and pH

°C	$K_w \times 10^{14}$	pK_w	pH
0	0.115	14.94	7.47
5	0.185	14.73	7.37
10	0.292	14.53	7.27
15	0.450	14.35	7.17
20	0.681	14.17	7.08
24	1.000	14.00	7.00
25	1.008	13.99	6.99
30	1.469	13.83	6.92
35	2.089	13.68	6.84
40	2.919	13.54	6.77

Table 11-6. Relations among pH, the seldom-used pOH, and equivalent acid and base normalities

pH	Acid normality	Base normality	pOH
0	1.0	0.00000000000001	14
1	0.1	0.0000000000001	13
2	0.01	0.000000000001	12
3	0.001	0.00000000001	11
4	0.0001	0.0000000001	10
5	0.00001	0.000000001	9
6	0.000001	0.00000001	8
7	0.0000001	0.0000001	7
8	0.00000001	0.000001	6
9	0.000000001	0.00001	5
10	0.0000000001	0.0001	4
11	0.0000000001	0.001	3
12	0.000000000001	0.01	2
13	0.0000000000001	0.1	1
14	0.00000000000001	1.0	0

undissociated water approximates 1.0, and K_W is simply the product of H$^+$ and OH$^-$, the numerator alone. The product is the tiny value 10^{-14} at 24° C. In absolutely pure water the ratio of the number of hydrogen ions to hydroxyl ions is 1.0, the overall reaction being neutral. Each occurs, therefore, in a concentration of 10^{-7}. These concentrations are expressed as moles (gram ions) per liter. The effect of temperature on the dissociation constant, $K_{W,}$ is set forth in Table 11-5.

In a neutral solution the number of hydrogen ions would equal the hydroxyl ions, but the masses would differ. For every metric ton of undissociated water molecules there would be 0.1 mg H$^+$ and 1.7 mg OH$^-$. The masses would be nearly similar, if they were reckoned and compared on the basis of the hydronium ion as the source of positive charge. With any departure from neutrality, one ion increases as the other diminishes (Table 11-6). A gain in H$^+$ to 10^{-6} moles per liter would signify a decrease in hydroxyl ions to 10^{-8}; their product, $10^{-6} \times 10^{-8}$, still equals 10^{-14}, or K_w. This constant relationship permits the notation of just one of the ions to describe whether a solution behaves as an acid or as a base. The hydrogen ion has been chosen for this purpose, and the logarithm of its concentration is used to describe the ratio of hydroxyl to hydrogen ions. Conventionally, the negative sign is dropped, and the exponent is designated pH. There are other ways of stating this. For example, pH is the logarithm to the base 10 of the reciprocal of the hydrogen ion molarity, or its cologarithm. Or, it may be stated that pH is the negative logarithm of the concentration of hydrogen ions in moles per liter.

$$pH = \log \frac{1}{[H^+]} = -\log [H^+]$$

At neutrality the molar concentration of H$^+$ is expressed as pH 7.0. (If it were commonly employed, pOH would then be 7.0.) An increase in H$^+$ is reflected in a lowered pH; below 7.0 designates a surplus of H$^+$ and an acid reaction.

At least two different methods serve to measure pH. First, indicators of various types are colored differently by acid and alkaline solutions. Color comparators that permit the matching of indicators (added to natural waters) to colored glass discs are accurate to ±0.1 pH units. More than 60 acid-base indicators ranging from pH 0 to 14 are available. A second method involves electrodes and either battery-operated meters in the field or line-operated instruments in the laboratory. This electrometric procedure has advantages in accuracy, but the simplicity of comparing the hues of indicator solutions has much to recommend it.

Sources of hydrogen ions

The main source of hydrogen ions within natural waters is carbonic acid in its various forms. One need not invoke other origins of protons to account for pH values somewhat below 6.0, approaching 5.0. One can generalize, then, that the providers of CO_2 in inland waters also supply hydrogen ions.

Rainwater in equilibrium with atmospheric CO_2 would have a pH of about 5.6, if only carbonic acid were involved. Analyses have shown, however, that lower values often prevail (Carroll 1962). The presence of SO_2 explains some of these acid rains; SO_2 is an extremely soluble gas and reacts readily with water to form sulfurous acid, which is rapidly oxidized to sulfuric acid. Studies of the inorganic content of rainwater over the United States (see the review by Kellogg and associates 1972) show that appreciable amounts of sulfate occur, and much of this is as H_2SO_4. Volcanic emissions and industrial smoke contaminate the atmosphere with SO_2. A reasonable estimate is that 100×10^6 metric tons of this gas is produced by burning coal and petroleum products each year.

Sulfurous fumes from the smelters of Sudbury, Ontario, have had an acidifying effect that resulted in high fish mortalities in the poorly buffered La Cloche Mountain Lakes (Beamish and Harvey 1972). Records of 150 lakes observed over the past decade show that in some there has been a hundredfold increase of hydrogen ion concentration; 33 of the lakes now have a pH below 4.5.

In addition to H_2SO_4, hydrochloric acid amounting to 1.8 mEq/liter has been found in rainwater near Mount Vesuvius. It owes its existence to that famous cone.

Some volcanic lakes are acid because of nearby active sources of sulfur compounds. Armitage (1958) wrote of one that occupied a crater in El Salvador and was ringed by sulfurous fumaroles and springs along its shores; its water had a pH of 2.0! Many Japanese volcanic lakes, similarly, are very acid. On the other hand, some volcanic lakes, and particularly those in arid regions, are characterized by unusually high pH values. They are soda lakes, with marked concentrations of Na_2CO_3 and $NaHCO_3$, the sodium having been provided by lava.

Pyrite, the so-called fool's gold, FeS_2, may be found within the drainage basin of a body of water or be present in anaerobic peats or bottom sediments. Oxidation of this mineral leads to the formation of sulfuric acid in the following manner:

$$4FeS_2 + 15O_2 + H_2O \longrightarrow 2Fe_2(SO_4)_3 + 2H_2SO_4$$

In anaerobic water, the gas H_2S may be evidenced by the rotten-egg odor that typifies it. Both phototrophic and chemotrophic bacteria can oxidize this compound to elemental sulfur and later to H_2SO_4. These events may be effective at the boundary of anaerobic and aerobic water in a stratified lake and, of course, are common in anoxic oozes.

Calcium sulfate is common in runoff waters and under some conditions can be present in rain. Any exchange between the bivalent cation Ca^{++} and hydrogen ions would form the strong acid H_2SO_4, and this is what comes about under certain conditions. A simple water softener based on ion exchange can be made from peat derived from *Sphagnum* moss. As water trickles through the peat, calcium is adsorbed and the plant material concurrently yields hydrogen ions; as a result sulfuric acid is produced. This is why *Sphagnum* bogs attain high acidity.

Experimental work by Bell (1959) underlined the fact that living *Sphagnum* takes up cations differentially, the trivalent and bivalent ions being adsorbed much more readily than the monovalent. Dead *Sphagnum* continues to act as an ion exchanger. The action of this moss is similar to that of the commercial resins and zeolites used in water deionizers. Zeolites make up a large family of natural hydrous aluminum silicates. They show molecular sieve effects and possess base exchange properties that make them valuable in water-softening procedures. Similarly, a complex system of minute pores in the cell walls of *Sphagnum* may be adapted uniquely for such a role. Gorham (1957b) found that metallic ions adsorbed on peat surfaces were sometimes more than 100 times the amount present in the water.

Sulfuric acid is not the only agent lowering the pH of bog waters. Organic acids, collectively called humic acids, are abundant in peaty materials. They arise from plant materials by a two-step process mediated by bacterial enzymes (Kononova 1961). First, there is decomposition of plant compounds to simpler substances; and, second, there is a synthesis of complex, high-molecular–weight, yellow-brown substances. The second step is the conversion of open-chain compounds into aromatic compounds that undergo subsequent polymerization. The results are condensation products of phenols, quinones, and amino compounds. As implied by their name, humic acids are common in soils, reaching lakes via runoff. They are stronger than carbonic acid, bringing the pH down to about 4.0, or slightly lower. Shapiro (1957) reported that purified preparations of the yellow acids of lake water lowered the pH to 3.6 in aqueous solutions. Thus, humic acids can neutralize carbonic acid, preventing its dissociation at about pH 4.4. In turn, humic acids are neutralized by strong mineral acids. In many bog lakes, H_2SO_4 depresses the pH to 3.0 or below, where neither carbonic acid nor the humic acids dissociate.

Berg (1962) studied the brown-stained humic waters of the Congo—waters where the pH was controlled largely by organic acids. In some instances the presence of metallic cations partially neutralized the African waters by forming salts, and those humates, thereby, contributed to alkalinity titers.

Bayly (1964) published results of research on some acidic Australian lakes that owed their acidity (pH 4.0) to humic acids. Generally, the acidity of northern bog lakes of North America is due to H_2SO_4, and humic acids are less important.

On the basis of work with the stained humic waters of the Congo, Berg (1962) described a method for ascertaining total acidity, noncarbonic acidity (humic and sulfuric), and carbonic acidity by subtraction. After determination of total acidity by NaOH titration to the phenolphthalein end point, the carbonic acidity is driven from a second sample by agitation under a vacuum, and residual acidity is titrated to the neutralization point of humic acid, pH 7.6. The residual acidity is the result of humic acids and perhaps strong mineral acids such as H_2SO_4. Carbonic acidity, if present, is detected by the difference between the total and residual titrations.

Despite the paragraphs devoted to acidity derived from strong mineral acids and organic acids, it must be reiterated that the pH range in most inland waters extends from 6.0 to 9.0 and that the carbonic acid system controls it. Residual acidity following aeration and agitation is rare.

There are interrelationships among various forms of CO_2, photosynthesis, and pH. If a water contains relatively great amounts of $Ca(HCO_3)_2$, with the equilibrium CO_2 that permits that solution, removal of the CO_2, as in photosynthesis, will disrupt the equilibrium. The reversible reaction below will proceed to the right with the precipitation of

$CaCO_3$:

$$Ca(HCO_3)_2 \rightleftharpoons CaCO_3 + H_2O + CO_2 \nearrow^{\text{assimilated}}$$
$$\downarrow$$
$$\text{precipitated}$$

This reaction, resulting in a rise of pH, is revealed sometimes by calcareous incrustations on plants and other submerged objects.

Further reactions are the hydrolysis of bicarbonate and carbonate and the appearance of hydroxyl ions with an accompanying increase of pH.

$$HCO_3^- + H_2O \rightleftharpoons H_2CO_3 + OH^-$$
$$CO_3^{--} + H_2O \rightleftharpoons HCO_3^- + OH^-$$

The addition of free CO_2 to the system by respiration, for example, reverses the reactions and lowers the pH.

The pH of a typical calcareous water is the result, then, of the ratio of hydrogen ions (arising from the two dissociations of carbonic acid) to hydroxyl ions (provided by the hydrolysis of bicarbonate and carbonate). The importance of photosynthesis is obvious here, for plants can successively absorb CO_2, eliminate bicarbonates, precipitate carbonates, and form hydroxyl ions. All these events account for rises in pH.

In very saline waters the picture may not be so simple. Wangersky (1972) presented data to support the view that the pH of seawater resists change through complex ion equilibria of all major ions. Moreover, he considers these reactions more important as a pH-stat than the carbonate buffering system in the seas, although this viewpoint is not uncontested.

BUFFER SYSTEMS

Buffers are solutions that resist changes in hydrogen ion concentration when other solutions, acidic or basic, are added. A weak acid becomes a buffer when alkaline substances are added, and a weak base may become a buffer when acid is introduced. A mobile equilibrium of a reversible reaction applies.

Mixing acidic and basic phosphates makes a common laboratory buffer. Because of the law of mass action, the pH of these buffers can be determined from the amounts of base and acid in the mixture. The association of a partially neutralized acid and its base has a certain pH, formulated below:

$$\text{pH} = \text{p}K' + \log \frac{C_B}{C_A}$$

In the above example, $\text{p}K'$ is the negative logarithm of the ionization constant of the acid *(A)*; C refers to the molar concentrations of the acid and its conjugate base *(B)*. As an example, a buffer of about pH 6.8 is made from a mixture of Na_2HPO_4 (a slightly acidic primary salt of phosphoric acid) and NaH_2PO_4 (an almost neutral secondary salt of phosphoric acid). If the mixture includes a 0.06 molar concentration of NaH_2PO_4 and 0.04 of the acid, Na_2HPO_4, then

$$\text{pH} = 6.8 + \log \frac{0.06}{0.04} = 6.8 + 0.18 = 6.98$$

Now, if 0.01 mole of HCl is added,

$$\text{pH} = 6.8 + \log \frac{0.05}{0.05} = 6.8$$

Or if 0.01 mole of NaOH is added,

$$\text{pH} = 6.8 + \log \frac{0.07}{0.03} = 6.8 + 0.37 = 7.17$$

This buffer system, beginning at pH 6.98, varied no more than 0.19 pH units with the addition of considerable quantities of strong acid and base. By contrast, a liter of 0.1 molar solution of unbuffered NaCl would be changed from pH 7.0 to 2.0 by the addition of 0.01 mole of HCl!

A water containing some carbonic acid and one of its salts qualifies as a buffer solution. This typifies most natural waters, and those with high total alkalinities are especially effective in resisting pH changes. When a strong base is added, it reacts with carbonic acid to form the bicarbonate salt and eventually carbonate, using up the base in the process. Likewise, when acid is added, it is used in the conversion of carbonate to bicarbonate and of bicarbonate to the undissociated H_2CO_3. These relationships explain why, in a natural body of water low in total alkalinity, the addition of respiratory CO_2 or the removal of CO_2 via photosynthesis results in far greater pH changes than in well-buffered water with a high total alkalinity.

METHODS OF ANALYZING FOR FREE CO_2
Titration

Limnologic field tests for free CO_2 are somewhat unsophisticated and have been replaced to a great extent by calculation. A freshly collected water sample is measured out in a Nessler tube or graduated cylinder; a few drops of phenolphthalein are added, and a rapid titration with NaOH or $NaHCO_3$ follows until the pink end point of phenolphthalein is attained. The normality of the base solutions are usually adjusted to facilitate ensuing calculations. For example, if 0.0227 N (1/44) NaOH is used and 100 ml of water is tested, the milliliters of titrant multiplied by 10 gives free analytic CO_2 in mg per liter. Despite the small surface exposed in using an elongate, narrow cylinder to hold the sample and despite the gentle stirring that must be performed during the titration, there is probably some escape of CO_2 into the air. Imagine how this would apply to summer samples brought from the deeps and subjected to a sudden decrease in pressure and an increase in temperature during the titration. To compound the problem, the pink end point is not easily judged; pink may flash through the sample only to disappear as the worker prepares to record the results. This fading may be repeated a time or two before a pink lingers for a minute or so and is then termed "permanent." Because of this delay, consider-

able free CO_2 may have escaped the final reckoning.

An example of how CO_2 can be lost from a sample is illustrated by a simple test with the issue from a spring. A sample of effluent from an underground source, placed in a beaker and tested with phenolphthalein, will probably be colorless. If the limnologist goes about his business for a few minutes, occupying himself with other tasks, he may return to find the container of spring water a reddish hue. Free CO_2 escaped from the water and the pH rose to 8.3 or above. Agitation or stirring would have hastened the process. This reveals something about the spring water as it first emerges: it contains gaseous CO_2; its pH is somewhere below 8.3; and there is no residual acidity, its hydrogen ion content being due to carbonic acid alone, rather than to mineral acids such as H_2SO_4.

Perhaps there is need for some gasometric equipment, based on sophisticated physiologic and medical techniques, that could be used easily in the field by the limnologist. A small sample of water could be analyzed under completely closed conditions, allowing the escape or the absorption of no gas. There are better ways of arriving at CO_2 than by titration in the field, however, and a discussion of these follows.

Calculation

Rough approximation. The relationships among bicarbonate, pH, and free CO_2 (including carbonic acid) shown in Fig. 11-1 permit calculation of any one when the other two are known. At the time of sampling, the pH of the water should be determined without delay and preferably in situ. If it is above pH 8.3, one assumes there is no free analytic CO_2; but if it is below this value, the assumption is that gaseous CO_2 occurs in company with bicarbonate ions, and computing its strength is possible. The bicarbonate determination can be de-

Table 11-7. Relationships among pH, total alkalinity (mg/liter as $CaCO_3$) and free CO_2 (mg/liter)

pH	Total alkalinity	Free CO_2	pH	Total alkalinity	Free CO_2
5.0	0	9.7	6.8	10	3.1
	1	24.3		50	15.4
	2	48.5		100	30.7
5.2	0	4.9	7.0	50	9.7
	2	26.5		100	19.4
	5	66.2		200	38.7
5.4	0	1.5	7.2	50	6.1
	2	16.1		100	12.3
	5	40.3		200	24.5
5.6	0	0.6	7.4	50	3.9
	5	24.7		100	7.8
	10	49.3		200	15.6
5.8	0	0.2	7.6	50	2.4
	5	15.5		100	4.8
	10	30.9		200	9.7
6.0	10	19.5	7.8	50	1.5
	15	29.2		100	3.1
	20	28.9		200	6.1
6.2	10	12.3	8.0	100	1.9
	20	24.5		200	3.8
	30	36.8		300	5.7
6.4	10	7.7	8.2	100	1.2
	30	23.2		200	2.4
	50	38.7		300	3.6
6.6	10	4.9			
	50	24.4			
	100	48.8			

Data from Moore (1939).

layed in most instances with little harm, although it is not difficult to measure it in the field.

A rough approximation ignoring temperature and ionic strength of the water being tested for CO_2 is shown first. The pH is evaluated and then compared with total alkalinity expressed as $CaCO_3$ in mg per liter. Table 11-7 and Fig. 11-2 can be used to make a crude approximation of the CO_2 to be expected. If pH were 7.2 and total alkalinity were found to be 185 mg/liter (Table 11-7), then the following equation would be closely applicable, even though it assumes arithmetic rela-

tions. Such are not truly the case, as indicated by the straight lines on the semilog plot of Fig. 11-2.

$$\frac{200}{24.5} = \frac{185}{x \text{ mg } CO_2 \text{ per liter}}$$

Solving for x yields about 22.7 mg uncombined CO_2 per liter. Using the graph (Fig. 11-2) and interpolating to judge the point where total alkalinity of 185 mg/liter would fall at a pH of 7.2, one can estimate about 22 mg free CO_2 per liter.

Table 11-7 and Fig. 11-2 are based on data and computations presented by Moore (1939) and are familiar to North

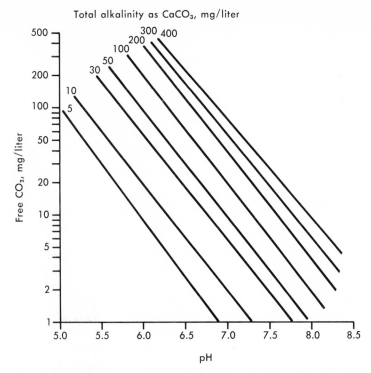

Total alkalinity as CaCO₃, mg/liter

Fig. 11-2. Free CO₂ in relation to pH and total alkalinity. (Based on data from E. W. Moore 1939.)

American limnologists because of their incorporation into *Standard Methods for the Examination of Water and Sewage* (Amer. Publ. Health Assoc. 1946). Later editions of this manual contain nomograms prepared by Dye (1952) that permit CO_2 approximations with corrections for the effects of temperature and other material dissolved in the water.

Rainwater and Thatcher (1960) presented some tables, based on the relationships between pH, alkalinity, and free CO_2 that permit rough approximations of free CO_2 within pH ranges 6.0 to 9.0. Their data were based on the following equation:

mg CO_2 per liter =
1.589 × 10⁶ [H⁺] × mg alkalinity per liter
(as HCO₃⁻)

The value of the term 1.589 × 10⁶ [H⁺] has been modified in Table 11-8 and shown for each 0.1 pH unit from 6.0 to

9.0; unlike Rainwater and Thatcher's presentation, these data apply to alkalinity expressed as $CaCO_3$, not as bicarbonate.

Using the factor for pH 7.2, which is 0.122 (Table 11-8), and multiplying by 185 mg/liter, results in 22.6 mg CO_2 per liter, in close agreement with the other rough approximations.

The effect of temperature. To correct for temperature's effect, the first dissociation constant (Table 11-2) can be used to write:

$$CO_2 + H_2CO_3 = \frac{[HCO_3^-]\ [H^+]}{K_1'}$$

The bicarbonate (HCO_3^-) is to be expressed in moles per liter. (Dividing the alkalinity by 0.8202 gives alkalinity expressed as mg HCO_3^- per liter. Shifting the decimal point three places to the left yields bicarbonate ions as g per liter, and dividing by 61.018, the ionic weight of HCO_3^-, gives the molar concentration of bicarbonate.)

Table 11-8. Factors useful in approximating free CO_2 in mg/liter at various pH levels*

pH	Factor	pH	Factor	pH	Factor
6.0	1.937	7.0	0.194	8.0	0.019
6.1	1.539	7.1	0.154	8.1	0.015
6.2	1.223	7.2	0.122	8.2	0.012
6.3	0.970	7.3	0.097	8.3	0.010
6.4	0.772	7.4	0.077	8.4	0.008
6.5	0.613	7.5	0.061	8.5	0.006
6.6	0.486	7.6	0.049	8.6	0.005
6.7	0.386	7.7	0.039	8.7	0.004
6.8	0.307	7.8	0.031	8.8	0.003
6.9	0.244	7.9	0.024	8.9	0.002

Modified from Rainwater and Thatcher (1960).
*Product of factors and total alkalinity, expressed as mg $CaCO_3$ per liter, yields free CO_2.

The H^+ in the formula, of course, refers to moles of hydrogen ions per liter. Because pH, the conventional way of expressing hydrogen ions, is the negative log of the hydrogen ion concentration, we know that a pH of 5.0, for example, means that the molar concentration of H^+ is 10^{-5}. Other values are shown in Table 11-4.

The K_1' values are those presented by Harned and Davis (1943). Their apparent first ionization constants of carbonic acid as affected by temperature are shown in Table 11-2.

The equation yields CO_2 in moles per liter. Moles of CO_2 per liter $\times$ 44.01 (grams per mole) equal grams of CO_2 per liter, easily converted to mg per liter, a conventional way of expressing the results. The values derived from this equation, assuming a water temperature of 20° C, pH 7.2, and total alkalinity 185 mg/liter (as $CaCO_3$) are: 225.6 mg or 0.2256 g HCO_3^- per liter, which is 0.00369 moles per liter; molar concentration of H^+ at pH 7.2, from Table 11-4, is 6.31×10^{-8}; and K' at 20° C is 4.15×10^{-7}. Thus, corrected for the effect of temperature, free CO_2 is:

$$\frac{(0.00369) \times (6.31 \times 10^{-8})}{4.15 \times 10^{-7}} = 0.00056 \text{ moles } CO_2 \text{ per liter}$$

Continuing, $0.00056 \times 44.01 = 0.0246$ g, or 24.6 mg of free CO_2 per liter.

Correcting for activity coefficient. A more nearly accurate method of computing free CO_2 would include correcting for the *activity coefficient, γ,* of HCO_3^-. This is a function of the ionic strength of the solution: the higher the ionic strength of the water, the more interference there is with the activity of bicarbonate and the lower is γ.

The ionic strength of the water is a mathematical quantity that is used to describe the intensity of the forces restricting the freedom of ions in solution, causing them to depart from ideal thermodynamic acitivity. Ionic strength is defined as μ, or one-half the sum of the products of each ion's molar concentration and the square of its charge. The more concentrated a solution, the higher its ionic strength, and the greater the restriction in activity of any given ion. Its relation to the activity of HCO_3^- is shown in Table 11-9 and Fig. 11-3. Different ions contribute different increments of ionic strength (Mg^{++} contributes about 1.6 times as much as an equal weight of Ca^{++}, for example). For this reason it is dangerous to generalize, but in most fresh waters multiplying the number that quantifies the total dissolved solids (mg/liter) by 2.50 to 2.55×10^{-5} approximates the ionic strength.

If, in the above example, the ionic strength had been 0.001 and the HCO_3^- molarity had been corrected *(a)* for a re-

Table 11-9. Approximate activity coefficient (γ) of HCO_3^- in relation to ionic strength of water (μ)

Ionic strength (μ)	Activity (γ) of HCO_3^-
0.0001	0.990
0.0005	0.975
0.0010	0.965
0.0050	0.930
0.0100	0.905
0.0500	0.815
0.1000	0.770

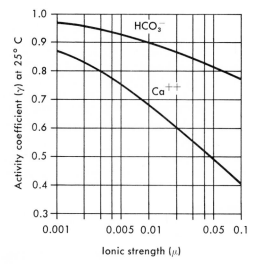

Fig. 11-3. Activity coefficients (γ) for HCO_3^- and Ca^{++} in relation to ionic strength (μ) of solutions.

duced activity of $\gamma = 0.965$, the ratio

$$\frac{[a\,HCO_3^-]\,[H^+]}{K_1}$$

would yield ultimately 23.8 mg free CO_2 per liter.

The titrations and calculations for free CO_2 are based on the assumption that the pH is essentially determined by carbonic acid relations. In waters containing strong mineral acids or organic humic acids, the relationships do not apply. Less obvious systems that introduce hydrogen ions could also invalidate calculations. The common utilization of ammonium ions by algae could set hydro-

gen ions free, along with ammonia as shown below:

$$NH_4^+ \rightleftharpoons NH_3 + H^+$$

In most instances, where the pH of natural water is no lower than 6.0, there is no reason to suspect a source of acidity other than the ionization of carbonic acid. By bubbling CO_2 into a water sample, one can reduce the pH to values well below 6.0, but waters below pH 5.0 probably owe their acidity to strong mineral acids.

CO_2, pH, AND PRIMARY PRODUCTION

In the final analysis, all carbon in living matter had its origin in CO_2 of the atmosphere, with photosynthesis as the basis of all plant and animal tissue. Primary productivity, the process wherein green organisms utilize a hydrogen donor to reduce CO_2, construct carbohydrate, and release O_2 as a by-product, has been the focus of attention for many ecologic workers over the past few decades. Indeed, Rodhe (1969) has recently emphasized the importance of the rate of carbon fixation in aquatic habitats to denote their relative place on a trophic scale. The rate at which autotrophic organisms, in the presence of radiant energy, produce organic compounds from inorganic CO_2 and water (the usual hydrogen donor in green-plant photosynthesis) can be estimated indirectly from the oxygen released or directly by assaying the rate at which CO_2 is absorbed.

In 1939 Rawson wrote that carbon dioxide "stands at the threshold of all production." Since then several methods for measuring the uptake of this gas in aquatic communities have been developed.

Assay by the radiocarbon method

Steemann Nielsen (1951), who measured carbon fixation in the oceans while serving on the Danish oceanographic vessel Galathea, introduced the radiocarbon method of measuring productivity. This method hinges on use of a radioactive isotope of carbon, ^{14}C, that has proved to be a relatively safe and effective tool because it is characterized by weak beta radiation and a half-life of about 5,700 years. Several types of Geiger-Müller detectors and liquid scintillators can be used in "counting" the radioactivity of ^{14}C.

The ^{14}C method for studying photosynthetic rates depends on taking samples, including the phytoplankton, from various depths and replacing them or incubating them under controlled light and temperature conditions in transparent bottles to which measured amounts of ^{14}C have been added. A small quantity of a dilute solution of $NaH^{14}CO_3$, amounting to 1 to 3 curies per 125 ml of sample, is injected into the bottles. This addition is followed by thorough shaking and about 4 hours of incubation. At the end of the chosen span of time the entire sample is filtered through a membrane to concentrate the algal cells that are then desiccated in preparation for future assay of radioactivity. The theory is that the assimilated ^{14}C in relation to the total ^{14}C available to the algae shows the ratio of the far more abundant nonradioactive ^{12}C assimilated to the total ^{12}C available. Thus

$$^{12}C \text{ assimilated} = \frac{^{14}C \text{ assimilated}}{^{14}C \text{ available}} \times {}^{12}C \text{ available}$$

The total carbon dioxide in the system must be calculated first and converted to carbon before the formula is useful and before the radioactive counts from the filtered residual plant cells become meaningful. A correction factor of about 6% compensates for the slower rate at which algae take up the radioactive isotope. Further correction is effected by subtracting appropriate background counts, and additional refinement is possible by use of a dark-bottle control so that any algal uptake of carbon in the dark is also taken into account. The details of the radiocarbon method of measuring photosynthetic rate are presented explicitly in a valuable manual edited by Vollenweider (1969).

The ^{14}C procedure, briefly described here, approximates net production because it measures the radioactive carbon remaining *within* the plant cells at the end of the photosynthetic incubation period. The ^{14}C that was taken in by the cells and respired during the same time is part of the filtrate, along with the added radioactive material not taken up by the algal cells that are present on the membrane filter. Even this explanation oversimplifies the picture because there may be a loss of organic material containing ^{14}C that had been assimilated during the incubation period in addition to the respired inorganic $^{14}CO_2$. Furthermore, the uptake of ^{14}C supplied as bicarbonate may result from reactions unrelated to photosynthesis. Scientific literature is rapidly accumulating on such phenomena.

The ^{14}C method of arriving at primary production is far more sensitive than the oxygen method. It is, therefore, superior in extremely oligotrophic waters because results may be obtained in 6 to 24 hours, while experiments based on oxygen changes might require several days. Where photosynthetic activity is great, the ^{14}C and oxygen methods are comparable, and satisfactory measurements can be made within a few hours using either technique.

Some biologic facts should be kept in mind while studying the uptake of CO_2. For example, certain aquatic plants cannot utilize half-bound CO_2 for photosynthesis. In this respect they resemble terrestrial plants, which depend on gaseous CO_2. Aquatic bryophytes are limited to regions where abundant free CO_2 prevails. For this reason one finds them near the orifices of springs or at impressive depths in clear lakes where light penetrates to strata moderately rich in dissolved CO_2, as in Thoreau's Walden Pond, Crater Lake (Oregon), and Lake

Tahoe. The spectacular freshwater red alga *Batrachospermum* is another classic example. It occurs in spring brooks and especially near subterranean sources, but farther downstream in reaches of the outflow where crucial amounts of CO_2 have been lost to the air, the alga is no longer present (Minckley and Tindall 1963). Recently, Hutchinson (1970b) analyzed the chemistry of habitats of some species of the aquatic angiosperm *Myriophyllum* and came to the conclusion that one species, *M. verticillatum,* is restricted to regions where free CO_2 abounds; the other species, possessing the typical versatility of higher aquatic plants, find bicarbonate an adequate source of carbon.

Estimate of primary production by pH changes

Relationships between hydrogen ion and CO_2 have led to a method of estimating primary productivity by studying pH changes in aquatic habitats. At dawn, for example, one might expect the lowest pH of the 24-hour period because the CO_2 of respiration and decomposition would have accumulated since the preceding dusk. With the morning sun, photosynthesis commences, and CO_2 is taken up by the green autotrophic organisms of the community. As CO_2 is absorbed, the pH rises at a rate that can be translated to the rate at which carbon is being fixed by plants. Theoretical equations and nomographs based on them afford a rough index of the effects of CO_2 changes on pH, if the bicarbonate content is also known. Verduin (1951) used the equilibrium equations of Moore (1939) to study CO_2 removal during photosynthesis and CO_2 evolution by respiration. This procedure had been attempted before by Osterhout and Haas (1918), who used colored indicators rather than a precise pH meter.

Other substances in lake water, however, could invalidate inferences based on theoretical carbonic acid equilibria, and these must be taken into consideration. Some controversy has existed concerning

a valid way to correct for these substances. Verduin (1956) was one of the first to realize that the theoretical curves, equations, and nomograms of Moore (1939), Dye (1944), and others do not apply to every body of water. To set the stage for studying photosynthetic rates of the phytoplankton in a given body of water, he studied effects of titrating with NaOH. Using filtered lake water, he would first lower the pH by introducing bubbles of CO_2. A differential titration with 0.01 N NaOH followed, the rise in pH being recorded after the addition of each increment, 0.1 or 0.5 ml of the standard base. The rationale is that each ml of 0.01 N NaOH will absorb 10 micromoles of H_2CO_3 and will thus convert it to $NaHCO_3$, or at higher pH levels will convert 10 micromoles of HCO_3^- to CO_3^{--}. These steps are close to what occurs when plants remove free and half-bound CO_2 from the environment as they fix inorganic carbon in synthesizing carbohydrate. The curve of pH plotted against the NaOH added may deviate markedly from the theoretical curve, yet it can be used to portray pH changes in terms of carbon dioxide withdrawn from the aqueous system as carbon is photosynthetically fixed. Similarly, 1 ml of 0.01 N HCl is equivalent to 10 micromoles of CO_2. Differential titration, starting from a higher pH and employing HCl, yields data from which a curve depicting the addition of respiratory CO_2 and its effect on pH can be plotted. It should be nearly identical to the NaOH curve, and either one can be used to find the effects of removing or adding known quantities of CO_2 to the water. With this technique, standard light-dark bottle experiments can be performed in the same manner as the oxygen method but based on the rate at which hydrogen ion concentrations change.

Beyers and Odum (1959) used a different approach, which they believed was superior to that of Verduin. Pure water, through which gaseous CO_2 has bubbled until saturated at a given temperature, is introduced in small increments to the water to be tested. The CO_2 content of each milliliter of titrant is computed on theoretical grounds, and the effect it has on lowering pH is noted and plotted to generate a curve from which the effects of CO_2 fluctuations in nature can be known in a given body of water. This method, Beyers and Odum argue, is preferable to titrating with a strong acid or base to construct a curve that mimics the effects of adding or removing CO_2.

ALKALINITY AS AN INDEX OF PRODUCTIVITY

While searching for essential factors contributing to productivity in some Minnesota fish-rearing ponds, Moyle (1949) came to the conclusion that total alkalinity up to a level of about 0.8 mEq/liter (48 mg HCO_3^- per liter) was directly related. Along with phosphorus, total alkalinity served as the best index to productivity. Phosphorus, present in tiny amounts, was a limiting factor in some ponds, but when phosphorus was adequate, the total alkalinity was the best index to productivity. Years before, Naumann (1932) had considered 0.88 mEq/liter to be at the upper limits for Swedish oligotrophic lakes.

In the Minnesota ponds and the Scandinavian lakes, alkalinity is due to carbonate and bicarbonate, and these are combined largely with calcium. Perhaps that alkaline earth metal is the key, for calcium plays important physiologic roles. Carbonate and bicarbonate, however, are forms of CO_2, the raw material of photosynthesis, and this must be taken into account. Total alkalinity was a measure of the reserves of CO_2 in Moyle's Minnesota ponds.

We recall that atmospheric gas would obey Henry's law with no complications in water poor in minerals, such as rain, snow melt, and pools in granitic and peaty regions. The dissolved CO_2 would find no $Ca(OH)_2$, for example, to join in forming the bicarbonate salt; therefore, alkalinity would approximate zero. Algal autotrophy would come to a halt when this limited supply of CO_2 was assimilated. A liter of pure water dissolves no more than 0.5 to 1.0 mg of CO_2, depending upon the temperature and pressure, and the photosynthesizing flora in that volume would soon deplete the gas.

In normal waters of higher alkalinity, the titrable base is bound or half-bound CO_2, and the latter is readily available as a source of carbon for most plants. Apparently in the Minnesota fish ponds, as in the Swedish lakes, total alkalinity above 40 to 44 mg/liter as $CaCO_3$ supplies adequate carbon dioxide; below this, the demands of photosynthesis outstrip the supply of inorganic carbon, and daily primary productivity rates may be thereby limited.

The greatest alkalinity titrations come from lake waters where carbonate is combined with sodium. In such situations the highest photosynthetic productivity in natural waters occurs. Talling and associates (1973) reported alkalinities of 51 to 67 mEq/liter in some Ethiopian soda lakes, with standing crops of the bluegreen *Spirulina* measured in terms of 10 to 20 g chlorophyll *a* per m^2. From this remarkable mass of photosynthetic pigment came gross primary production rates amounting from 13.4 to 17.8 g carbon fixed per m^2 each day, despite the shading brought about by the phytoplankton reducing the euphotic zone to 0.6 m. Probably no natural waters can match such intense primary productivity, although some features of sewage ponds are reminiscent of these Ethiopian sodium carbonate lakes.

HYPOLIMNETIC CO_2 INCREASE AS AN INDEX OF PRODUCTIVITY

Methods for estimating the amount of inorganic carbon fixed per unit of time have been discussed. These, as in the case of O_2 production, can be referred to activities within volumes of water or related to what occurs beneath the average m^2 or cm^2 of water surface.

An indirect index of productivity within a lake, a value that can be used to compare one lake with another, was proposed by Ohle (1952). This index more nearly approximates the total amount of organic material decaying in the hypolimion than does the rate at which oxygen disappears. It is the rate at which hypolimnetic CO_2 accumulates.

If all the CO_2 were produced by the aerobic decay of simple carbohydrates, this gas would appear in amounts equalling the disappearance of oxygen. The respiratory quotient (RQ = CO_2/O_2) would be 1.0. The materials that decay and are respired, however, include lipids and proteins, as well as other substances in various proportions. Because of these substances, the ratio of CO_2 produced to oxygen consumed is less than 1.0. An average figure of 0.85 seems to be a reasonable approximation of the RQ involving a mixture of organic compounds.

The moles of oxygen that disappear during a given time multiplied by 0.85 should approximate the CO_2 simultaneously produced by aerobic decay and respiration. Thus, if 1,000 molecules of oxygen were used by the bacteria, 850 molecules of CO_2 would be liberated.

An anomaly sometimes occurs when more CO_2 is produced per unit of time than would be expected on theoretical grounds. This extra CO_2 results from anaerobic decay and is not, therefore, related to oxygen consumption. Certain bacteria that attack the celluloses of plant origin and some lipolytic microbes can function under anaerobic conditions. The appearance of CO_2 generated by their actions must be reckoned in computing the organic matter that is decaying in the hypolimnion. In addition, it is assumed that only about one half of the organic matter broken down by anaerobic events

is reflected in this CO_2 production; the other half is represented by the marsh gas CH_4, methane. Methane is strictly a product of anaerobic decomposition of plant and animal remains. Bacteria of the genera *Methanobacterium, Methanosarcian,* and *Methanococcus,* especially, give rise to CH_4 at the expense of fatty acids, ketones, alcohols, and carbohydrates. These bacteria are immotile, obligatory anaerobes that gain energy from an oxidative decomposition of organic compounds accompanied by the reduction of CO_2 to CH_4. Thus, the excess of free CO_2 that comes from anaerobic decay contains about one half of the carbon involved in that decay; the other half is represented by methane. The carbon in the two gases indicates more nearly the total organic material that underwent decomposition within the hypolimnion than does the oxygen that disappeared.

Just as the rate of a hypolimnetic areal oxygen deficit can be calculated to derive an index of lake productivity, so the rate of CO_2 increase beneath unit area of hypolimnion can be computed for comparative purposes. The validity of both indices can be influenced adversely by organic allochthonous material, temperature, and morphologic relations.

CARBON AS A FACTOR LIMITING PRIMARY PRODUCTIVITY AND ITS ROLE IN EUTROPHICATION

The concept of the limiting factor is used so frequently by ecologists that they may have forgotten the contradictory and confusing nature of the term. A toxin, which limits or hinders growth, is *not* termed a limiting factor. A limiting factor is an essential nutrient or other requirement, but this is only a partial definition. A necessary element that is always in adequate supply is not considered to be a limiting factor. If demand becomes greater than supply of such a needed element, it becomes limiting and governs growth or production despite the presence of all other requisites in adequate amounts. When an essential factor is in such short supply that it is limiting, its addition to the environment will cause a spurt in growth.

Carbon dioxide is so common that it has rarely been considered a limiting factor in primary productivity, even though its quantities in bound or half-bound state (alkalinity) have long been theorized to account in part for the trophic nature of lakes. There is evidence, however, that in dense algal populations there may be brief effective limitations of growth due to carbon shortages. Sometimes, after phytoplankton populations have reached a plateau where addition of some nutrient has no effect, supplemental carbon dioxide stimulates a burst of new growth.

Numerous observations have shown photosynthesis proceeding in epilimnetic strata where no free CO_2 could be demonstrated. This absence might lead to the erroneous conclusion that carbon dioxide is not necessary for photosynthesis! Closer to fact, however, is that in such instances, the green autotrophs utilize CO_2 as rapidly as it is produced; some temporary limiting effect might be inferred from this.

Lately, nutrient supply has received much attention because of man's acceleration of eutrophication processes that bring about nuisance blooms of blue-green algae. These blooms seem to be the key to most of the events that diminish lake quality. For this reason, the search for the most important element inducing blooms has been the aim of much research, because with this information, effective purification of the sewage entering lakes can be achieved. The rationale, in simplistic terms, is that the culprit (element, ion, or compound), normally in limited supply, can be removed or intercepted before it reaches the lake.

A readily available source of recent information on these matters is the volume on eutrophication (National Academy of Sciences, Washington, 1969), and more to the point are the collected papers, *Nutrients and Eutrophication,* from the symposium of the American Society of Limnology and Oceanography (Likens 1972).

At this time it is not unusual to read of a spirited controversy over the key chemical in eutrophication—the chemical, usually in limited supply, that stimulates massive algal blooms when added to lakes. Despite disagreement, the rational view held by most limnologists is that: limiting factors vary; there is not always just one limiting factor; and the problem is complex. As the following examples attempt to show, however, limnologists recognize that carbon dioxide may be a factor in establishing qualitative changes in phytoplankton, and occasionally CO_2 may be in short supply locally, despite its abundance in the world. Evidence for the triggering of eutrophication by its abrupt and massive addition via human activity is questionable; the finger points with a greater degree of accuracy to phosphorus as the element that can initiate such an event.

Phosphorus is an abundant and necessary element in plant and animal tissues. Its stores in the universe, however, are not great. Because of its scarcity, there is little doubt that phosphorus is often the master factor. Its meager supply limits the growth of fresh-water phytoplankton. There are, however, other requisite elements that can hold back algal growth by their scarcity. Furthermore, at times blue-greens do not predominate in situations where the phosphorus supply is extraordinarily great.

Nitrogen, although an essential element, is usually less critical than phosphorus. It is more abundant than phosphorus, and, in addition to edaphic sources, the rich atmospheric store of nitrogen is made available in part by some nitrogen-fixing bacteria and a few blue-greens. Oceanographers have found, however, that in coastal marine waters the nitrogen supply is often more limiting to algal growth than phosphorus. Early biologic tests performed by Potash (1956) showed that the algae of two Cornell ponds found phosphorus in short supply at one season and nitrogen compounds critical at another time of year. In addition, many experiments have shown that plant growth is stimulated best by the addition of a *mixture* of nitrogen and phosphorus compounds. Also, there are times when a marked response comes about from the addition of one of many trace elements, such as cobalt and molybdenum, or even common ions and compounds, such as SiO_2 (Goldman 1972).

In Shriner's Pond, Georgia, Kerr and co-workers (1972) found evidence that the addition of the nutrients nitrogen and phosphorus caused a rapid increase in the heterotrophic bacteria before the larger, autotrophic algae responded. Increased bacterial decomposition of organic material made CO_2 available to the algae and stimulated their growth, an in-

direct effect of adding nitrogen and phosphorus.

Allen (1972) studied little Star Lake in Vermont, where total inorganic carbon supply was very low. A pronounced diel cycle in the waning and waxing of carbon took place. Free CO_2, present in the morning and largely a product of nocturnal respiration, was depleted by algal populations by noontime, and the bicarbonate level also fell. Allen theorized that, in poorly buffered Star Lake after the morning uptake of CO_2, a second source of carbon for bacteria and phytoplankton served to maintain a rather high production rate during the remainder of the daylight hours. This second supply of carbon was the release of organic compounds that algae and benthic macrophytes had produced during morning hours.

Schindler (1971c) reported the results of experiments on a Canadian lake, extremely impoverished in total CO_2 (about 1.1 mg/liter), that led him to conclude that CO_2 supply rarely limits phytoplank-

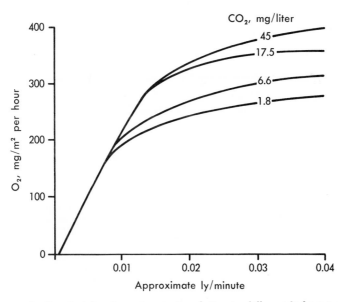

Fig. 11-4. Primary production in laboratory streams in relation to different light intensities and free CO_2. (Modified from McIntire and Phinney 1965.)

ton growth. The addition of nitrate and phosphate salts to the lake increased the standing crop of planktonic algae thirty-fold, measured in terms of chlorophyll a, despite the initial low stock of carbon. Invasion of gaseous CO_2 from the air supplied the carbon needed for the excess productivity. Thus, the gradient set up by the stimulated algal population removing CO_2 allowed more than 700 mg of CO_2 to move across an average square meter of epilimnion surface each day. Schindler's report leads to speculating that in sunny epilimnion waters, where no free CO_2 can be demonstrated, there may be more photosynthesis proceeding than that which utilizes HCO_3^- as a carbon source. Gaseous CO_2 may still be important, although it is used up as rapidly as it invades from the atmosphere or is produced by respiration.

On the other hand, Foster (1973), studying two ponds containing tertiary-treated waste water from the city of Phoenix, came to the conclusion that CO_2 supply sometimes limited photosynthetic rate. The water entering the ponds carried a mean of 14.1 mg phosphate per liter; the algae utilized it to such an extent that on the average only 2.2 mg soluble PO_4 per liter was present in pond-water samples. The latter is a tremendous amount when compared to that in natural lakes and is far above a limiting threshold. Nitrogen also was abundant, averaging 1.2 mg/liter throughout the year. Foster found that, despite the plentiful stores of nitrogen and phosphorus, the rate of production often decreased spectacularly by noon. In some instances inhibition by intense incoming solar radiation was involved, but at other times free CO_2 seemed to be the limiting factor. The possibility of atmospheric CO_2 keeping pace

with productivity in the Phoenix ponds seems remote; the amount of carbon fixed in 1 hour was usually greater than the entire daily input from the atmosphere over unit area of Schindler's Canadian lake. Several earlier studies on sewage lagoons had suggested, prior to Foster's work, that in such extremely fertile habitats carbon is often in short supply and is the limiting factor. This is probably rare in less polluted waters.

McIntire and Phinney (1965) studied experimental laboratory streams to which light and CO_2 input could be regulated. Some of their results (Fig. 11-4) show that primary productivity increased as a function of light intensity, up to about 0.005 ly/minute. After that, the carbon dioxide supply showed its effect: 45 mg CO_2 per liter resulted in 1.5 times the photosynthetic rate of 1.8 mg/liter. In this artificial system with phototrophic producers being periphytic algae, the limiting effect of CO_2 was obvious.

Wiegert and Fraleigh (1972) used a natural situation with little modification to demonstrate some effects of carbon limitation. In a stream charged with free CO_2 and issuing from a hot spring in Yellowstone National Park, they found diminished primary productivity of blue-green algae at a downstream station. Solar radiation and phosphorus supply were unchanged from the source to the station in the lower reaches, but much free CO_2 had been lost to the atmosphere by then. Its decrease was assumed to be responsible for the lessened productivity.

The relations of CO_2 and phosphorus to objectionable blue-green growth in lakes are complex. In the extremely polluted waters of sewage lagoons one would expect the bluegreens to be dominant. Often, however, this is not the case;

mixed populations of small green algae occur, winning the competition with the bluegreens in these rich environments. Recent papers by King (1970) and Shapiro (1973) give some clues to this. In the presence of nutrients, high pH, and very little free CO_2, the bluegreens, efficient at utilizing CO_2 from low concentrations, predominate. When pH is lower and carbon dioxide tensions are higher, certain chlorophytans thrive and exclude their prokaryote competitors. In poorly buffered sewage lagoons, photosynthetic activity raises the pH to a high level; free CO_2 is at a premium; and bluegreens flourish just as they do in alkaline soda lakes. In well-buffered lakes, the pH may not rise to the threshold favoring bluegreens.

Brock (1973) presents evidence that bluegreens do not exist in habitats where the pH is below 4.0 (and rarely occur where pH is below 5.0), although eukaryotic species representing many genera thrive. Perhaps, because the prokaryotes arose first in organic evolution, their inability to colonize acidic environments left habitats open where the higher algae could develop later without competition.

Shapiro (1973) showed in a series of experiments that natural populations of blue-green algae were replaced by chlorophytans when, after enrichment with phosphorus and nitrogen, carbon dioxide was added or the pH was brought down with acid, thereby making more CO_2 available from bicarbonate. The addition of phosphorus and nitrogen compounds alone stimulated the bluegreens to some extent, but the increments of CO_2 and hydrogen ions caused them to lose in competition with green algae.

12
The major ions in inland waters

SOURCES OF IONS

It is easy to speak of the chemical composition of the average fresh water of the world or of different continents, but at least two things must be kept in mind when this is one. First, there is no ideal toward which inland waters are evolving; and, second, the average depends upon what waters have been assayed and how the results have been weighted in the computations. Table 12-1 shows often-quoted data that were derived from Clarke (1924), Conway (1942), Livingstone (1963b), and Rodhe (1949). The first three authors were interested in the dissolved substances carried to the sea each year by the rivers of the world, and they estimated some data that describe the average chemical content of the world's rivers. The last author described a "standard" fresh water. The relative abundance of the major ions in lakes and rivers varies from continent to continent and region to region. Generally, students of aquatic habitats assume proportions much like those shown in Table 12-1.

Gorham's (1961) paper dealing with the major ions in inland waters is an excellent

Table 12-1. Some estimates of the chemical composition of the world's rivers and of a "standard" fresh water

Ions	Clarke (1924) Percent mEq	Conway (1942) Percent mEq	Rodhe (1949) Percent mEq	Livingstone (1963b) Percent mEq	Means Percent mEq	Livingstone mg/liter
Anions						
CO_3^{--}	73.9	73.5	74.3	67.9	72.4	58.4
SO_4^{--}	15.9	16.5	15.6	16.5	16.1	11.2
Cl^-	10.1	10.0	10.1	15.6	11.5	7.8
				Totals 100		77.4
Cations						
Ca^{++}	63.4	64.0	63.5	52.6	60.9	15.0
Mg^{++}	17.5	17.0	17.5	24.0	19.0	4.1
Na^+	15.7	16.0	15.6	19.2	16.6	6.3
K^+	3.4	3.0	3.4	4.1	3.5	2.3
				Totals 100		27.7

There are, in addition, about 13 mg SiO_2 per liter; 1.0 mg NO_3^- per liter; 0.7 mg Fe per liter. TDS (total dissolved solids), therefore, are about 120 mg/liter (Livingstone 1963b).

source of information. He underscores the factors operating to bring about and maintain the differences among fresh waters. Five obvious factors are: climate, geography, topography, biotic activity, and time. These are not completely independent; they interact to produce variety.

The atmosphere—which receives materials from the sea, the soil, volcanoes, industrial and domestic pollution, and organic detritus blown aloft—contributes ion-laden rain, snow, gases, and dry fallout.

The soil and weathered rocks are sources of edaphic ions. The mechanisms that release these ions are: solution, including the complexities of solubility differences; oxidation and reduction, increasing or decreasing weathering and availability; chelation or other forms of complexing; and the action of hydrogen ions, supplied especially by carbonic acid but not restricted to that source.

TOTAL DISSOLVED SOLIDS AND SPECIFIC CONDUCTANCE

Total dissolved solids (TDS) or filterable residue is measured with some inconvenience. A tedious gravimetric procedure is one means of evaluating it. The concept is simple. One filters a water sample (100 ml is convenient) and evaporates it at $105° \pm 2°$ C in a tared container until a constant weight is achieved. In samples from saline lakes, several weeks may pass before a constant weight is reached; for that reason a smaller aliquot, perhaps 25 ml, should be dried, although it could ultimately introduce a greater error. The TDS includes salts and organic residue. Further burning, this time at 500° to 550° C, would leave only the inorganic ash. The weight lost would be a measure of the organic content or may be best expressed simply as loss on ignition, with no mention of the specific organic designation. The residual ash represents the total salt content of the water. Usually, the filterable residue remaining after evaporation is all that is determined; this is TDS.

The mean of many analyses presented by Livingstone (1963b) suggests that the world's rivers contain an average of about 120 ppm of TDS. There is a remarkable range to be considered in lakes. For example, the ultraoligotrophic Waldo in Oregon has filterable residue from 1.0 to 5.5 ppm, averaging about 3.6 (Malueg and others 1972). Eutrophic Lake Itasca waters contain about 185 ppm. In the sea, the

TDS value is about 35,000 ppm; in the Great Salt Lake of Utah the value is roughly 220,000 ppm, representing an unusually concentrated solution.

Rawson (1951) showed something about the importance of TDS in lake productivity. He reviewed his earlier finding that the Slave River contributes about 54,000 metric tons of dissolved matter, along with 36,000 tons of silt, per summer day to Great Slave Lake. Another great lake 400 km northeast, Great Bear, has no comparable influent, nor does it have so vast a drainage area. Although the climatic environment of Great Bear is more severe, the two lakes are comparable in many ways and share a similar edaphic heritage. The TDS of the southern portion of Great Slave, where the Slave River enters, is about 160 ppm, compared with Great Bear's 98 ppm. Great Slave supports a limited commercial fishery; Great Bear, being more oligotrophic, cannot. The role of influent streams and the edaphic factor are illustrated further in Great Slave's eastern region, where streams draining the granitic pre-Cambrian Shield enter. Dissolved solids in that part of the lake range from 22 to 82 ppm.

Similarly, Hooper (1951) found that Demming Lake, receiving its water only via precipitation, seepage, and a very small drainage area, has a dissolved mineral content far less than that of nearby drainage lakes (those with influent streams). The result is a very low productivity in Demming, when compared with its neighbor lakes.

A short cut in analyzing for TDS is testing for specific conductance (conductivity). A conductivity meter tests the flow of electrons through the water. The electron flow in the presence of electrolytes is heightened; in distilled water, however, resistance to electron flow, ohms, would be very high. Conductance is the reciprocal of resistance. It is symbolized by reverse spelling of the name of the nineteenth-century German physicist, George

S. Ohm, who elucidated a law of electric currents dealing with electric resistance. Conductance is set down as mhos per cm, or more often as micromhos per cm at some specified temperature. If the resistance were expressed for a cube with sides of 1 cm, the reciprocal could be stated simply in terms of the unit micromho.

The flow between electrodes in a solution of electrolytes is increased with temperature elevation; a compensating factor of 0.25 for every degree rise has been suggested. It is easy to establish an empirical factor in a given body of water by fixing upon the conductance of a single sample at various temperatures in the laboratory. The data acquired allow one to express conductance at any specified temperature. A favorite standard is 25° C, but many limnologists select 18° C, perhaps because it represents a temperature more often met in the field.

Taking the TDS data from a given lake or lake district through the seasons and comparing them with concurrent conductivities reveals a relationship. A graphic plot of the affinities will show a line from which TDS can be inferred from conductance; this method precludes further filtering-evaporation procedures. The worker can establish a value for c in the formula $Kc = T$. In this, K is the conductivity in micromhos per cm at a specified temperature; c is a coefficient empirically determined to yield T, short for TDS. Thereafter, a simple assay of conductivity referred to a standard temperature could be used to find total dissolved solids.

Williams (1966) showed that in 62 samples from 41 Australian lakes, ranging from 0.05% to 20% salinity, there was excellent correlation between TDS and conductance. Caution should be observed, however, in transforming conductivity to TDS in samples above 5% salinity. In hypersaline waters there are inherent errors that are not significant in fresh water, because all ions do not contribute identical specific conductance. In the diversified ionic proportions of different hypersaline lakes, the sum of conductances could differ even when salinities are identical.

EXPRESSION OF CHEMICAL RESULTS

In most instances one can generalize that mg/per liter and parts per million by weight (ppm) are identical ways in which to express concentrations present in water. One ppm represents 1 mg of solute per kg of solution; 1,000 ppm is 1 part per 1,000, and 10,000 ppm is equivalent to 1%. Results reported in mg/per liter are weights per volume, and the conversion to ppm is permissible if it is assumed that 1 liter of water weighs 1 kg. In the realm of desert limnology, an important error may be introduced by not correcting for dissolved minerals that raise the density of water substantially above unity. When mineral concentrations are greater than, roughly, 7,000 ppm, the conversion to or from mg/per liter requires a correction factor to account for the change in solution density:

$$ppm = \frac{mg/liter}{specific\ gravity}$$

Other volume concentration units are molarity and normality; the former is especially useful. Milliunits are appropriate. They describe typical freshwater concentrations without using values less than unity, such as mg per liter, and are preferred over grams per liter. Gases dissolved in water are often expressed as millimoles per liter. the quotient of the weight in mg divided by molecular weight. Twelve mg CO_2 per liter, then, equals 12/44, or 0.272 mM/liter.

Recently there has been a move to express water analyses in terms of chemical equivalents of the ions. This can be justified because it takes into account the combining or equivalent weights of ions (ionic weight/ionic charge), thereby permitting exploration of the cation-anion balance to see if some gross error has

Table 12-2. Factors to convert milligrams of common ions per liter to milliequivalents per liter and vice versa

Ions	mEq/liter = mg/liter ×	mg/liter = mEq/liter ×
Ca^{++}	0.04990	20.04
Mg^{++}	0.08224	12.16
Na^+	0.04350	22.99
K^+	0.02558	39.10
HCO_3^-	0.01639	61.02
CO_3^{--}	0.03333	30.01
SO_4^{--}	0.02082	48.03
Cl^-	0.02820	35.46

marred the chemical analyses. The equivalent sum of the cations should equal the equivalents due to the major anions. Usually ions are treated as milliequivalents per liter. The mEq/per liter value is the mg of an ion per liter divided by its equivalent weight. Thus, the equivalent weight of Ca^{++} is 40.08/2 = 20.04. The equivalents in 1 g of calcium ion is 1/20.04 = 0.0499, or 49.9 mEq. Converting mg Ca^{++} per liter to mEq per liter is brought about by multiplying by the factor, 0.0499. The reciprocal, 1/0.0499 = 20.04, the equivalent weight of calcium, and serves as a factor to convert calcium from mEq per liter to mg per liter (Table 12-2).

Nonionized materials cannot be reported in mEq. This leaves total iron, silica, and oxygen, for example, to be expressed in terms of weight-based units, mg/per liter or ppm, or as molarity. The conglomeration called TDS must be reported as mg/per liter or ppm.

SALINITY VERSUS CHLORINITY

Titration for chloride ions has been standard oceanographic procedure for many years. The results for seawater having around 535 mEq/liter should be expressed as chlorinity rather than salinity. It is true that the assay of chlorinity in seawater gives a good index to whether salinity is low, as at a river's mouth, or relatively high, as in the Gulf of California, where evaporation is consequential. An empirical formula is:

$$\text{Salinity} = 0.03 + 1.805 \text{ (chlorinity)}$$

This is expressed in grams of solid material dissolved in 1 kg of seawater, being parts per 1,000. Oceanographers define salinity as total grams of solid material in 1 kg of seawater after organic matter has been completely oxidized, all carbonate has been converted to oxide, and bromine and iodine have been transformed to chloride equivalent. In inland waters the chloride titration is not necessarily directly proportional to salinity, because there are numerous combinations of the various ions, while seawater and coastal brackish waters, by contrast, are rather stable with respect to ratios of major constituents.

Among limnologists the term salinity refers to the sum of anions and cations; its meaning is less restricted than that of chlorinity and perhaps less restricted than the word salinity as used by oceanographers.

Salinity can be determined by measuring electrical conductivity. Among oceanographers this conversion is applicable universally; limnologists, by contrast, must make a few comparisons before they arrive at an empirical formula to convert conductivity to salinity in some body of water, and the formula may differ from lake to lake.

CARBONATE

In most dilute fresh water in humid regions of the world, the principal anion is carbonate (see table 12-1). Actually it occurs most often as bicarbonate ion, and usually with calcium. When it is compared by weight with other ions in solution, bicarbonate ion is customarily expressed as CO_3^{--} because evaporation of a known amount of calcium bicarbonate solution leaves only the carbonate of cal-

cium to be weighed. During evaporation, gaseous CO_2 and water are lost from bicarbonate ions, converting them to a lesser weight (factor 0.4917) of carbonate.

$$Ca(HCO_3)_2 \xrightarrow{\text{evaporation}} CaCO_3 + CO_2 \nearrow + H_2O \nearrow$$

In the previous chapter much has been discussed about carbonate. It is unnatural to separate carbonate from discussions of CO_2, pH, alkalinity and even calcium in "typical" fresh water. Alkalinity is usually a measure of carbonate, and, despite pitfalls, the alkalinity titration usually quantifies this ion, the principal anion in most fresh waters.

Compounds of carbonate

Indirectly, alkalinity measures cations that are balanced against carbonate and other ions that are important in buffering action. Because the typical inland water can be described as a calcium bicarbonate solution, most carbonate is combined with calcium. This may be found in nature as *calcite* or, less commonly, as *aragonite,* which has the same chemical formula ($CaCO_3$) but is crystallized differently (in an orthorhombic system rather than hexagonal) and is unstable at ordinary temperatures. Aragonite precipitates from thermal waters (usually above 30° C) and is contained especially in the shells of freshwater molluscs. *Magnesite,* the carbonate of magnesium ($MgCO_3$), and *dolomite,* a double carbonate of calcium and magnesium, $CaMg(CO_3)_2$, are relatively common. Carbonates of barium ($BaCO_3$) and strontium ($SrCO_3$) also occur.

In some arid regions precipitates of carbonate combined with sodium abound. They include *natron* ($Na_2CO_3 \cdot 10\ H_2O$) and *trona* ($Na_2CO_3 \cdot H_2O$). Ponds and lakes rich in Na_2CO_3 and the less soluble $NaHCO_3$ are called alkali lakes or soda lakes. They may be extremely high in total alkalinity but in no way can be termed "hard," as are the waters containing calcium and magnesium salts of carbonic acid. The potash ponds, occupying depressions among sand dunes in Nebraska, display noteworthy quantities of K_2CO_3. (The sodium borate mineral called borax, $Na_2B_4O_7 \cdot 10\ H_2O$, contributes to the alkalinity titrations of some desert lakes of the western United States but, of course, is not a measure of carbonate.)

In the stagnant, anoxic, summer hypolimnion waters of eutrophic lakes, ferrous bicarbonate—$Fe(HCO_3)_2$—is often plentiful, as is ammonium bicarbonate—NH_4HCO_3. The high alkalinities from hypolimnetic samples even in calcareous regions thus indirectly reflect more than the abundance of alkaline earth or alkali metals. Conversely, large resources of those metals would go undetected in alkalinity determinations if they were present as sulfates, chlorides, or nitrates.

The carbonate of calcium is abundant in the earth's soils, although feebly soluble. In pure water, devoid of free CO2, and at 1 atmosphere, only 6.2 mg $CaCO_3$ per liter would dissolve at 25° C (Schmalz 1972). Its solubility decreases as temperature rises and increases in the presence of free CO_2. Thus, at equilibrium with normal atmospheric CO_2 the solubility of $CaCO_3$ increases to nearly 10 times that found in the absence of CO_2.

It is customary to say that $CaCO_3$ is insoluble except in the presence of acid. With carbonic acid, it becomes $Ca(HCO_3)_2$. Because of this, it seems reasonable to express alkalinity titrations in terms of bicarbonate ions; but on the other hand, $Ca(HCO_3)_2$ is unstable to such an extent that when natural water is evaporated to determine its contained dissolved salts, the bicarbonate of calcium is destroyed and only carbonate remains.

Magnesium carbonate is about eight times more soluble than calcium carbonate, but of the common carbonates in nature the only truly soluble forms are Na_2CO_3, K_2CO_3, and $(NH_4)_2CO_3$. The first of these, abundant in some lakes of arid regions in Africa and North America, is more soluble than its bicarbonate form, $NaHCO_3$. The nature of these carbonates is taken up in greater detail in the treatment of cations in inland waters.

Biota of alkaline carbonate waters

In extremely saline environments, where relatively few organisms persist, there may be at least two distinct physiologic groups of salt-tolerant species. One of these inhabits chloride and sulfate waters. The second group includes the natriophils (L. *natrium,* sodium), typical of the alkali carbonate waters.

Certain blue-green algae, such as *Arthrospira* and *Spirulina,* flourish in soda lakes, where the zooplankton may contain the rotifers *Hexarthra fennica* and *H. jenkinae,* the American cladoceran *Moina hutchinsoni,* or its Old-World counterpart, *M. mongolica. Diaptomus sicilis,* a North American calanoid copepod, may belong to such a group; it is significant that its synonymy includes an older name, *D. natriophilus. Diaptomus spinosus,* from saline ponds in the deserts of Asia and Africa could be an ecologic equivalent of *D. sicilis.* Corixid bugs, especially those species referable to the genus *Corisella,* commonly appear in sodium carbonate pools. The larvae of one mosquito frequent alkali waters to such an extent that the species is appropriately named *Aëdes natronius* (Gr., *aedes,* unpleasant).

There is danger in generalizing about these two salt-tolerant groups of organisms. Species that occur in all saline situations often blur distinctions. Moreover, different populations, assigned to the same species by taxonomists, may each represent distinct physiologic races or separate species. For example, *Artemia salina,* the brine shrimp, is extremely rare in soda lakes, and laboratory experiments have shown that some stocks cannot survive in high concentrations of carbonate. There are, however, a few populations of *Artemia* thriving in "lethal" waters, quite unaware of the danger and of the fact that they have never been classified with the natriophils (Cole and Brown 1967).

Diaptomus sicilis occurs in the Laurentian Great Lakes of North America as well as in alkali pools far to the west. At least three possible reasons account for this: that calanoid copepod is remarkably euryhaline; there are distinct physiologic races within the species; or there may be a complex of unrecognized, morphologically similar species lumped as one by taxonomists.

SULFATE
Some forms of sulfur

The sulfate ion, SO^{4--}, is usually second to carbonate as the principle anion in fresh waters, although chloride occasionally surpasses it.* Sulfate is discussed elsewhere in relation to sources of hydrogen ions and with respect to the cations with which it combines to form minerals. The minerals are treated in greater detail when cations are discussed.

Free, or elemental, sulfur is inactive at ordinary temperatures. Therefore, beds of "brimstone" (sulfur in an uncombined state) are not rare. The beds are especially abundant in regions of recent volcanic activity. This element can combine with both metals and nonmetals to form many compounds. Beginning biology students are acquainted with free sulfur as an important constituent of protoplasm; it is in protein and specifically within those amino acids having sulfhydryl (SH) bonding; examples are cystine, cysteine, and methionine.

When sulfur is combined with hydrogen or oxygen, a series of reduced and oxidized forms of sulfur can be demon-

strated. The most reduced state is sulfide (S^{--}), and the most important sulfides to limnology are the gas, hydrogen sulfide (H_2S), and ferrous sulfide, (FeS). At the other end of the series, spanning SO_2 and SO_3, is the most oxidized form of sulfate (SO_4^{--}). Sulfate combined with hydrogen as sulfuric acid and with the alkaline earth and alkali metals is the most abundant form of sulfur in lakes and streams.

The evaluation of sulfate ions has become relatively easy in recent years with the development of spectrophotometry. Older gravimetric procedures have been replaced by measuring the turbidity of acidified samples treated with barium chloride. In most samples of fresh water, the only ion that precipitates with barium is sulfate; it forms crystals that approach uniformity in size and remain in suspension. In waters stained by humic acids and naturally turbid from particulate materials, the direct turbimetric method has drawbacks, and more sophisticated treatment is necessary to remove interfering substances.

Sources of sulfate

Atmospheric sources of sulfate have increased since the onset of man's industrial activities, although volcanic emissions have added sulfur compounds to the air for eons. Man now contributes about 10 times more SO_2 than the annual contribution from volcanoes about (10^7 tons) to the atmospheric load of this gas (Stoiber and Jepsen 1973). Coal combustion is especially notorious, and copper smelting and paper manufacturing also produce gases and runoff rich in sulfur compounds. Indeed, sometimes an important index of industrial water pollution is the presence of unusually high sulfate and sulfite levels.

Sulfate in seawater amounts to more than 2.6 g/liter. Intense evaporation in some arid-region lakes has concentrated sulfates well above that value, but fresh waters are usually 100 times or more

---

*Silica often outranks sulfate, but very little is ionized in most fresh waters, so it is not considered here.

below the marine level for the ion. Interestingly, those lakes nearest the sea, as is true for bodies of waters nearest industrial sites, show greater sulfate concentrations than comparable lakes farther inland. Sea spray swept aloft can be carried inland, but evaporation probably occurs before much reaches the lake surface. Even so, salt particles serve as nuclei for cloud condensation, and ultimately raindrops carry the sea salts to inland lakes.

The edaphic contribution is of paramount importance, however, and high-sulfate waters usually reflect the presence of old marine sediments. Calcium sulfate, especially, is to be considred in such instances, although sodium sulfate deposits can be of oceanic origin also. In addition, oxidation of sedimentary pyrites supplies sulfate.

The two most important stores of sedimentary sulfur are the minerals of $CaSO_4$ and the metal sulfides, especially pyrite, FeS_2. Those of the first type are essentially evaporites; the sulfides are largely a result of microbial action. There are four stable isotopes of sulfur, the commonest two being ^{32}S (95.1%) and ^{34}S (4.2%); ^{33}S and ^{36}S comprise less than 1% of the total. The proportions of ^{34}S and ^{32}S vary remarkably—up to 11%. This is probably because some sulfur bacteria fractionate the isotopes, selecting the lighter of the pair,^{32}S, to enrich sedimentary sulfides, while the residual material is relatively enriched in ^{34}S. Evaporites tend to have a higher $^{34}S/^{32}S$ ratio than precipitated sulfides.

Moyle's (1945 and 1956) studies of the regional limnology of Minnesota clearly show an interrelationship among geologic history, soils, forest types, water quality, and lacustrine flora and fauna. There are three distinct soil types in the state. In the southwestern part, Cretaceous seas left their mark, and it is in this region that sulfates are abundant in lake waters, ranging up to 500 mg/liter. The aquatic seed plants and the fish in this edaphic area differ markedly from those in the other two regions. *Ruppia,* a submerged pondweed called widgeon grass, flourishes in that region, recalling the stands of this species in the brackish waters of estuaries on the Atlantic coast, and in some saline pools in western North America. It would be sought in vain, however, in other parts of Minnesota where terrestrial sulfate stores are meager.

Sulfate lakes

Certain bodies of water can be termed sulfate lakes. In most fresh waters bicarbonate is the principal ion, but some unusually dilute Nova Scotian lakes studied by Gorham (1957a) contain chloride and sulfate concentrations superior to bicarbonate. In some cases sulfate surpassed chloride by weight, although not on an equivalent basis. The proximity of the lakes to the sea coast results in a major contribution of sulfate from the rain. There is no satisfactory terminology to describe these lakes. Some resemble extremely dilute seawater except for the high SO_4^{--} level when compared with chloride.

In geologic tracts where rocks contain abundant $CaSO_4$, the water chemistry reflects this. Calcium sulfate is, however, the least soluble of the common sulfate compounds, and with concentration it precipitates from solution. For this reason it is uncommon in markedly arid regions, except when issuing from underground sources before evaporation has had its effect.

Sodium sulfate lakes are not rare in desert regions. Algerian *chotts,* which we would term playa lakes, contain this compound, as do the many saline bodies of water in southern and central Saskatchewan and the Bottomless Lakes of New Mexico. Magnesium sulfate waters are less common; Hot Lake, Washington, is one of these.

Sulfur cycles and productivity

Mann (1958) described an annual cycle in some British ponds that brings to mind the acid titration employed in alkalinity evaluation. The bicarbonate level was low in the spring, rising during the summer to an autumnal high that dwindled during the winter months. Sulfate concentrations, however, were high in spring, diminishing during the summer to a low point in fall. The decrease in sulfate was attributed to its reduction to sulfide, some of which entered the anaerobic sediment as the insoluble ferrous sulfide. Oxidation of sulfide to sulfate during winter circulation resulted in the formation of some H_2SO_4, which converted calcium bicarbonate to calcium sulfate. The action was in effect as though a partial titration, lowering the alkalinity, had been performed.

Similarly, indicator drops added to a measured water sample from streams receiving effluent from coal-mining operations often show the final end-point color before the titration has begun. There is no alkalinity; the "titration" has already been brought to completion by sulfuric acid from the mines, and the end point of pH 4.4 has been attained and passed.

Sulfate's effect on aquatic organisms is rarely obvious, although there are times when it may be a limiting factor in growth. The amino acids containing the sulfhydryl groups are normal in plant protein, and for this reason sulfur deficiency can inhibit algal populations, perhaps by hindering chlorophyll synthesis in some way. Probably in most instances, however, the sulfates are more than adequate for freshwater productivity.

About 20 years ago some experiments were done at Cornell University by Potash (1956), who demonstrated sulfate's adequacy by the commonly used technique of nutrient enrichment. He studied the response of algae to nutrients added to filtered pond water collected through-out the seasons. A green alga was added to the fresh water samples and allowed to grow for 10 to 12 days under constant conditions of light and temperature. In most instances the alga flourished as well in the unfertilized control water as in the media containing nutrients. On occasion nitrate or phosphate deficiencies were noted in the pond water, as evidenced by the greater growth in media containing these ions, but the alga always grew in the unmodified control water as well as it did in the water to which sulfate had been added. The inference is that adequate sulfate prevailed throughout the year in the rather ordinary ponds that Potash studied.

There has been a controversy in limnology concerning the effect of low levels of sulfate in Lake Victoria and some other large African Lakes. It began when Beauchamp (1953) suggested that the impoverished phytoplankton crop in Lake Victoria is a function of a low level of sulfate, which he said ranged from 0.8 to 1.8 mg/liter. Lake Victoria and some other large African lakes, marked by poor SO_4^{--} content, lie in regions where sedimentary rocks containing this ion are rare; yet the lakes contain less sulfate than their inflowing rivers. Sulfate is lowered to critical levels by at least two processes: protein synthesis locks up much of it, its recycling being dependent on decomposition rates that seem to be slow; and much of the decaying protein releases H_2S, which forms less soluble metallic sulfides that precipitate and become buried in the sediments. Shallow African Lake George, by contrast, is extremely rich in phytoplankton despite its poor sulfate content, 0.5 mg/liter or less. A high decomposition rate in Lake George, Beauchamp reasoned, accelerates all biologic cycles, and sulfate is regenerated so rapidly that it does not appear to be limiting.

Beauchamp's explanation is interesting

because it outlines a mechanism whereby low concentrations of sulfate could limit phytoplankton crops, but later workers pointed out flaws in his argument. Fish (1956) showed that sulfate added to cultures of phytoplankton (not from Lake Victoria) in the lake's water, indeed, seemed to stimulate growth. Later, Evans (1961) reported that the predominant alga in the lake, a species of *Melosira,* showed no response to $MgSO_4$ added to cultures of lake water in which it grew, although phosphate additions stimulated its growth. The green alga *Ankistrodesmus falcatus* from Victoria responded to enrichment with nitrate, sulfate, and phosphate, in that order, yet blue-green algae from the lake showed no effects from the addition of any of the three nutrients. It seemed from these experiments that sulfate could be limiting at certain times but not always. Then Livingstone (1963b) questioned Beauchamp's quantitative data concerning the amounts of SO_4^{--}, pointing out records of at least 3.4 mg/liter of sulfate from Lake Victoria's water. In 1965, Talling showed that on an areal basis the photosynthetic rate in Lake Victoria was high, amounting to a mean of approximately 7 g O_2 per m^2 per day, although the phytoplankton, measured as chlorophyll *a,* was a "decidedly modest concentration." Later, Talling and Talling (1965) agreed that the sulfate level is unusually low in Lake Victoria and some other East African lakes but suggested that the analyses of Beauchamp and others had underestimated the amount. The analytical method whereby barium salts of sulfate are precipitated yields too low results when sulfate is scarce; a method using ion-exchange columns (Mackereth 1963) reveals two or three times more sulfate.

The Lake Victoria example of sulfate being so rare that it limits growth may be a myth, but there are probably some lakes where sulfate is critical. For example, algae from some lakes in New Zealand's South Island respond to sulfate enrichment of these lake waters (Goldman 1972).

Hydrogen sulfide

Hypolimnia of stratified eutrophic lakes or the monimolimnia of meromictic lakes may contain appreciable quantities of the very soluble gas H_2S. This is especially marked in lakes of regions high in edaphic sulfate, for that ion is the main source of hydrogen sulfide, and its concentration is directly related to H_2S. Meromictic Big Soda Lake, Nevada, and Soap Lake, Washington, are two outstanding North American examples, with recorded monimolimnetic amounts of 786 and 6,000 mg/liter, respectively. Some fjord lakes also contain great amounts. Hydrogen sulfide is poisonous to aerobic organisms because it inactivates the enzyme cytochrome oxidase.

Water samples from the anaerobic deep strata of eutrophic lakes may give off the characteristic rotten-egg odor of H_2S, while little or no sulfate can be detected because it has been chemically reduced. By contrast, epilimnetic waters may be practically odorless and contain significant quantities of sulfate. Moreover, collections from the stagnant hypolimnion may resemble dilute India-ink suspensions because of the presence of ferrous sulfide. The meromictic Black Sea owes its name to the dark waters lying 150 to 200 m below its surface. At least 99% of the H_2S in the Black Sea comes from the reduction of sulfates; the remainder is from decomposition of dead organic matter.

The reduction of sulfate to sulfide probably does not occur until the redox potential falls, under anoxic conditions, below 0.1 volt, perhaps in the neighborhood of 0.06 (see Table 13-1). It is largely a phenomenon of anaerobic sediments, although occasionally it is reflected in overlying water or atmosphere. This leads into the field of bacteriology, following some generalizations about mineral cycles.

Sulfur bacteria

Most students know the textbook example of carbon dioxide being reduced to an organic photosynthate with the evolution of oxygen as a by-product. This reduction process, in which solar radiation is the energy source and water serves as a hydrogen donor, is brought about by organisms—conspicuous green organisms. The reverse oxidation process, likewise, is well known. A similar cycle whereby sulfates are reduced or hydrogenated to form SH groups of amino acids and, thereby, innumerable proteins, lacks the visibility of photosynthesis. It is carried on in dim subsurface strata, anaerobic marsh sediments, the organic oozes in the bottoms of lakes and seas, and even in blackened anoxic layers a few centimeters below the surface of sandy beaches not far from the water's edge.* Organisms are involved in this reduction and in the reverse oxidation reaction, just as in the synthesis and destruction of carbohydrate, but most are not conspicuous. They are minute bacteria living in most instances in anaerobic habitats where they, lacking the enzyme catalase, escape the lethal effects of free oxygen. There is a varied array of metabolic processes by which bacteria deal with sulfur and its compounds. It is unnatural to treat them as divorced from oxygen and iron cycles, but this shall be done.

The sulfur bacteria fit three main groupings on the basis of their morphology. There are pigmented species and large colorless forms, both filamentous

*Green plants obtain their sulfur by similar metabolic processes, but this assimilatory sulfate reduction is neither so rapid nor on such a large scale as the bacterial reduction.

and nonfilamentous. A physiologic or metabolic classification is preferable.

Sulfate reducers

When oxygen is absent and redox potentials fall below 0.1 volt, the sulfate-reducing microbes begin their work. Indeed, in many such extreme habitats no other organisms can survive. *Desulfovibrio desulfuricans* is one of these; its metabolism is much like that of the denitrifying bacteria. This sulfate reducer, while transforming sulfate to sulfur and hydrogen sulfide, precipitates $CaCO_3$ at the same time. A simple way of showing this is in the two following reactions:

$$CaSO_4 + 2C \rightarrow CaS + 2CO_2$$
$$CaS + CO_2 + H_2O \rightarrow CaCO_3 + H_2S$$

The carbon shown in the first reaction is from decaying organic matter. Notice that organic compounds have been oxidized, not an unusual source of energy except that sulfate rather than oxygen was used as the oxidant.

Another group of reducing bacteria are those that attack organic material, liberating H_2S from the proteins with no accompanying calcite precipitation. These anaerobic bacteria of putrefaction degrade the sulfur-containing components of protein—cysteine, cystine, and methionine.

The value of anaerobic oozes and peats, where microbes can survive and carry on reducing activities, was elegantly expressed by Deevey (1970) in his essay "In Defense of Mud." In these dark anoxic sediments, SH groups necessary for protein building are regenerated, and H_2S is formed to escape to the atmosphere. There it is oxidized and joins other oxides of sulfur, originating naturally from volcanoes and from combustion of coal and petroleum mixtures. Recently the amount of sulfur derived from fossil fuels has overtaken the natural output to the air (Stoiber and Jepsen 1973). In light of mounting industrial pollution that adds more than 100 million tons of H_2SO_4 to the atmosphere each year, any ecosystem where sulfuric acid can be chemically reduced is worth saving. Those who make a plea for the preservation of wetlands have many good points to present.

Sulfur oxidizers

The sulfur-oxidizing microbes comprise another category of anaerobic bacteria and have attracted attention because some are pigmented and photosynthetic. Those classified as the Chlorobacteriaceae are green species that oxidize the inorganic reductant, H_2S, to free sulfur. They contain a pigment, bacteriochlorophyll, that occupies a place in the absorption spectrum where the familiar green pigment of algae and higher plants is largely ineffective. This bacterial pigment is effective in wavelengths from 700 to 800 nm, within the infrared range.

In anaerobic habitats where the level of H_2S attains 50 mg/liter or more, the non-motile, green sulfur bacteria may be found. They are phototrophic, utlizing H_2S as a hydrogen donor for the reduction of CO_2 and regenerating elemental sulfur as a by-product of carbohydrate synthesis. The following simple reaction illustrates how similar their action is to the photosynthesis of higher green plants, which utilize water as a hydrogen donor to reduce CO_2 and release free oxygen as a by-product.

$$CO_2 + 2H_2S \xrightarrow{\text{light}} (CH_2O) + H_2O + 2S$$
$$\text{cell material}$$

Chlorobium is one of these autotrophic bacteria. Physiologically adapted to dim light, it often forms dense plates below the aerobic algae, including the bluegreens. One can generalize that these plates occur ordinarily near the contact layer between oxidative and reductive zones where light is less than 10% of that falling on the lake surface. *C. limicola* forms green layers because its carotenoids are yellowish and do not mask the green pigments. At least two other species have brown carotenoids that hide their green color. They form red-brown layers in subsurface anoxic strata where hydrogen sulfide prevails and where the absorption peak of their carotenoids (about 460 nm) is most efficient at absorbing wavelengths that reach those depths.

The purple sulfur bacteria Thiorhodaceae, such as the motile *Chromatium* and *Thiopedia,* usually contain pigments with absorptive properties from 780 to 900 nm and another peak in the green-yellow wavelengths, about 500 to 600 nm. They form pink or red layers in meromictic lakes, saline lagoons, and in the sands of tropical beaches.

With the chlorophyll *a* of the bluegreen and higher plants considered, almost all wavelengths from 400 to 900 nm can serve as energy sources for pigmented prokaryotes and eukaryotic autotrophs.

Most purple sulfur bacteria, even more than their green relatives, are adapted for dim light and are inhibited photosynthetically by intense bright light. Furthermore, they function optimally at high temperatures. When purple bacteria form elemental sulfur, they keep the granules within their cells, rather than on the outside as the green bacteria do. The sulfur can be oxidized later to sulfuric acid with a gain of energy in a reaction such as the following:

$$2H_2O + 2S + 3O_2 \rightarrow 2H_2SO_4$$

In most ponds where this reaction is effected, there is little or no increase in hydrogen ion concentration because bases are abundant enough to neutralize the acid.

The Leucothiobacteria include colorless species that also oxidize inorganic substances, such as H_2S, but are aerobic. They are autotrophic organisms but chemotrophic rather than phototrophic. The energy they require is attained by direct oxidation of H_2S and of elemental sulfur:

$$2H_2S + O_2 \rightarrow 2H_2O + 2S$$
$$2S + 2H_2O + 2O_2 \rightarrow 2H_2SO_4$$

Thiobacillus is one of these acid formers, and, as one might guess, it can thrive in extremely acid environments.

The gliding, filamentous *Beggiatoa* is a spectacular member of the colorless sulfur bacteria. Its cells, stuffed with sulfur granules, are arranged in trichomes, reminiscent of the blue-green alga *Oscillatoria.* Assemblages of *Beggiatoa* are found at the boundary of aerobic and anaerobic waters, appearing like wispy cotton strands. The two requirements, a low oxygen tension and H_2S, make it necessary for these colorless autotrophs to occupy this subsurface, watery interface.

CHLORIDE

Authors who have summarized preexisting data to present the chemical composition of the rivers and freshwater lakes of the world have shown that chloride usually ranks third among the anions (see Table 12-1). Much depends, however, on the "World" sampled. An Australian limnologist finds the fresh water in his "down under" world to be quite different from "standard" waters. Although chloride's position may vary in some Australian states, it directly follows total ionic content; in Victoria and Tasmania it usually takes precedence.

Chlorine is an element of the halogen group that includes also fluorine, iodine, and bromine. It is by far the most abundant of these, surpassing other members of this group in the sea, in inland saline and polluted waters, as well as in the purest of lakes or streams. Molecular chlorine (Cl_2) is a heavy, yellow, lethal gas; but in most natural waters, it is dissociated as chloride ions, which combine with all common cations. Where chloride is most abundant, as in the sea and in concentrated desert pools, most of it combines with sodium. The Dead Sea, representing an extreme in concentration of salts, is an exception; it contains some 35.6×10^9 tons of $MgCl_2$ and $NaCl$. (The former compound is 64% of the total.)

Chloride is the major halide stored in most freshwater algal cells, although the marine kelps and other brown algae are noteworthy for their uptake and concentration of iodide. In the American southwestern deserts an exotic tree has established itself along the few surviving water courses, competing with the native cottonwoods. This is the salt-cedar, *Tamarix.* It takes up sodium chloride and exudes it from its leaves to the ground below.

Sources of chloride

Edaphic. The igneous rocks are a minor source of chloride, although the feldspathoid called *sodalite,* $Na_8(AlSiO_4)_6Cl_2$, contains it. The issue from hot springs, if *magmatic* water, is by definition derived from molten igneous rock and is often rich in chloride. In many instances, however, the heated water passes through other sources, dissolving salt on its way. Some of this water may be *juvenile,* never having circulated before and defined as newly released water that had been combined in minerals or dissolved in igneous rocks. It is not known how much juvenile chloride enters natural surface waters, but it is estimated to surpass a million metric tons each year.

Evaporites are very important as edaphic chloride sources. Extensive beds of salt derived from evaporation of former bodies of water are common. Chloride coming from such stores can be called *cyclic;* it has been in the oceans at least once before and will return.

Atmospheric. The atmosphere carries windblown chloride inland from the seacoasts. Many measurements of this meteoric chloride have been made in rainwater. This falls under the classification of cyclic Cl^-, as does the salt in ancient sedimentary beds. Cyclic, meteoric chloride is pronounced in some surface waters of Australia, many of which resemble dilute seawater in chemical constitution (Williams 1964).

Windblown chloride may be immediately derived from the sea or may have been part of seawater no more than a few months before. The classic example of the latter is the Rann of Cutch in India. During the annual dry season a great arm of the sea dries, and the new evaporite is transported inland via the winds.

Volcanic gases contribute chloride to the air, accounting for some acidity. Hydrochloric acid is one result of volcanic emission.

Pollution. In certain lake districts contamination from domestic sewage can be monitored by chloride assays. Comparatively high concentrations imply that the lake in question may be receiving pollutants. This is because human and animal excretions contain, on the average, 5 g Cl^- per liter. Thus, subsurface seepage from septic tanks introduces soluble chloride salts to nearby lakes. High chloride levels are found in some desert pools in the American Southwest and in the so-called *r'dirs* of the North African desert; they are water holes, polluted by the wastes of domestic and wild animals.

A further source of chloride in northern United States and adjacent Canada is the winter salting of city streets and highways (Judd 1970). Runoff and melt water, or storm sewers entering directly, introduce dense solutions of NaCl and $CaCl_2$. In some instances deep density layers formed in winter prohibit complete mixing at the spring overturn, and incipient meromixis results. Thus, the bottom fauna is subjected to more than increased salinity; longer anaerobic periods are induced and only the hardiest species survive.

CALCIUM
Sources of calcium

The predominant compound in most interior waters, $CaCO_3$, is also one of the least soluble. Only a small amount can be dissolved in pure water,* but in the presence of carbonic acid it is represented

---

*According to Schmalz (1972, Fig. 3) pure water in contact with the atmosphere containing a partial pressure of CO_2 equaling 0.035% could dissolve about 66 mg of $CaCO_3$ per liter, or roughly 26 mg of calcium.

abundantly as the soluble $Ca(HCO_3)_2$. Thus, a treatment of the silvery white alkaline earth metal named calcium can hardly be divorced from earlier discussions of the forms of carbonic acid or CO_2, pH, and the anion CO_3^{--}.

The earth's crust contains an ample store of calcium as a constituent of certain silicates. For example, *anorthite* ($CaAl_2Si_2O_8$) is a common member of the feldspar group of silicates; feldspars are the most abundant of all minerals and make up about 60% of the earth's coating. In addition, over extended periods of time, immense deposits of sedimentary $CaCO_3$ have been laid down by living things. They are now a substantial part of the calcium reserve, awaiting the attack of meteoric water, rich in CO_2, that will change them to the soluble bicarbonate that may enter aquatic environments.

When lake basins lie in noncalcareous soils and their total ionic content is low, the edaphic contribution of calcium may be surpassed by that of atmospheric origin. Thus, Gorham (1958b) pointed out that several small lakes in the English Lake District having no more than 0.2 mEq total salts per liter receive more than half their calcium and in excess of 80% of their magnesium from rain. Weathering of soil supplies the remainder of these alkaline earth metals to the water as bicarbonate. Dust blown aloft from the ground is the main source of calcium found in snow and rain.

Calcium carbonate is the main constituent of chalk, limestone, and the metamorphosed rock called marble. Its common form is the mineral *calcite*, the most stable type at normal temperatures and low pressures. Formed under a much narrower range of conditions than calcite is *aragonite*, a less prevalent type of $CaCO_3$. Its crystalline structure differs from calcite, and it has a higher specific gravity. Because it changes spontaneously into calcite, there are no ancient aragonites. It is represented in deposits from hot springs and geysers, cave stalactites, and in some molluscan shells.

Solubility of calcite

Much interest has been aroused in the solubility of $CaCO_3$, and a great deal of research has been directed toward this phenomenon. Certain engineers, especially, have focused attention on this because precipitation of $CaCO_3$ in steam boilers and in water pipes has economic import. The limnologist finds this subject engaging because of the biogenic precipitation of calcite by photosynthesizing organisms and by the events occurring at or slightly downstream from spring orifices, where conspicuous concretionary deposits often form. In each instance the loss of CO_2 caused a shift to the left of the reaction $CaCO_3 \rightleftharpoons Ca(HCO_3)_2$. Equilibrium that had been achieved beneath the ground was disturbed when the water emerged, and the pressure on it was suddenly released, permitting the escape of CO_2. Phototrophic species trigger the reaction to the left by absorbing CO_2.

At least four names apply to calcareous deposits in lakes, streams, and at spring sources. The differences among them are not always clear-cut, and the use of terms may differ from one geographic region to another. Common usage denotes *marl* as the calcareous material in the littoral region of hard-water lakes. It is usually fine grained, although marl pebbles are common, and the coarse contributions from gastropod and clam shells may be important. Individuals of some species of *Chara* are encrusted with flaky limestone that they have precipitated from the water. This accounts for the application of the name stonewort to this large alga. Through the years the accumulation of dead *Chara* contributes to littoral shelves of marl. The photosynthesis of microscopic algae and bluegreens, both planktonic and benthic, also precipitates $CaCO_3$, but in diminutive particles. In the deeps of the lake, most of the $CaCO_3$ may

be dissolved to $Ca(HCO_3)_2$ by the acid nature of hypolimnion water. Because of this, marl deposits are especially prominent features of lake margins where pH values are high and photosynthesis is intense during sunny hours. Thus, biogenesis is important in marl formation, and the results are typically a soft, calcareous-clay sediment of whitish hue.

Sinter is a general term applied to chemical sediments deposited by mineral springs. Some are siliceous, building terraces of *geyserite*, such as those around the hot springs of Yellowstone National Park familiar to North Americans. Calcareous sinter is called *tufa* or *travertine*. It is deposited from solution in ground waters, as evidenced by stalactites and stalagmites in limestone caves, or from surface waters not long after they have emerged from subterranean sources. When travertine is extremely porous, it is termed calcareous tufa or *spring deposit*. The name tufa has also been applied to some siliceous sinters.

Despite the importance of organisms in the formation of marl, many lakes with rich organic sediments and suspended detritus are not active marl formers. This may be attributed in part to the CO_2, derived from decay, that dissolves marl and hinders its deposition. The littoral marl benches or shelves reported to modify the morphology of some Michigan lakes were not conspicuous in these waters until they had attained alkalinities of at least 105 mg/liter (Hooper 1956). Although this concentration is above the level of calcium carbonate saturation, it is not extraordinarily so when compared with some lakes having higher rates of organic sedimentation.

The symmetrical curves that represent the dissociation of carbonic acid as a function of pH (see Fig. 11-1) imply that almost no carbonate is below a pH of 8.3. This suggests that $CaCO_3$ would not be precipitated below the point on the scale where phenolphthalein becomes colorless. However, other factors, such as temperature, may be involved. The solubility of $CaCO_3$ decreases as the temperature rises from 0° to 35° C. Moreover, the nature of ions other than calcium and carbonate and their concentrations affects the ionic strength of the solution and thus the activity of individual ions. The activities of bicarbonate and calcium are especially important for any consideration of the solubility of calcium carbonate. The total concentration of ions present may not reveal the amounts available to participate in chemical reactions because activity coefficients can be well below unity. Dissolved materials may thus remain in solution, though simple theory would predict their precipitation. In laboratory experiments sodium and potassium salts increase the solubility of $CaCO_3$ even in the absence of free CO_2.

Investigation of subterranean water at spring orifices reveals that $CaCO_3$ can be saturated and precipitate at pH levels well below the 8.3 that is shown on curves in the idealized graphs portraying solutions containing only species of carbonic acid (see Fig. 11-1). The point at which saturation occurs, therefore, may lie at a greater hydrogen ion concentration than one would expect for the conversion of bicarbonate to carbonate and its subsequent precipitation.

There are certain ways of expressing the degree of saturation in a body of water. Usually Langelier (1936) is credited with defining the pH of saturation (pH_s). In a given solution where the alkalinity and calcium contents are known, Langelier's pH_s is at a point where the water is neither undersaturated nor oversaturated with $CaCO_3$. An *index of saturation* can be set down if we know the difference between observed pH (pH_{obs}) and the computed pH_s. If the index is positive, equilibrium would be attained by precipitation of $CaCO_3$. If, however, $pH_{obs} - pH_s$ is negative, the water is undersaturated and equilibrium could be established by the

dissolution of $CaCO_3$ or, as the engineers might say, by "corrosion, rather than scaling." Thus, water with a calculated pH_s of 7.8 and with an observed pH of 8.0 has a positive index, 0.2, and is obviously oversaturated; if the observed pH were 7.6, the index would be −0.2, indicating undersaturation. When water emerges from a subterranean origin, it is probably in equilibrium at pH_s, but the nature of the solution changes as free CO_2 escapes to the air. The index of saturation becomes positive, to be followed soon by precipitation of $CaCO_3$ to reestablish a condition of equilibrium in which $pH_{obs} - pH_s = 0$. Indices of saturation based on the differences between pH_{obs} and pH_s are not precisely quantitative. They do disclose, however, the directional tendency that must be followed to achieve equilibrium.

An entirely different way of expressing the degree of saturation would be the ratio of the thermodynamic ionic product of Ca^{++} and CO_3^{--} (corrected for activity, a) to its solubility-product constant, K_{sp}.

$$\frac{aCa^{++} \times aCO_3^{--}}{K_{sp}} = \text{relative saturation}$$

A quotient of 1.0 represents equilibrium; a figure less than 1.0 denotes undersaturation; and of course a figure greater than 1.0 reveals supersaturation.

A direct test to see whether water is saturated or not was explained by Weyl (1961), who devised a "carbonate saturometer." It is essentially a slightly modified electric pH meter. The water sample is tested immediately after collecting; crystalline calcite is sprinkled in, contacting the glass electrode, and any pH change is noted. If the water is saturated with calcium carbonate, no pH change occurs; pH_{obs} is pH_s, and its degree of saturation is 1.0. Had the water been oversaturated, the added calcite would have provided nuclei for carbonate precipitation with release of hydrogen ions and falling pH. Had calcite been added to water undersaturated with $CaCO_3$, hydrogen ions would have been consumed with a rise in pH. To understand these events we recall the second dissociation of carbonic acid:

$$HCO_3^- \rightarrow CO_3^{--} + H^+$$

The changes occur within 2 minutes after the addition of calcite crystals when a pH plateau is reached and held for about a minute before drifting on. The magnitude of the pH deflection to the plateau affords an index of the degree of undersaturation or oversaturation.

$CaCO_3$ is precipitated from water when various factors interact to bring it above the equilibrium level. The generalization is valid, but some others are not always applicable. A long-prevailing idea has been that marl accumulates only at the margins of lakes where littoral calcareous shelves are perceptible and that in the acid milieu of the hypolimnion, carbonate is dissolved and, therefore, cannot be deposited in profundal ooze. Megard (1968) disclosed that the calcareous nature of some profundal sediments need not be explained only by erosion of relatively large particles from marginal banks. He demonstrated that in some Minnesota lakes, precipitation of profundal calcium carbonate comes about during the spring overturn, even though the calcium concentration in hypolimnion waters had been higher during winter stagnation before the profundal marl was laid down and even though the pH was circumneutral rather than above 8.3. The vernal phytoplankton pulse, with its accompanying photosynthetic activity, removed enough CO_2 to disturb the equilibrium and effectuate the deposition of marl. Even more remarkable is the deposition of a layer of calcite each summer in the deeps of meromictic Fayetteville Green Lake; the sedimentation occurs beneath monimolimnetic water of pH 7.1 (Brunskill 1969).

Other minerals of calcium

After the silicate and carbonate minerals of calcium, the sulfates rank as its most abundant store. These are *gypsum* ($CaSO_4 \cdot 2H_2O$) and *anhydrite* ($CaSO_4$). Sedimentary beds containing these two minerals are usually of marine origin, but evaporation of saline inland lakes accounts for some terrestrial deposits. Anhydrite precipitates from seawater at high temperatures (about 42° C and above) and at lower temperatures in the presence of high salinity. At ordinary temperatures gypsum is usually the first mineral thrown down as seawater evaporates; later, when salinities have mounted, anhydrite is deposited. The latter can be converted to gypsum by the action of rainwater, and, conversely, some anhydrite sediments are thought to have been formed by dehydration of earlier gypsum beds.

The solubility of the sulfate of calcium in pure water surpasses that of the carbonate by about 120 times. In normal seawater 970 mg of calcium sulfate per liter would represent approximate saturation, but this is because of the reduced activities in water of high ionic strength. Inland waters in contact with gypsum rocks become rich in $CaSO_4$ because of this increased solubility, which does not require carbonic acid. $CaSO_4$ must be considered a compound of fresh water, however, because it precipitates when concentrated in saline basins. It is about 50 times less soluble than sodium sulfate, the least soluble of the abundant compounds in the typical concentrated waters of arid regions.

To many Americans, the impressive dunes of White Sands National Monument in New Mexico typify gypsum. That state boasts an immense gypsum resource, and because of the solubility of the mineral some interesting lakes occur there. These are solution basins, circular in outline or in the design of a figure 8 where adjacent lakes have coalesced. They are protected now within the Bottomless Lakes State Park. Some have steep-walled sides, recalling the Yucatan cenotes far to the southeast. The cenotes, however, mostly occupy limestone pits, and carbonic acid contributed much to their genesis, although many have waters high in $CaSO_4$ (Covich and Stuiver 1974).

The most soluble of the common compounds of calcium is its chloride. It is 30,000 times more soluble than $CaCO_3$. There are only a few good examples of calcium chloride waters. For example, the issue from Clifton Hot Springs in Arizona contains much $CaCl_2$, although surpassed by NaCl. Also, there are 5.4×10^9 tons of $CaCl_2$ in the Dead Sea, though outstripped 6.5 times by NaCl and $MgCl_2$. A remarkable body of water, Don Juan Pond in Antarctica, definitely belongs to the $CaCl_2$ category. It is a shallow pool upon the bottom of which lie needle-like crystals. These are $CaCl_2 \cdot 6H_2O$ and were new to science when first described and named *Antarcticite* in 1965 by Torii and Ossaka.

Marl lakes

In the glaciated region of the Laurentian Great Lakes there are many bodies of water called marl lakes. These are oligotrophic, distinguished by low primary productivity as well as scanty littoral periphyton and macrophyte growth. Certain diatoms flourish in marl lakes, but low levels of phosphorus, iron, calcium, and potassium serve to restrict other algae and the bluegreens. Their waters, overlying beds of calcareous sediments, are high in pH and saturated concentrations of bivalent cations. In extreme cases, the monovalent ions Na^+ and K^+ are surpassed tenfold by Ca^{++} and Mg^{++}. Nutrient elements such as iron, manganese, and especially phosphorus are scarce because they are bound in an unavailable form or have precipitated out with the cations. The coprecipitation of phosphorus and calcium is especially important in taking phosphate out of circulation. Phosphate adsorbs on calcium carbonate, and they precipitate concurrently when the pH rises to values near 9.0. Otsuki and Wetzel (1972) suggested that in the microenvironments at algal-cell and macrophyte surfaces, where CO_2 removal leads to high pH, the resultant coprecipitation of carbonate and phosphate limits plant growth, serving as a density-dependent control on populations in marl lakes. Moreover, based on their study of marl lakes, those authors suggested that the speed of eutrophication, following the introduction of phosphate, would be greater in low-calcium, soft-water lakes than in hard-water lakes.

Biota of calcium waters

Among plants and animals there are some that can be classed as *calciphiles* (calcium lovers) and others as *calciphobes* (haters of calcium). In certain taxonomic groups all species favor calcium, and species numbers decrease as that element becomes scarcer. Probably most of the Pelecypoda and Gastropoda typify the strict calciphiles.

Other groups have both calciphilic and calciphobic species. The planktonic rotifer genus *Brachionus* includes common species, such as *B. calyciflorous, B. angularis,* and *B. quadridentata,* said to be typical calciphiles, while other members of the genus are less restricted to high-calcium waters. Some other rotifers are restricted to acidic waters low in calcium and high in hydrogen ion concentration.

The family Desmidaceae of the green algae is composed of hundreds of species, including many planktonic forms. The finest desmid floras flourish in acidic waters low in calcium, although certain species can be found in high-calcium habitats. (Moss 1972b) brought up the complexities of these relationships. In laboratory experiments even desmid species deemed to be oligotrophic do not behave like calciphobes.

An excellent example from the Cladocera is *Holopedium gibberum.* Typical of the calciphobes, it swims in the plankton of waters low in both calcium and pH. An upper limit of 20 mg Ca^{++} per liter has long stood in the literature, but Martin A. Hegyi, a student of the genus, has come upon specimens in water containing at least 36 mg/liter.

Although extremely important to higher plants, calcium is no more than a micronutrient to most algae; therefore, relatively small quantities suffice for large phytoplankton populations at times. Calcium abundance, however, can mirror the presence of rarer and essential plant nutrients and a favorable edaphic heritage. Many calcareous soils are well endowed with phosphorus, for example. Dilute, soft water, poor in calcium, may also be low in most other ions. Lack of calcium may play a role in promoting dystrophy, decreasing the rate at which organic substances are precipitated, mineralized, and recycled for use by the primary producers.

MAGNESIUM
Sources and types of magnesium compounds

Magnesium is usually the second most abundant cation in inland waters of temperate regions. Its source is both silicate and nonsilicate minerals of the earth's crust. Also, near the seacoast some waters have high magnesium concentrations believed to represent aerial transport of ocean spray. A liter of seawater contains about 1.3 g of magnesium.

Magnesium is represented in most of the main subclasses of the silicates that compose continental rocks. One such as *forsterite* (Mg_2SiO_4) can be altered by carbonic acid to form silica, carbonate, and *serpentine* ($H_4Mg_3Si_2O_9$) in the following manner:

$$5Mg_2SiO_4 + 4H_2O + 4CO_2 \rightarrow$$
$$2H_4Mg_3Si_2O_9 + 4MgCO_3 + SiO_2$$

The process of serpentinization produces $MgCO_3$ from several types of silicate minerals. This carbonate can be dissolved by carbonic acid in the same manner as limestone, although it is about 8 times more soluble than calcite in pure water.

The magnesium carbonate *magnesite* and a double carbonate called *dolomite,* $CaMg(CO_3)_2$, are less common than calcite. Dolomite represents an intermediate step in the replacement of calcite by magnesium-bearing solutions and contains varying proportions of the two elements calcium and magnesium. It resists weathering more than calcite, and yet it releases magnesium and calcium in approximately equal ratios despite the greater solubility of most magnesium compounds.

Epsomite, known as Epsom salt, is a soft, whitish sulfate of magnesium ($MgSO_4 \cdot 7H_2O$). It is 150 times more soluble than gypsum. It occurs in some mineral spring deposits, in salt sediments of lacustrine and marine origins, and in caves. The best example of a body of water typified by magnesium sulfate is the small, saline Hot Lake in the arid eastern region of Washington. Hot Lake occupies a shallow depression that came about through mining operations for epsomite. Magnesium sulfate's source is directly edaphic in this lake, rather than climatic, with relative enrichment brought about by evaporation and the precipitation of less soluble compounds.

Magnesium chloride ($MgCl_2$), like calcium chloride, is extremely soluble. Its occurrence in marked concentrations is typical of the most condensed of desert waters. A well-known example is the Dead Sea.

When seawater is evaporated and most of its salts have crystallized and precipitated, the "mother liquor" that remains is called *bittern.* It contains bromides and magnesium salts. For this reason, the Dead Sea and other bodies of saline water, such as Lake Macdonnell in the Australian desert, can be termed specifically bittern lakes, signifying their high magnesium content.

Because most magnesium compounds surpass similar calcium compounds in their ability to remain in solution, they precipitate at different rates. Calcium usually surpasses magnesium in fresh waters because there is a preponderance of calcium over magnesium in sedimentary rocks. With evaporation and resultant concentration, however, magnesium may assume more importance. Ca/Mg ratios in waters change first when the solubility product of $CaCO_3$ is reached and calcite precipitates. For this reason the relative amounts of these two metals in lacustrine sediments or encrusted on aquatic plants usually favor calcium when compared with the adjacent lake water. A further example of the different solubilities of calcium and magnesium is provided by events in the stream leaving Montezuma Well. At the start the Ca/Mg ratio approximates 2.8 on the basis of mEq per liter, but only 1 mile (1.6 km) downstream it has dropped to 2.2. This is because the loss of free CO_2 and the rise in pH, accompanied by some evaporation, cause precipitation of $CaCO_3$, while magnesium compounds remain in solution. Similarly, the Ca/Mg ratio is 3.2 in the world's rivers running to the sea (see Table 12-1), but it is reduced to about 0.2 in seawater.

Magnesium lies at the heart of the chlorophyll molecule and seems to occupy, therefore, a chosen position in community events. Too much of this light metal, however, is detrimental. For example, magnesium salts, especially $MgSO_4$, produce anesthesia in both invertebrates and vertebrates. In laboratory experiments it has been demonstrated that pure 0.25 M solutions of $MgCl_2$ are slightly toxic to the hardy *Artemia*. Rawson and Moore (1944) found it puzzling that Last Mountain and Echo Lake were more productive than about 60 other somewhat saline lakes they had studied within the same district of Saskatchewan.

Point after point were compared with no fundamental differences coming to light. The only thing that set these two lakes apart was the low magnesium content of their waters when compared with the others.

The concept of hardness

Cations that form insoluble compounds with soap contribute to what is termed "hardness" in discussions of water quality. An early method of quantifying hardness was based on titration with a standard soap. The soap-consuming power of the water is lowered by heavy metals and the alkaline earth metals. The two most common bivalent cations of lake water, calcium and magnesium, usually account for most of the hardness. At present, total hardness is determined by titration with ethylenediaminetetraacetic acid (EDTA) or some other compound that chelates magnesium and calcium. This is more nearly accurate than the older soap method, and furthermore, the titrant is usually standardized to give results equivalent to mg $CaCO_3$ per liter just as in alkalinity titrations.

The carbonate hardness of water includes the portion equivalent to the bicarbonate and carbonate in the water. This has been called "temporary" hardness, for it is the part that disappears as water is softened by boiling and by the ensuing precipitation of calcium carbonate and magnesium carbonate. Noncarbonate or "permanent" hardness is the difference between total and carbonate hardness. Permanent hardness is caused by the sulfates and chlorides of bivalent cations. The SO_4^{--} and Cl^- ions are not revealed by alkalinity titrations, and their compounds of calcium and magnesium do not precipitate with boiling. Silica, on the other hand, may be part of alkalinity titrations, but does not contribute to hardness, even though it forms incrustations as does $CaCO_3$.

The generality that magnesium compounds are more soluble than molecules containing calcium does not apply in the case of the hydroxide, and this phenomenon is utilized in hardness assays. First, total hardness, mostly the sum of calcium and magnesium, is established. A dye that shows a reddish hue in the presence of the two cations is added to the sample, and an EDTA titration follows until the two cations are completely chelated and the dye no longer indicates them. A second titration is performed on a sample that is treated with strong KOH, which precipitates $Mg(OH)_2$. The result yields calcium hardness, expressed as $CaCO_3$. The difference between total and calcium hardness is magnesium hardness.*

In the upper midwest of the United States and adjacent Canada, where North American limnology got its start, hardness is often equated erroneously with alkalinity. Calcium is the common cation associated with carbonate, and the acid titrations of alkalinity assays indirectly measure most of that earth metal. The monovalent alkaline metals such as sodium and potassium are used in the manufacture of soap, and obviously they do not contribute to hardness. For this reason, some concentrated waters of arid zones are extremely soft, although their alkalinities are high. All students of limnology should experience titrating and recording some 6,000 mg total alkalinity per liter in a sample that has practically no hardness. (The sample might be from a soda lake such as Moses Lake, Washington.) This exercise would serve as a reminder that the words "hardness" and "softness" cannot be used interchangeably with alkalinity.

---

*Interference from iron and manganese are bothersome in many instances, and this description of methodology may be too idealized. Despite this, if the titrations are referred to mg $CaCO_3$ per liter, the calcium hardness × 0.4 approximates the calcium ion content in mg per liter, and the magnesium hardness multiplied by the factor 0.243 gives the value of Mg^{++}.

SODIUM
Sources of and types of sodium compounds

The monovalent cation sodium is the sixth most abundant element in the lithosphere. This alkali metal is very reactive and soluble; when leached from the rocks, its compounds tend to remain in solution. For this reason it is at least the third most abundant metal in lakes and streams, and in many instances it ranks first. Among igneous rocks, the feldspars, aluminosilicates of alkali, and alkaline earth metals are the most abundant of all minerals. A representative of them, *albite,* is sodium feldspar ($NaAlSi_3O_8$). When attacked by carbonic acid, albite decomposes to yield sodium carbonate, silica, and clay minerals.

When alkali-rich sources of igneous rocks are deficient in silica, they form a type collectively called the feldspathoids. Such rocks react with silica to form feldspars, a reaction that explains their absence in the presence of quartz. At least three common types of feldspathoids contain sodium; of these, *nepheline* ($NaAlSiO_4$) is predominant.

The commonest water-soluble mineral is *halite* or simply NaCl. A liter of seawater contains about 28 g of this and, therefore, roughly 11 g of sodium. Extensive beds of rock salt, representing evaporation of seawater, are impure halite, a common source of sodium chloride in some springs. Ocean spray, swept up by the wind and carried inland, is believed to account for the high NaCl values in Australian (Williams 1964) and Nova Scotian lakes (Gorham 1957a). Solid salt, swept up from dried inland basins such as the flat floor of ancient Lake Bonneville, can be carried by winds to add to aquatic sodium concentrations far inland.

Mirabilite ($Na_2SO_4 \cdot 10H_2O$), a more euphonious name for Glauber's salt,* may serve as a source of sodium in some

---

Glauberite is more of a mixture—$Na_2Ca(SO_4)_2$.

instances. Other sources are natron and trona, deposits of hydrated Na_2CO_3. Such sedimentary accumulations of sodium compounds should be thought of, however, as having been derived from concentrated waters (by evaporation or freezing-out effects) rather than as being a common source of sodium for waters of humid regions. Man's agricultural activities involving irrigation in arid zones may put old salts back into solution. The Salton Sea in southern California is a good example of this. Its salts were deposited by pluvial Lake Cahuilla.

Types of sodium lakes and the blue-green algae

In arid tracts where closed basins hold concentrated waters, there are at least three types of sodium lakes: *salterns,* the commonest and much like concentrated seawater with a preponderance of NaCl; lakes typified by much Na_2SO_4, such as saline lakes of Saskatchewan (Rawson and Moore 1944); and the soda lakes characterized by $NaHCO_3$ and Na_2CO_3, termed alkali waters because of their high pH.

Some of the most luxuriant populations of blue-green algae in the world are known from the soda lakes, and there has been suspicion that sodium might be a minor factor in eutrophication. Provasoli (1969) brought together the experimental evidence founded on laboratory experiments that showed Na^+ and K^+ are necessary for bluegreen growth and that increasing concentrations of alkali metals leads to flourishing populations of these prokaryotes. As the enrichment of lakes via cultural eutrophication has proceeded, concomitant increases in sodium and potassium have scarcely been noted, despite the fact that these monovalent cations are essential nutrients for the bluegreens. The general abundance of these alkali metals, however, precludes their being limiting factors, except in rare situations. Furthermore, the pH and car-

bonate ion of soda lakes may be keys to the tremendous blooms of bluegreens they support. The concentrated salterns and sodium sulfate waters do not exhibit such large populations; this suggests that sodium per se does not always favor enormous blooms.

POTASSIUM
Sources and types of potassium compounds

Potassium, a close relative of sodium, is usually the fourth ranking cation in lake water. In some closed basins it surpasses sodium, but this is unusual. It is weathered from various feldspars that have the formula $KAlSi_3O_8$ but does not remain in solution so well as sodium. It recombines easily with other products of weathering, being removed from solution by adsorption on clay, for example. Moreover, the feldspathoids containing potassium do not weather so readily as the sodium minerals. *Leucite* ($KAlSi_2O_6$), one of the potassium types, exists as crystals within volcanic rocks. Potassium also tends to form micas, which are insoluble and unavailable to aquatic ecosystems. All these phenomena interact to make potassium rarer in water than sodium is but superior to it in the world's rocks.

In plants, both extracellular and intracellular fluids contain an excess of K^+ over Na^+. In animals, extracellular Na^+ often surpasses potassium. There is some evidence that highly concentrated waters with a pronounced potassium content are lethal to many aquatic animals, the Na/K ratio being less than 10. Some habitats are known, however, where K^+ surpasses Na^+, and euryhaline species, such as *Artemia,* thrive.

Plants take up potassium to such an extent that an important commercial source of the element has been wood ash. Conversely, 90% of the world's production of potassium salts is used for fertilizers, to be taken up by domestic plants.

Potash is the name for K_2CO_3, but the word has been used indiscriminately to refer to KOH and potassium oxide. The so-called potash lakes, occupying depressions among the sand dunes in Nebraska, serve as sources of potassium-rich brines. In many of these waters potassium surpasses the other common alkali metal, sodium. The source of the potash is puzzling but is thought to be the ashes of ancient fires.

Sylvite (KCl) is less common than halite, but occurs with it and gypsum in old marine deposits.

Older analyses of water constituents lumped Na^+ and K^+ because of the difficulty in the chemical procedures for measuring them. With the development of flame photometry in the early 1940's, the detection and evaluation of these two metals became simple. Sodium burns with a yellow flame, and potassium produces violet. With proper filters, these two elements can be detected, and the intensity of the color can be related to a standard curve prepared by flaming known amounts. Today. ratios between sodium and potassium are common in accounts of water quality. (Calcium, magnesium, and lithium are often assayed by flame photometry because filters have been developed to screen out all but the characteristic wavelength of each individual flame.) The use of atomic absorption spectrophotometry is now replacing the older flame technique.

Some confusion exists in terminology where certain potassium and sodium compounds are concerned, but this has little limnologic importance. *Caliche* ($NaNO_3$) is also known as "Chile saltpeter." In the southwestern United States and in Mexico, caliche is the name applied to the hard-pan layer beneath the surface of desert soils where leached minerals have precipitated; much of this evaporate is $CaCO_3$. Also, KNO_3 is termed saltpeter but without the Chilean prefix.

WATER CHEMISTRY AND DESERT LIMNOLOGY

Desert limnology is best defined in terms of hydrography and limited to regions where no runoff reaches the sea—the climes where closed basins occur. Closed basins exist only where evaporation substantially exceeds precipitation; this broadens the concept of desert to include a spectrum from semiarid steppes or prairies to the most parched and bleak landscapes of the world. A terrestrial ecologist would, perhaps, balk at this and define only about 21×10^6 km^2 of the world's surface as desert. The climatic region of closed basins is more expansive. Desert waters are similar by being high in electrolytes and are quite different from the dilute waters of humid regions. The chemical limnology of arid lands deals especially with evaporation, concentration, precipitation of compounds, and the relative changes in ionic abundance. A review of desert limnology was published by Cole in 1968, and Bayly and Williams (1973) have summarized further details.

Fig. 12-1 reveals comparative solubilities of the common compounds of fresh water. The common compounds of dilute inland waters, the carbonates of the alkaline earth metals, are the first to achieve their solubility products and precipitate. Thus, $CaCO_3$ and $MgCO_3$ are diminished, with marked relative increases in SO_4^{--}

	Cl^-	$SO_4^=$	$CO_3^=$
Ca^{++}	1.5	0.006	0.00005
Mg^{++}	1.3	0.9	0.0004
Na^+	1.0	0.3	0.4

Fig. 12-1. Relative solubilities of some compounds in distilled water at 10°C; NaCl = 1.0. The three compounds bounded by dotted line are typical of dilute water only.

and Cl^-. The next precipitate is $CaSO_4$, leading to the comparative importance of Na^+ and Mg^{++} among the cations. The subsequent precipitation of sodium sulfate leads to a water dominated by compounds of chloride. If all carbonate were not deposited with calcium and magnesium, that linked to sodium would precipitate next, followed by $MgSO_4$, and the sodium chloride saltern would result. These salterns, such as the Great Salt Lake of Utah, are fairly common in North America. The theoretical stages when only the extremely soluble chlorides of the alkaline earths persist are rare, but bitterns such as the Dead Sea do exist. Calcium chloride is the most soluble compound shown in Fig. 12-1, but one would not expect its occurrence at the termination of an evaporation sequence, because calcium precipitates earlier with carbonate and sulfate. The shallow Antarctic Don Juan Pond is a notable exception; it is a $CaCl_2$ pool. Some subterranean waters emerging in Arizona springs

are remarkably endowed with $CaCl_2$. If they led to closed basins where intense evaporation could proceed, they might form calcium chloride lakes, but none are known.

Desert lakes are often less concentrated than would be theorized on the basis of their age and the annual input of salt. Moreover, many are quite different in ionic composition from the salterns and bitterns toward which evaporating waters seem to be proceeding. Such discrepancies are explained by two facts: first, there are seven or eight mechanisms by which salt can be lost from closed basins; and second, the dilute waters that initiate the evaporative series may be strikingly different ionic mixtures. Details of these methods were reviewed by Hutchinson (1957) and Cole (1968).

There are two main groupings of arid-land waters and a terminology to describe them. Sodium chloride waters, similar to concentrated ocean brine or brackish waters (best described as dilute

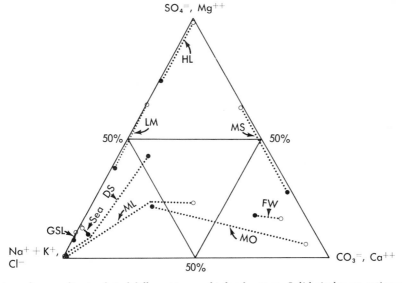

Fig. 12-2. Triangular coordinate plot of different types of inland waters. Solid circles are cations; open circles are anions. *FW*, "Standard" fresh water, from Rodhe 1949; *MO*, Moses Lake, Washington, soda lake; *MS*, Monkey Spring, Arizona, gypsum water; *ML*, Mono Lake, California, "triple" water; *DS*, Dead Sea, Israel, bittern; *GSL*, Great Salt Lake, Utah, saltern; *LM*, Little Manitou, Saskatchewan, sodium sulfate lake; *HL*, Hot Lake, Washington, magnesium sulfate lake; Sea, mean sea water.

sea water), are termed *thalassohaline.* Others quite different from seawater in relative ionic content are *athalassohaline.* Fig. 12-2 was devised to portray the different types of water, including seawater. The examples chosen show a typical thalassohaline saltern, the Great Salt Lake and the Dead Sea bittern. Athalassohaline examples include: a "typical" dilute freshwater calcium carbonate lake and a gypsum spring (neither of which could exist in a concentrated state); a soda lake; two other types of sulfate lakes; and Mono Lake, California, as an example of "triple water" with the ions CO_3^{--}, Cl^-, and SO_4^{--} in nearly equal proportions.

Biota of saline waters

The biota of concentrated inland waters includes hardy species typified by fresh-water ancestry. Bayly (1967) constructed a biologic classification of Australian aquatic environments, coming to the conclusion that marine and interior saline waters are at opposite ends of a spectrum. Bayly, a student of calanoid copepods, showed that Australian centropagids, characteristic of the highest salinities, seem to have had direct freshwater ancestors and were less closely related to marine and brackish water forms.

In general, the diversity of species is inversely correlated with salinity. There is risk in setting down exact tolerance limits because relative proportions of major ions may be more important than total salt content. There is, however, only a meager list of species found in solutions in excess of 10% salinity. Usually, specific bluegreens and diatoms persist in concentrated water where green algae no longer survive. Notable exceptions are the branched green alga *Ctenocladus cir-*

cinnatus and the green flagellate *Dunaliella.* Cells of the former survive surrounded by crystallized salt, and the latter thrives in water saturated with NaCl.

Euryhaline invertebrates include cosmopolitan species and others that are more local in distribution but represented from region to region by ecologic equivalents. The rotifer *Brachionus plicatilis* and the brine shrimp *Artemia salina* are examples of the first category. The calanoid copepod *Diaptomus nevadensis* of North America and *D. salinus* of the Old World exemplify the latter. The Diptera have many hardy species, including ephydrids, culicids, and tabanids. To a lesser degree, certain species of the chironomids are capable of life in concentrated waters. A few Coleoptera and Hemiptera, especially corixids in the latter group, are found in hypersaline environments.

Seemingly, an invertebrate adapted for terrestrial existence would be preadapted for the osmotic hardships of hypersaline water. Both habitats are, in a sense, arid. Examples are scarce, although in Australia *Haloniscus,* a member of the terrestrial oniscid isopods, lives in concentrated pools.

Among the Vertebrata, some cyprinodont fishes are extraordinarily euryhaline. The southwestern pupminnows, *Cyprinodon,* have been found in pools of at least twice the concentration of seawater.

The species that occur in concentrated thalassohaline and athalassohaline waters are capable of withstanding major fluctuations in physicochemical features of the environment. They are found in lakes having a wide range of salinities. Marine species, by contrast, have evolved in a stable habitat, and most plants and animals from the sea that are found also in inland waters are not capable of any remarkable osmoregulation. They occur in waters differing little in salinity from seawater. Many marine species, such as the mullet *Mugil cephalus* and the edible blue crab *Callinectes,* are capable of progressing inland and move up rivers in gradients of decreasing salinity.

Researchers usually focus on saline lakes as habitats where physiologic stress on the biota is accented and where extreme adaptations are necessary for survival. Williams (1972) chides them gently for not going further to recognize the value of salt lakes for fundamental ecologic research. He points out that there are several factors lessening the difficulty of trophic-dynamic studies in saline lakes compared with investigations of freshwater ecosystems. These are: (1) a far less complex biota with greatly decreased biotic diversity and, therefore, simplified trophic relations; (2) the discreteness of the salt-lake habitat that always lacks outflow and often permanent inflow and shows minimal contact with contiguous ecosystems; and (3) the relatively low habitat heterogeneity in shallow saline lakes that often lack littoral macrophytes, for example. Moreover, it is interesting that extremely high rates of primary production are known from condensed desert waters, and following this plant growth, some unusual secondary production occurs. Perhaps this is partially due to the remarkable efficiencies of the animals, as studies on the typical saline-water grazer *Artemia* suggest. Also, organisms from the simple ecosystems represented by some desert waters are amenable to laboratory experimentation, contributing, therefore, to our understanding of the entire ecosystem. Data from desert lakes may be more rewarding for mathematic and computer simulation than are those from more complex ecosystems.

13
Redox, metals, nutrients, and organic substances

OXIDATION AND REDUCTION: REDOX POTENTIAL

Long-standing definitions of chemical oxidation and reduction of a substance are, respectively, the combining of oxygen with it and the removal of oxygen from it. Broader definitions, such as the loss and acquisition of hydrogen atoms, still represent too narrow an approach. However, without going further at the moment, one must be aware of: the two possible states (the oxidized and the reduced) of an ion, atom, or molecule; the reversible nature of these states; and the various ratios in which mixtures of the two may occur.

A current will flow between two solutions that differ in their ratios of oxidized to reduced substances. To bring this about, the solutions must be linked by a neutral salt bridge and a conducting filament connecting nonreactive electrodes of a noble metal (such as platinum) that are inserted into them. To achieve equilibrium, electrons pass from the mixture containing an excess of reduced substances to its electrode; in the solution containing an excess of oxidized substances, electrons flow from the electrode as it becomes charged positively. Herein lies a more nearly complete definition of oxidation and reduction: the excessively reduced mixture loses electrons and becomes oxidized; the predominantly oxidized mixture receives electrons and, thereby, is reduced. Oxidation is the loss of electrons; reduction is the gain of electrons.

Ferrous iron can be oxidized to the ferric state by giving up an electron, and ferric iron can be reduced by the addition of an electron. These events can occur without the participation of oxygen or hydrogen.

$$Fe^{++} \rightarrow Fe^{+++} + e^-$$
$$\text{ferrous} \quad \text{ferric}$$
$$\text{iron} \quad \text{iron}$$

Both processes are changes in the availability of the outer orbital electrons of chemical elements. Some resist rearrangement of these electrons more than others do. Sodium, for example, is very resistant to reduction, normally existing in an oxidized state.

Reduction and oxidation occur simultaneously, for an ion can be reduced only by the gain of electrons that arrive from an outside source as another ion is oxidized by their loss. This permits us to think of oxidation-reduction pairs, such as ferric and ferrous iron. Also, inherent in the theme of oxidation-reduction is the relative nature of an element or ion. When compared with aluminum, sodium is a strong reducer, giving up electrons to become oxidized. However, compared with lithium, another alkali metal, sodium is a weaker reducer and more of an oxidant. Thus ion A may reduce B, but in turn is reduced by C. Or stated in another fashion, A oxidizes C but is oxidized by B.

Some of the above is reminiscent of the principle upon which a common battery, the voltaic cell, is produced. A copper sulfate solution and a zinc sulfate solution are joined by a wire and salt bridge. The copper solution, a stronger oxidant than the zinc, takes up electrons. As a result electrons flow through the wire, oxidizing Zn to Zn^{++} as Cu^{++} is reduced to Cu. The voltage is about 1.10 but would be different if some reductant other than zinc were compared with the copper oxidant. The tendency of a copper–copper sulfate mixture to oxidize by taking electrons from other pairs is relative.

The relative difference in potential that drives a current is expressed as voltage. It is analogous to the difference in hydraulic pressure that forces water through a pipe. The intensity of the current flowing in the wire that connects two contrasting mixtures is a function of their relative states of oxidation or reduction and is measurable. It is the oxidation-reduction potential, or simply the redox potential, the difference in voltage that can be quantified by the counterpotential needed to bring the current to a halt. The electromotive force is termed Eh.

Potential and voltage imply comparisons. A single solution, a mixture of a redox couple (an oxidant and its reductant), must be compared with some standard. The standard generally selected is the hydrogen electrode,* where the redox pair is molecular hydrogen (the reductant) and hydrogen ion (the oxidant). The electrode is a glass tube through which gaseous H_2 at a pressure of 1 atmosphere can be passed over an included foil of platinum. The platinum adsorbs hydrogen but, being less active, does not lose or gain electrons itself. The electrode is immersed in a 1-normal acid solution; the pH, therefore, is zero. The flow of electrons may be toward the electrode of the mixture being compared or toward the standard hydrogen electrode, which can

---

*The calomel electrode of $HgCl$ or Hg_2Cl_2 is another common arbitrary standard. It has a positive voltage of 0.242 compared with the hydrogen electrode at pH 0.

act as an anode, with hydrogen molecules giving up electrons to form hydrogen ions:

$$H_2 \rightarrow 2H^+ + 2e^-$$

Or it can perform as a positive pole, a cathode, receiving electrons:

$$2H^+ + 2e^- \rightarrow H_2$$

The direction of flow indicates whether the mixture being tested tends to oxidize, taking up electrons readily, or whether it is a reducing solution, giving off electrons to the hydrogen system. The redox potential of the H^+-H_2 pair is arbitrarily defined as zero. Other redox couples and complex mixtures with potentials greater than zero are those that take up electrons and oxidize the hydrogen electrode; negative potentials are those shown by mixtures that yield electrons to the standard electrode. High positive voltage indicates oxidizing mixtures; decreasing voltage reflects an increase of reducing elements. A surplus of the reducing elements, when compared with the hydrogen standard, is shown by negative voltage. This scheme is the so-called European-sign convention. Confusingly, it is sometimes reversed, with positive values signifying that the reduced member of a redox pair is a more effective reducer than the H_2 in the H^+-H_2 couple.

Hydrogen ion concentration affects Eh to such an extent that it is necessary to correct voltage to some standard pH, usually 7.0; Eh is then expressed as E_7. At 18° C a lowering of one unit of pH is attended by an increased potential of 0.0577 volt; at 20° C this is 0.0581. Temperatures in this range are considered normal, and customarily, solutions tested at any pH have their potentials referred to pH 7.0 by adding 0.058 volt for every unit above neutral or by subtracting the same for each unit of the sample below pH 7.0. From data based on such manipulations, it appears that oxygenated epilimnion waters usually have an E_7 voltage near 0.5, although the oxidant-reductant

Table 13-1. Redox values of limnologic interest: voltages at which important reductions and oxidations occur and associated oxygen concentrations

Redox couples	E_7 (volts)	Dissolved O_2 (mg/liter)
NO_3^- to NO_2^-	0.45 to 0.40	4.0
NO_2^- to NH_3	0.40 to 0.35	0.4
Fe^{+++} to Fe^{++}	0.30 to 0.20	0.1
SO_4^{--} to S^{--}	0.10 to 0.06	0.0

Data from Mortimer 1941-1942.

couple, O_2-H_2O, theoretically have a potential of about 0.82 volt.

As oxygen tensions decline, there may be little change in potential. In small fertile lakes, however, there is an increasing tendency for reduction to accompany the decrease of hypolimnetic oxygen, and negative voltages often accompany anaerobic water. At and just below the profundal sediment-water interface, sharp Eh changes are to be expected in rich, stratified bodies of water.

As certain voltages are reached in lake waters and sediments, limnologically important ions are reduced as shown in Table 13-1. Mortimer (1941-1942) has shown that the conversion of trivalent to bivalent iron, occurring at E_7 voltages between 0.3 and 0.2, is especially significant. This change can be witnessed in stratified eutrophic lakes when depletion of oxygen and accumulations of reduced substances bring about iron reduction (Fig. 13-1).

In Table 13-1 a sequence of conversions from oxidized to reduced states can be seen. In a summer hypolimnion, nitrite, for example, begins to be reduced to ammonia as voltage falls to 0.4; sometime later, ferric iron may be reduced. It must be understood that the voltages shown in Table 13-1 are those at which the reactions have been found to occur; they are not the potentials of the redox pairs opposite them. In a neutral solution, for example, the potential (E_7) of the triva-

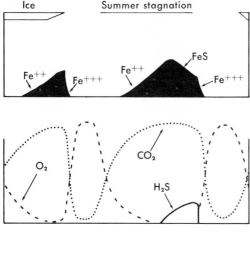

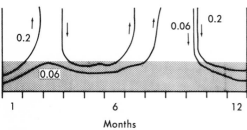

Fig. 13-1. Schematic presentation of events due to anoxic and intense reducing conditions in the hypolimnion of a dimictic, eutrophic lake. Lowest block shows the progress of two critical isovolts throughout the year within the sediment and the overlying hypolimnetic water; 0.2 volt line represents the redox potential at which ferric iron is reduced to ferrous iron; 0.06 volt line represents the redox potential at which sulfate is reduced to sulfide. Top block shows the appearance of Fe^{++} in the water beneath winter ice and subsequent precipitation of Fe^{+++} at the vernal overturn, the appearance of Fe^{++} during the summer stagnation, the precipitation of some iron as FeS when the redox potential falls to 0.06 volt, and the precipitation of Fe^{+++} at the fall overturn. Middle block shows the appearance and disappearance of the gases O_2, CO_2, and H_2S in hypolimnetic waters.

lent-bivalent iron couple is about 0.36 volt.

IRON

Iron is an abundant and important element, unsurpassed by any other heavy metal in the earth's crust. In living systems it is associated with numerous en-

zymes—peroxidase, catalase, cytochrome oxidase, and others. Iron is necessary to photosynthesizing plants, where it is the metal part of at least two plant cytochromes that function in the transfer of electrons during photosynthesis.

Iron is found in two states, the oxidized ferric (Fe^{+++}) and the reduced ferrous (Fe^{++}). Reducing and acid conditions promote the solubility of iron. Most ferrous compounds are soluble; a noteworthy exception is FeS (Fig. 13-1). In aqueous environments the common ferric compounds are insoluble; as a result, iron precipitates in alkaline and oxidized conditions.

Many of the conversions reducing and oxidizing iron are mediated by microorganisms. Chemosynthetic bacteria belonging to the *Thiobacillus-Ferrobacillus* group possess enzyme systems that transfer electrons from ferrous iron to oxygen, and this transfer results in ferric iron, water, and some free energy that is used for synthesizing organic compounds from CO_2. Bacteria in this group work at a low pH (below 5.0) where the oxidation of ferrous iron would proceed very slowly without enzymatic aid. Other bacteria use the energy derived from oxidizing iron to assimilate, rather than create, organic material. Generally, the microbial iron reducers cause the acceptor to act in low pH and Eh environments but not necesssarily in anoxic habitats.

Bacteria and plants can modify environments so that iron becomes either self-oxidizing or self-reducing. The elevation of oxygen values and the consumption of CO_2 promote oxidation and, hence, precipitation of iron. Some bacterial metabolic products, such as the H_2SO_4 produced by *Desulfovibrio*, promote iron solubilization.

At pH values from 7.5 to 7.7, a threshold is reached where iron in the form of $Fe(OH)_3$ is precipitated automatically. This means that iron would not be found except in acid to neutral water that is very low in oxygen and with redox potentials of 0.3 to 0.2 volt—such as in the hypolimnion of a stratified eutrophic lake. There it would be present in the soluble reduced state. With the introduction of oxygen at circulation, the iron would be oxidized and precipitated. A similar phenomenon is seen in streams contaminated by the acidic wastes from coal mines. Rusty-colored masses of precipitated flocculent $Fe(OH)_3$ mark a recovery zone where pH has risen and oxygen increased. These flocculated accumulations of ferric hydroxide, called "yellow dog," often damage the fish by clogging their gills in a seemingly habitable stream region.

Chelating agents

It is significant that some conversions of insoluble ferric iron to a soluble state do not require chemical reduction of the metal. Adding chelating agents results in an increase in solubility, and it is this available soluble iron, not total iron, that is important in algal nutrition.

Chelators are a class of compounds, organic and inorganic, that can hold metal atoms or ions. The metals are held between atoms of a single chelator molecule, frequently being pinched between two nitrogen, oxygen, or sulfur atoms. Chlorophyll is a chelate molecule with a magnesium atom held by nitrogen atoms. Some natural chelators, mostly polypeptides, are present in the extracellular products of bluegreens and make iron and other metals, often trace elements, available to plant populations by solubilizing them. Alanine and glycine are two amino acids with known chelating properties, and the porphyrins represent another common type of organic chelator.

Wetzel recently conducted research on alkaline marl lakes where soluble iron is scarce. In a 1972 publication, he reviewed much of his experimentation and discussed the results that follow additions of various chelators. Most iron present in marl lakes is sestonic or ad-

sorbed to particles as ferric compounds. The increase of algal primary production following the addition of chelators is a response to the sudden availability of iron through solubilization. In Wetzel's marl lakes, amino acids, citrate, and the synthetic chelators EDTA (ethylenediaminetetraacetic acid) and NTA (a trisodium salt of nitrilotriacetic acid) are effective. The EDTA is used to chelate calcium and magnesium in hardness tests; NTA* has achieved prominence in recent years because it was tested as a substitute for phosphates in laundry detergents in Canada.

The iron cycle in lakes

A most important limnologic feature of iron is its seasonal behavior in the hypolimnion. We owe much of our knowledge of the iron cycle in lakes to Mortimer (1941-1942). In well-oxygenated waters, ferric iron occurs but is rare because of its insolubility. During the spring overturn, most of it is in the sediments. In the profundal ooze it exists as ferric hydroxide, ferric phosphate, and perhaps a ferric silicate and ferric carbonate complex. An oxidized microzone of iron-containing molecules in a complex colloidal layer seals nutrients within the sediments, and little escapes to the overlying water. This would be the condition throughout the summer stagnation period in a stratified

---

*Hamilton (1972) reviewed much of what is known about this chelating compound. Although lacking the important nutrient phosphorus, NTA could possibly accelerate algal growth by making iron and other essential metals available. Moreover, NTA contains nitrogen and decomposes to form glycine and glycollic acid during biodegradation. These are probably useful to some algae, and certainly they may be deaminated to ammonia, which is readily available to phytoplankters. In any habitat where nitrogen rather than phosphorus is limiting, the substitution of NTA for phosphoric acid detergents will not prohibit eutrophication. The coastal seawaters, receiving tremendous quantities of sewage, are this type of habitat (Ryther and Dunstan 1971).

oligotrophic lake. In a eutrophic lake, by contrast, CO_2 collects, oxygen becomes scarce or absent, the pH falls, and the redox voltage drops to 0.3 or 0.2. Then conversion of ferric to ferrous iron commences (Fig. 13-1). Because this reduced iron is soluble, the oxidized seal disappears. The various substances mobilized with ferrous iron—including phosphorus and silica—then become abundant in hypolimnetic waters. Ammonia also may be profuse, having been produced at higher redox potentials by the reduction of nitrite (Table 13-1) and having arisen as a result of microbial action on decaying protein. Much of the well-known increase in summertime hypolimnion alkalinity, unaccounted for in terms of $Ca(HCO_3)_2$, is due to ammonium bicarbonate and ferrous bicarbonate.

The disappearance of the oxidized barrier and the release of nutrients to the supernatant water lead to the consumption of more oxygen and perhaps to the escape of even more nutrients. Thus, the first appearance of a reduced microzone at the water-sediment interface during the course of a lake's history must be a momentous event. The surface-oxidized sediments of oligotrophic lakes serve to keep elements of fertility from being recycled and to maintain the trophic state at an oligotrophic equilibrium.

The hypolimnetic agents of fertility, however, are not completely mixed throughout the lake, because oxygenated conditions at the autumnal overturn cause rapid conversion of Fe^{++} to Fe^{+++} and the immediate precipitation of $FePO_4$ and other iron compounds (Fig. 13-1). The hypolimnion has been likened to an iron trap: most of the iron that arrives there is retained, alternating between mobile soluble and immobile insoluble states. This explains a minor source of the world's iron ore, the so-called bog iron—*siderite,* $FeCO_3$; *hematite,* Fe_2O_3; "ochre," $Fe(OH_3)$—occupying concavities that were former lake basins.

In large lakes, where seiches are effective, internal waves might bring hypolimnetic waters close to the surface at the windward end of the lake. This upwelling could be followed by some mixing and transport of the rich water into the trophogenic zone.

Iron is not abundant in waters of meromictic lakes. The reason for its scarcity is the same as that which accounts for a decline in iron as summer stagnation proceeds (but *before* the overturn) in some polluted eutrophic lakes (Fig. 13-1). In both instances intense anaerobiosis and reducing conditions (as are met in the monimolimnia of meromictic lakes) bring redox potentials below 0.1 volt, and sulfate is reduced to sulfide (Table 13-1). Much of the sulfide, in addition to forming H_2S, combines with iron as FeS. Ferrous sulfide is insoluble and precipitates to contribute to the shiny black luster of sapropel. The precipitation of FeS represents the final stage in summer stagnation, although in many eutrophic lakes the overturn terminates stagnation before this stage is reached.

MANGANESE

Very close to iron in the economy of lakes and behaving in much the same manner is the heavy metal manganese. Manganese has four valence states, and it alternates between reduced soluble and oxidized (less soluble) conditions.

Manganese is a necessary nutrient for plants and animals. It stimulates plankton growth perhaps by activating enzyme systems and by having at least some effect on the vitamin thiamine. Its abundance in the igneous rocks and soils is perhaps no greater than 0.5%, but this amount seems adequate, and manganese deficiencies are rare.

Manganese, being especially soluble in the bivalent state, is reduced and mobilized at a higher redox voltage than iron. Under strong oxidizing conditions, manganese is part of the colloidal microzone seal and serves with iron as a barrier between deeper sediment and supernatant water. At this time manganese is probably in the tetravalent or trivalent condition.

During summer stagnation, manganese goes into solution earlier than iron, but it is precipitated later than iron when the overturn occurs. Manganese, then, is more apt to be lost in lake outflows than iron is. The hypolimnion is not so effective a trap for manganese as it is for iron. Because of this difference, past oxidizing-reducing conditions have been inferred from Fe/Mn ratios changing in the sediments. Mackereth (1966) published some instructive data based on analyses of cores from the eutrophic English lake, Esthwaite Water. Changing Fe/Mn ratios imply fluctuations in reducing oxidizing environments during the postglacial history of the lake. When oxidizing conditions began to be replaced by a reducing environment, there was an increase in the Fe/Mn ratio, signifying chemical reduction and solubilization of manganese, some of which was lost. Later, as redox conditions brought about the mobilization of ferrous iron, the ratio diminished. Similarly, the advent of oxidizing situations led to initial increases in the ratio because iron precipitated first; the later arrival of manganese in the sediments lowered the Fe/Mn value again.

PHOSPHORUS

Phosphorus is absolutely necessary to all life; it functions in the storage and transfer of a cell's energy and in genetic systems. The universality of ATP (adenosine triphosphate) as an energy carrier and the presence of phosphate groups in nucleotides, and hence nucleic acids, underscores living things' need for phosphorus. Found in meteorites, rocks, soils, and even in the sun's atmosphere, it is not one of the rarest elements. Phosphorus is much scarcer, however, than the other principal atoms of living organisms (carbon, hydrogen, oxygen, nitrogen, and sulfur). Its abundance at the surface of the earth is about one tenth of 1% by weight. It is taken up rapidly and concentrated by living things.

Phosphorus oxidizes very readily and occurs in the earth's rocks principally as orthophosphate (PO_4^{---}). The main source of this ion is igneous rocks containing the phosphatic mineral *apatite*, $Ca_5(PO_4)_3^+$ united with either OH^-, Cl^-, or fluoride. The reduced, gaseous phosphine, (PH_3) is but a fleeting state because it oxidizes so rapidly. It is thought that the eerie lights sometimes flickering over marshes, will-o'-the-wisps, could be phosphine and perhaps other gases produced by anaerobic decomposition burning on contact with air. There is little other phosphorus in the earth's atmosphere save what adheres to dust and debris. The five other major elements of tissue are represented, sometimes abundantly, in air and rain.

Igneous rock was the original source of phosphorus on earth. Subsequent weathering, probably aided by carbonic acid, liberated much of the phosphorus, which was redeposited or carried to the seas. The flow from continents to seas was the major movement. Phosphorus accumulations of biotic origin formed near the oceans when upwelled phosphate was taken up by planktonic organisms and concentrated by marine fish that served as food for guano-producing sea birds. Great accumulations of guano were built up on dry cliffs and islands, especially off the west coast of South America. In addition, phosphorus is concentrated in the skeletons of vertebrate animals as an important constituent of bone. Phosphate accumulations are reminders of the major role played by organisms in concentrating this essential element.

With industrial and agricultural use of guano beds there has been a reverse flow from the sea to the continents. Since the phosphorus from rocks, both igneous and sedimentary, is also mined and used, phosphorus has been spread throughout a large part of the globe. It is now being washed seaward, some of it for the second time, with much of it reaching lacustrine basins en route.

The decay and mineralization of plant and animal corpses is a source of phosphorus to the living components of ecosystems; the bacteria change it from organic molecular phosphorus to inorganic orthophosphate, which can be utilized by plants. This recycling does not represent a steady income of phosphorus from without. Only the rocks and the material from the seas can supply that.

There are some troublesome areas in analyzing and presenting data for phosphorus. The usual method of testing for it is based on the reaction of acidified ammonium molybdate with inorganic phosphate (orthophosphate). The reaction forms a molybdophosphoric acid that turns blue when reduced. Stannous chloride, the usual reducing agent, causes the development of molybdenum blue when soluble orthophosphate is in the sample. (Contamination of glassware, being more critical than it is in many water-chemistry routines, may be a source of error here.) Organic phosphates, known as meta- or polyphosphates, are not shown by this test. They are revealed after being hydrolyzed to orthophosphate by heat and acid. The molybdate test on such a hydrolyzed sample gives total phosphate, and by subtraction (total PO_4 minus ortho-PO_4) the organic phosphate can be rated. Testing filtered and unfiltered samples adds further dimensions; the categories of soluble and particulate phosphate come to light.

The reactive soluble orthophosphate is the fraction that is immediately useful for autotrophic plants. The tests for it, however, yield slightly high results because of some hydrolysis of soluble polyphosphates in the acid medium during the time it takes the blue color to appear.

There are pitfalls to watch for when one reads reports on phosphorous tests. Briefly, some authors have been careless in reporting their data and have confused orthophosphate with orthophosphate-P, and total phosphate with total phosphorus. Phosphate amounts are 3.07 times the phosphorus atom in the ion.

In 1957 Hutchinson presented a table that showed the mean of samples from several lake districts was about 20.8 mg total P per m^3 (or that same amount in micrograms per liter); this equals 0.0208 mg total P per liter or 0.0638 mg total phosphate per liter. Far greater amounts have been reported from saline basins of arid climates. Hutchinson listed Goodenough Lake, British Columbia, with 208 g/m^3, which is 10,000 times the mean from dilute lakes in humid regions. The concentrated waters of Red Pond at the Long-H Ranch, Arizona, had more than 150 g/m^3 one summer following the sudden crash of a flourishing *Artemia* population.

Phosphorus cycles have engaged limnologists for a long time because the element is often a limiting factor for primary production and, therefore, for fish yield. The picture has changed however—now there is concern about too much phosphorus!

Early investigations were restricted to measuring changes over periods of days or monitoring algal response after addition of phosphate. Commonly, only traces of orthophosphate are found in the water when photosynthesis is proceeding at a good rate. This situation resembles the apparent absence of free CO_2 on sunny days in rich waters while primary production is considerable. The phosphate of course, as is true for CO_2, has been taken up by the plants, and its scarcity in the water in no way implies unimportance. The rate at which it is taken up and recirculated could only be guessed by early investigators, although they presumed rapid cycling.

With the availability of radioisotopes after World War II, there arose the possibility of quantifying phosphorus dynamics by using ^{32}P in a phosphate. Hutchinson and Bowen (1947 and 1950) at Linsley Pond and Coffin and co-workers (1949) in Canada were the first to add radiophosphorus directly to lakes and follow it as best they could. There was good evidence that phosphate was absorbed rapidly by the plankton and transferred, presumably by sedimentation, to the hypolimnion. Subsequently, inorganic phosphorus was released from the sediments. A few years later when ^{32}P was available in greater quantities, Hayes (1955), Hayes and Phillips (1958), and Rigler (1956 and 1964) made some important contributions in Canada. Rigler (1964) published the results of tracer studies in bog lakes that revealed very rapid cycling of phosphorus. He added radiophosphate to the epilimnion, and the results agreed with earlier reports: it had but a brief time in the upper waters. More important, Rigler discovered that low levels of phosphate, remaining constant for hours, did not reflect the inability of plankton cells to take up the ion. Rather, a metabolic loss matched the uptake, and soluble inorganic phosphate was replaced many times during an hour. By separating phytoplankters from bacterial cells, Rigler demonstrated that the bacteria were more responsible for the rapid cycling of phosphorus. The turnover time, which was approximately 5 minutes, suggests that aquatic bacteria are formidable competitors with the algae where this scarce element is concerned.

Rigler found in his tracer study that 77% of the radiophosphate added to the water was gone within 4 weeks, but only 3% ended up in the sediments, and only 2% left via the lake's outlet. The remainder had been taken up largely by the littoral organisms. Uptake of phosphate through the leaves as well as the root system may be possible for many aquatic macrophytes.

A common concept of the phosphorus cycle assumes that a dead organism, starting as particulate organic phosphorus, becomes soluble organic phosphorus and, eventually, soluble inorganic phosphorus. (The changes are mediated by bacteria.) This is probably a little too simple. Living plankton organisms excrete organic phosphorus compounds that soon become colloidal and account for most of the filterable phosphorus in lake waters, according to Lean (1973). Also, the eelgrass *Zostera* in shallow marine environments seems to take up phosphorus from the sediments via the roots and to pump it into the water by way of the leaves (McRoy and associates 1972).

Although new data continuously accumulate on the complexities of the phosphorus cycle in lake waters, some generalities can be made. First, the speed with which phosphorus is whisked back and forth between the abiotic and biotic worlds emphasizes the aptness of the ecosystem concept and leads to the conclusion that the best figure to use in quantifying phosphorus in a body of water is *total* phosphorus, including sestonic as well as dissolved values. Second, there is a mechanism whereby the normal accumulation of phosphorus in a lacustrine system does not lead rapidly to a condition favoring the production of a soupy mass of bluegreens. This is because of rapid sedimentation, followed by little return of phosphorus in oligotrophic lakes and only more or less seasonal releases in eutrophic lakes. According to Megard (1972), the total phosphorus at any one time in the waters of Lake Minnetonka is about equal to the annual increment from outside sources.

Jones (1972) examined 16 lakes in the English Lake District in search of indices that best correlated with high summer standing crops and degree of eutrophication. Total phosphorus stood at the top of the list. Interestingly, the *alkaline phosphatase* activity of epilimnetic samples was also significant. (The enzyme is an excellent indicator of biomass in the English lakes.) Berman (1970) reported on the annual fluctuations of this enzyme in Israel's Lake Kinneret and showed its importance to the algae and dinoflagellates of that lake. This enzyme affords algae access to the total phosphorus of the ecosystem by making some of it available as dissolved inorganic phosphate, the useful state of the element.

Unappealing eutrophication resulting from sewage and other pollutants associated with human activity in bringing phosphorus back from the seas has stimulated research on ways to keep phosphorus out of lakes. One approach is to reduce or eliminate the use of high-phosphate detergents. Another scheme is to modify sewage before it can enter a waterway. This method has been successful in Switzerland, where ferric chloride precipitates about 90% of the phosphate from the sewage as ferric phosphate (Thomas 1969). (A similar phenomenon occurs in a eutrophic lake at the overturn.) A third method is to be certain that domestic wastes do not reach the lakes; the successful bypassing of Lake Washington has been documented by Edmondson (1969 and 1972b).

NITROGEN

The versatile element nitrogen is found in four recognized spheres of the earth. Stevenson (1972) assembled data that estimate 16,734.328 $\times$ 10^{13} metric tons as the total, with 97.6% in the lithosphere and a little less than 2.3% in the atmosphere. The tiny fraction remaining belongs to the hydrosphere and biosphere. The approximation of about 386 $\times$ 10^{13} metric tons of nitrogen in the atmosphere is probably the most trustworthy datum. Despite the relatively small portion in the biosphere, most nitrogen cycling is brought about by organisms.

The free, inert nitrogen so abundant in the atmosphere and pressing down on us at about 755 g/cm^2 is denied to higher plants and animals without the aid of other organisms. Only a few prokaryotes can convert the strongly bonded molecules of gaseous nitrogen to useful compounds.

Nitrogen, although absolutely necessary for life as we know it, does not command the attention that phosphorus does, because nitrogen is more abundant and has more sources for living things. The tremendous atmospheric stores contribute in more than one manner. Rainwater contains various forms of nitrogen, some of which the rain is returning to the lithosphere. Nitrate and perhaps other oxides of nitrogen in the rain may have been formed photochemically or to a lesser extent by electrical discharge. Perhaps the oxidation of ammonia, common in rainwater, is also a factor in the origin of the nitrate.

Molecular nitrogen dissolves readily (see Table 10-2) and enters the hydrosphere or the soil where a few organisms can convert it to useful compounds. During industrial techniques or laboratory procedures, the covalent triple bonds of the N_2 molecule ($N \equiv N$) can be broken only at high pressures and temperatures. A few bacteria and bluegreens have the remarkable ability to break this bond at ordinary temperatures and pressures; this is certainly one of the most important events on earth.

There are two main groups of organisms that achieve the biochemical steps ranging from cracking the molecular bonds of nitrogen to producing protein. They are the symbiotic fixers and the nonsymbiotic type. The symbiotic fixers, or reducers, reduce N_2 in association with eukaryotic plants and have long been known. They are made up of a half dozen species of *Rhizobium* living in root nodules of leguminous plants. The agricultural technique of planting alfalfa and clover to improve soil is common knowledge.

The rather high nitrogen content of desert waters has been attributed to the abundance of wild legumes in arid lands. Many species of catclaw *(Acacia)* characterize the Australian deserts and have been suspected of being responsible. In the American Southwest *Acacia,* mesquite *(Prosopis),* and ironwood *(Olynea)* have been assumed to be the source of edaphic nitrates.

Many nonlegumes have root nodules harboring colonies of nitrogen-fixing microorganisms. At least 15 species of alders *(Alnus)* are known to have root nodules, and many grow in moist soil near water. Goldman (1961) showed that alder leaves falling in oligotrophic Castle Lake, California, accounted for one third of the lake's nitrogen supply.

Rhizobium's fixation of nitrogen involves an enzyme (or series of enzymes), nitrogenase, which reduces nitrogen to an ammonium ion that can be aminated by photosynthetic primary producers. Conversion of ammonia to amino acids is the mechanism by which inorganic nitrogen enters the biosphere. Green plants can use some organic forms of nitrogen, but most is taken up as the inorganic forms, ammonia or nitrate. After assimilation, nitrate is reduced to ammonia, which is built into aspartic and glutamic acid. These two amino acids serve as forerunners of all other nitrogen compounds.

The nonsymbiotic N_2 reducers include free-living bacteria, such as the aerobic *Azotobacter,* members of about a dozen genera of anaerobic bacteria, and roughly 50 species of blue-green algae, especially those of the family Nostocaceae. Nitrogenase has been demonstrated with certainty only in prokaryotes. The energy source for reduction is organic matter for most of the bacteria and is light for the bluegreens and photosynthetic bacteria such as *Rhodospirillum.* Because *Rhodospirillum* is an obligate anaerobe, its distribution is limited. Often it occurs in anoxic zones beneath algae and utilizes wavelengths not absorbed by algal pigments. Bluegreens, by contrast, are broadly distributed.

Drewes (1928) demonstrated that pure cultures of blue-green algae fixed nitrogen. One of the first reports of blue-green nitrogen fixers in nature concerned *Anabaena* in rice paddies (De 1939). Soon thereafter a soil-dwelling *Nostoc* capable of reducing gaseous N_2 was discovered.

Bluegreens are abundant in desert soils, and it is possible that they are implicated in the high nitrogen levels, usually attributed to legumes in desert waters (Cameron and Fuller 1960). Certainly there would be unusual opportunities for concentration of edaphic nitrogen compounds in climates where rainfall is a rare event.

Aquatic animals, in contrast to most terrestrial forms, commonly excrete ammonia as a waste product of metabolism. Most of this gas dissolved in water, however, comes from bacterial mineralization of dead plants and animals. The microorganisms of decay assimilate some of the organic material in the dead remains to build their cells. Other organic material is converted to NH_3, and this in turn is oxidized to nitrite (NO_2) and thence to nitrate (NO_3). Both aerobic and anaerobic bacteria function in the ammonification, while only aerobic forms participate in nitrification. This explains in part why ammonia accumulates in the anaerobic eutrophic hypolimnion. *Nitrosomonas* and *Nitrobacter* are the principal genera gaining energy, first, from oxidizing ammonia to nitrite and, second, from oxidizing nitrite to nitrate.

Working in the biogeochemical cycling of nitrogen is a group of facultative anaerobic microbes that restore the gases N_2 and N_2O to the atmosphere. The process is called dentrification.

Before industrialization, the amount of nitrogen fixed by bacteria and bluegreens was probably balanced by natural denitrification. Thus, nitrogen was returned to the air in an inert state that could be converted to a useful condition only by the work of another set of prokaryotes. Man's learning how to fix N_2 industrially (at 500° C and several hundred atmospheres) has changed the picture. The annual industrial production approximates 50 million tons, and the denitrifying bacteria are hard pressed to keep pace with this extra substrate. Because denitrification proceeds best in anaerobic environments, the preservation of swamps, marshlands, and tundra has even more to recommend it than the esthetic worth of these habitats.

Early techniques used to study the fixation of N_2 by bluegreens were less sensitive than subsequent methods; algae were grown in media free of combined nitrogen, and any gains in total nitrogen were noted. A later improvement was filtering out the nitrogen from the gas mixture in the experimental containers (Fogg 1942).

Using the heavy isotope of nitrogen, ^{15}N, one can test for nitrogen-fixing ability with greater accuracy. Molecular heavy nitrogen is introduced after all the gas has been removed from the medium. If the bluegreen is capable of using molecular nitrogen, it will be found in its cells after a given period (Burris and others 1943).

Today, however, nitrogenase activity is usually measured by testing it with an electron acceptor. Nitrogenase is a versatile enzyme that reduces a variety of substrates in addition to N_2. For example, it reduces acetylene ($HC\equiv CH$) to ethylene. Organisms that lack nitrogenase cannot bring about the reduction of acetylene. The ^{15}N isotope still is useful for other nitrogen studies, however. Using nitrate labeled with ^{15}N, one can test for the rate of nitrate uptake by algae. In laboratory cultures, the Michaelis-Menten kinetic expression is useful in enzyme-substrate studies and describes the results well. In this expression, V = velocity of uptake of nitrate-nitrogen per unit of particulate N

in the algae; V_{max} = the maximum velocity of uptake; S = concentration of substrate, the nitrate nutrient in this case; and K_m, the Michaelis-Menten constant, is the value of S when $V = \frac{1}{2} V_{max}$.

$$V = \frac{V_{max} S}{K_m + S}$$

MacIsaac and Dugdall's (1969) experiments with natural population of phytoplankters have shown that K_m is rather high in eutrophic regions and lower in oligotrophic areas. This suggests that there may be an adaptation for taking nitrate up rapidly where it is scarce.

The site of nitrogen fixation (reduction of gaseous N_2) is thought to be the heterocyst in bluegreens. Only species with heterocysts have the ability to fix nitrogen. All genera of the Nostocaceae possess heterocysts, and the family rates high as a reducer of inert N_2. Representatives of some other families, such as *Gloeotrichia* of the Rivulariaceae, have heterocysts and also fix molecular nitrogen. *Aphanizomenon*, having a lower ratio of heterocysts to vegetative cells than *Anabaena*, is inferior to the latter in fixing N_2 (Horne and Fogg 1970). Horne and Goldman (1972) found that the spring peak in nitrogen reduction in Clear Lake, California, was due to *Aphanizomenon* and correlated with the ratio of heterocysts to vegetative cells in the filaments; the autumn peak was brought about by planktonic *Anabaena circinalis* and correlated with the total number of heterocysts in the population. These two prokaryotes fixed 18 kg N_2 per ha during the year.

There has been some contradictory evidence, however. Ohmori and Hattori (1971) recently reported that vegetative cells of *Anabaena cylindrica* fix molecular nitrogen at the same rate as do heterocysts. Van Gorkom and Donze (1971) found that in aerobic situations nitrogen is fixed almost exclusively by the heterocysts, but vegetative cells can do this work anaerobically. Carpenter (1973) is one of the latest workers to report nitrogenase activity by a nonheterocystous blue-green alga in the sea; this is a species of *Trichodesmium* (placed in *Oscillatoria* by some authors, including Carpenter). Nevertheless, freshwater *Oscillatoria* lack heterocysts, and their ability to fix nitrogen with their vegetative cells has not been substantiated. Interestingly, the species *O. rubescens,* said to foretell the onset of cultural eutrophication, is nitrogen limited and does not appear in lakes until nitrogen content rises.

Ryther and Dunstan (1971) came to the conclusion that nitrogen is the critical limiting factor in coastal marine waters. Their calculations show that the phosphorus received via sewage and terrestrial runoff in general is more than adequate for plankton growth. There are two reasons for the relative scarcity of nitrogen in coastal marine waters: (1) there is a low nitrogen/phosphorus ratio in contributions from sewage and other land-derived wastes; (2) phosphorus regenerates more rapidly than does ammonia from decomposing organic matter. A third factor might have relevance—there are no great marine populations of nitrogen-reducing bluegreens such as those found in inland lakes. There is a generalization to be derived here: when phosphorus is added to an aquatic system experimentally or by way of sewage or other terrestrial import, nitrogen often becomes a limiting factor even though it outranked phosphorus at first.

SILICA

Silicon is the second most abundant element in the lithosphere. Its main source in fresh and sea waters is weathering of the extremely abundant feldspar rocks. In inland waters it ranges from 0.1 to 4,000 ppm, representing the extremes from snow melt to hot mineral springs. In rivers and lakes silicon commonly ranges from 2 to 25 ppm, and is usually expressed as silica (SiO_2) in water analyses.

Silica is an essential nutrient for diatoms, which build their frustules of this glassy material. It may also be essential for the growth of planktonic chrysophyceans such as *Dinobryon, Uroglena,* and *Mallomonas,* which construct silicified scales and spores. Among freshwater animals, the main users are the sponges, building their glassy spicules with silica. In the sea, silica is scarce, averaging about 5 mg/liter; this has been attributed to the uptake by radiolarians, silico-flagellates, siliceous sponges, and diatoms.

The chemical test that is commonly employed for silica works only when this compound is in a soluble state; the particulate frustules of diatoms in a sample are not reactive. Because solubility of silica increases directly with temperature, high concentrations are found in geyser waters and hot springs. Concentrations of silica are reported in parts per million or milligrams per liter rather than in milliequivalents per liter because it is usually not ionized. Dissolved silica tends to complex with H_2O, perhaps as $SiO_2 \cdot 2H_2O$ or H_4SiO_4. The latter only dissociates above pH 9.0; thus silicate ions become important in alkalinity titrations only at low hydrogen ion concentrations.

The relationships between silica and the biotic segment of the aquatic ecosystem have been clearly demonstrated. In an early study Birge and Juday (1911) described a Wisconsin lake with a metalimnetic stratum of diatoms that accounted for a positive heterograde oxygen curve and a striking silica minimum at the same level. Lund (1964) showed that the course of events through the years reveals an inverse ratio for the diatom crop and the soluble silica in the water (Fig. 13-2). The crash of the diatom populations at the end of summer is accompanied by a slow rise in reactive soluble silica in the water samples. The decay is slower for silica than for or-

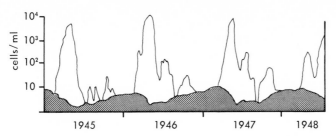

Fig. 13-2. The relationship between soluble silica (dark area) and the waxing and waning of diatom populations (cell numbers shown by thin line). The greatest SiO_2 concentration shown here is about 2.5 mg per liter. (Modified from Lund 1964.)

ganic compounds, and many frustules may be buried and lost. Because of this, the paleolimnologist can read the record of the past from the siliceous remains of diatoms in vertical cores of lake sediments.

Although many sedimentary diatom frustules may be lost, there is an increase in hypolimnetic silica during stagnation. Presumably, much of this could be distributed to the epilimnion at the overturn. Some, however, may be precipitated with iron.

Kilham (1971) hypothesized that diatom sequences were governed by ambient silica. From a search of the literature, he found that some lake species were not numerically dominant until silica concentrations seemed to match their demands. A variety of *Melosira granulata* bloomed when mean SiO_2 was 13.4 mg/liter; *Stephanodiscus* was predominant while much lower levels (0.6 mg/liter) of silica prevailed. These species were the extremes.

Kilham's hypothesis is relevant to a scheme later proposed by Schelske and Stoermer (1972). They showed a possible route to eutrophication as evidenced by the recent appearance of bluegreens at the expense of diatom phytoplankters in Lake Michigan. The addition of phosphorus stimulates growth of diatoms, which utilize more silica as their populations increase. After their growing season, the diatoms sink, and much of their

siliceous material reaches the sediments before decaying. Some is buried by subsequent deposition of other material and is lost from the open-water silica cycling. Nonsiliceous algae then compete successfully with the diatoms, eventually replacing them. The authors pointed out that during the past 40 years silica has diminished steadily in the waters of Lake Michigan, and recently the dominance of the diatoms has lessened as bluegreens have become more abundant.

The ideas of Kilham, Schelske, and Stoermer may readily explain the disappearance of *Melosira* from two lakes. In man-made Tom Wallace Lake, first filled in the winter of 1946-1947, *Melosira* was present in the plankton during the first 3 years of the lake's existence but was not seen after 1950. Two tons of commercial fertilizer had been applied annually for the first 5 years, and a blue-green flora developed. The last bloom was in the summer and early autumn of 1952; the fertilization program ended with the 1951 application (Cole 1957). In Crystal Lake, Minnesota, the profundal sediments are topped with 10 or 12 cm of sapropel overlying gyttja. *Melosira* frustules are lacking in the upper 4 or 5 cm of sapropel but occur abundantly below. Swinyard (1933) found *Melosira* abundant in plankton taken from Crystal Lake in 1931 and 1932, but none was present from 1947 through 1949 when repeated sampling was done (Cole 1955).

TRACE METALS

A group of metals that are needed in trace quantities by many organisms can be no more than touched on here. Most trace minerals do not affect limnology except indirectly in nutritional studies. However, knowledge of some interesting lacustrine metal cycles is likely to accumulate with the increased use of atomic absorption spectrophotometry for detecting minute quantities of elements.

Copper and zinc probably behave much like iron and manganese; they are insoluble in oxidized states and in intensely reducing environments where they form sulfides. Other elements, such as vanadium, chromium, and selenium, are soluble when oxidized (the opposite is true of iron). Cobalt and nickel behave somewhat similarly, but their oxidation-solubility pattern may resemble that of iron to a degree. The list of minor elements in lake waters could include boron, cadmium, iodine, rubidium, and poisonous forms, such as lead, mercury, and arsenic.

The heavy metal *molybdenum* (Mo) occurs in seven stable and five radioactive isotopes, and its importance to the growth of higher plants has been known for decades. In 1960 Goldman demonstrated that its deficiency limits primary production in Castle Lake, California, where addition of this element stimulates algal growth. Apparently, the beneficial effect of molybdenum is based on its relation to the enzyme systems that reduce N_2 (the nitrogen-fixing enzymes) and to those that reduce nitrate. It is directly incorporated into nitrogenase.

Molybdenum's lacustrine cycle is similar to the iron cycle because it decreases at the same time $Fe(OH)_3$ and FeS are removed by precipitation. As might be suspected, it is commoner in deep water and is concentrated in plankton cells and sediments. Dumont's (1972) report of the annual fluctuations of molybdenum in a eutrophic pond showed seasonal changes recalling the iron cycle. It was scarce in winter water samples when the sediments were oxidized; coinciding with the release of phosphorus, it appeared in abundance early in the summer; and it decreased during later summer when H_2S was obvious in the lower waters.

Cobalt is a trace element essential to life; when wanting, it leads to inactivation of certain enzymes. It is found in vitamin B_{12}, which in turn is a major requirement for bluegreens, diatoms, and dinoflagellates (Provasoli 1969). Vitamin B_{12}, properly termed cyanocobalamin, is unique because no other known vitamin contains a metal ion.

Copper is one of the few trace minerals that has been studied limnologically. Riley (1939) followed the annual copper cycle in some Connecticut lakes and found its abundance to vary more than twentyfold during the course of a year.

Copper in the form of $CuSO_4 \cdot 5H_2O$ has been used as an algicide for many years in aquatic ecosystems. It accumulates as copper carbonate especially in the sediments of hard-water lakes where it may be detrimental to the bottom fauna. Copper carbonate has been used for decades for killing the snail hosts of the flukes that cause a dermatitis called "swimmers' itch." The cercarial larvae leave the snails and burrow into the skin of a wrong host—the human (McMullen 1941). Recently, organic algicides and molluscicides have largely replaced copper.

Horne and Goldman (1974) found in the eutrophic Clear Lake, California, that additions of copper, on the order of 0.005 times the amount usually needed for algal control, severely inhibited nitrogen fixing by blue-green algae. The trace amounts added were believed to be effective because the chelating capacity of the lake water was saturated; experimental chelation of copper by such artificial compounds as EDTA renders copper harmless to phytoplankton populations in many natural waters.

Zinc is significant to living systems. A metal constituent of dehydrogenases, it is required in photosynthesis as an agent in hydrogen transfer. Another metabolic role of zinc is in the synthesis of protein. It is probably never in short supply because the rain carries from 2.5 to 12 mg/m^3. It precipitates in the lake sediments as a sulfide and coprecipitates with $CaCO_3$ and $Fe(OH)_3$. The radioisotope ^{65}Zn has served in studies of the uptake of this metal by organisms.

Vanadium has assumed importance in medical geology because it inhibits cholesterol synthesis; the incidence of vascular disease is said to be low where vanadium is present in soils and water. It increases the rate of photosynthesis in the green alga *Scenedesmus,* and substituting for molybdenum, it can be used by *Azotobacter* as a catalyst for nitrogen reduction.

DISSOLVED ORGANIC SUBSTANCES

Data from various authors agree with the early report by Birge and Juday (1934) that freshwater lakes contain from 0.1 to 50 mg dissolved organic compounds (DOC) per liter. Various free sugars, amino acids, organic acids, polypeptides, and other substances have been reported.

There are probably five sources of these dissolved materials: organic compounds of allochthonous origin, soluble organic stuff from the decay of aquatic organisms, photosynthates or extracellular metabolites excreted from phytoplankton, extracellular metabolites or photosynthates secreted by littoral macrophytes, and excretions from the lake fauna.

Humic material, causing the yellow stain in coastal marine waters as well as inland lakes, comes from the decay of vegetable material in the soil and from autochthonous plant detritus. The materials are a complex mixture; many are derived from polymerization of plant polyphenolic compounds.They are soluble in dilute bases or salts of complexing ions, but insoluble in mineral acids and alcohol, and remarkably resistant to decay. The $-COOH$ radical is common in the mixture, and they are commonly called humic acids.

Shapiro (1957) published results of intensive studies on these yellow organic acids. He called them *humolimnic acids* to distinguish them from the humic acids of soils, aromatic structures with much higher molecular weights. Shapiro assigned a mean molecular weight of 456 to humolimnic acids; the molecular weight of soil humic acids was about 1400. Actually, in some lake waters there are polymerized compounds of the humic acid type with molecular weights from 700 to 10,000. Perhaps they are of allochthonous origin, since true humolimnic acids of autochthonous origin are lighter.

Povoledo (1964) stated that the colored material in the nondialyzable fraction of lake sediment and lake water differed from soil humic acid. Shapiro considered the association of nitrogen with the yellow acid molecules to be fortuitous, but Swain and co-workers (1959) suggested that humolimnic acids can be connected to amino acids in various fashions. Povoledo (1964) found that 14 amino acids associated with the humic acids of Lake Maggiore differed somewhat from those reported from soil humic substances.

The humic materials in lake waters hold in suspension remarkable quantities of metallic ions compared with their solubilities in pure water. Shapiro (1966) reported high iron concentrations in membrane-filtered humic waters, suggesting that humic materials peptize (chelate) the metal, thereby keeping it in solution at pH and redox levels where it would normally precipitate. In the absence of complex-formers, the solubility of ferric iron in the pH range of 6.0 to 9.0 does not exceed about $10^{-8}M$, roughly 0.56 μg/liter (Stumm and Morgan 1970).

Saunders outlined the chelation of trace metals by humic substances can have four important effects on algae: it can lower concentrations until algal growth is limited; reduce excesses of toxic trace elements to nontoxic levels; remove an ion antagonistic to a metallic poison, thus increasing the toxicity of the poison; and keep an essential trace element in solution at concentrations well above its normal solubility, making it available for algal growth.

Bacterial action and autolysis effect the decay of dead plants and animals, which release soluble organic compounds. Otsuki and Hanya (1968) described what happened to decaying *Scenedesmus,* a green alga. Initially there was a rapid production of soluble organic carbon and nitrogen. The final organic material at the end of the decay was much like the resistant yellow organic stain.

For some time it has been known that a loss of newly formed photosynthates is sustained by phytoplankton cells. A substantial fraction of the carbon fixed during photosynthesis, especially in glycollate, may be leaked directly into the water. This leakage has been considered more typical of the blue-green algae than of the other phytoplankton taxa (Saunders 1972b). However, Aaronson (1971) found that a species of *Ochromonas,* assignable to the chrysophytes, secretes macromolecules of all sorts (including carbohydrates and nucleic acid-like molecules) and bits of membrane debris.

Recently, Wetzel (1969) reported on the excretion of DOC from the submersed macrophyte *Najas,* and later studies by Allen (1971) show that the littoral zone of lakes is an important source of soluble organic substances because of leaks from the emergent *Scirpus* as well as *Najas.*

The excretion of both organic and inorganic P compounds from zooplankters is well known, and DON (dissolved organic nitrogen) is liberated especially from the decaying bodies of aquatic organisms.

Many algae are heterotrophic to some measure; they are able to utilize dissolved and organic substrates as carbon and energy sources. The flagellated green cell *Chlamydomonas mundana* is common in anaerobic sewage lagoons where it perpetuates, rather than alleviates, anaerobiosis; its feeble oxygen production via photosynthesis does not compensate for its oxygen consumption in absorbing acetate. Eppley and MaciasR (1963) showed that *C. mundana* uses light in assimilating the acetate and is, therefore, more like a photosynthetic bacterium than an alga. Species of two other common sewage genera, *Scenedesmus* and *Chlorella,* consume CO_2 and release oxygen abundantly. They may utilize acetate to some degree, but the forms in waste waters generally have rather high phosphorus requirements. The interesting little *Ochromonas malkamensis* is remarkable because it contains only chlorophyll *a* but lacks the chlorophyll *c* that is typical of the chrysophyceans; it grows far better in an organic substrate than it does without. It has been suggested that the absence of this accessory pigment may reduce its photosynthesizing ability. Saunders (1972a) used autoradiography to show that *Oscillatoria aghardii* cells take up acetate and glucose labeled with ^{14}C. This is the species that forms positive heterograde oxygen profiles in some lakes.

VITAMINS

Growth-promoting substances such as thiamine, biotin, and vitamin B_{12} are common in lake waters and essential for the growth of some algae. Biotin is not required by the bluegreens, chlorophytes, and diatoms, but it is needed by the euglenoids, chrysomonads, and dinoflagellates (Provasoli 1969).

The large predaceous rotifer *Asplanchna* makes clear-cut reponses to α-tocopherol (vitamin E), which it receives second hand from herbivorous prey that feed on the algal source. Vitamin E causes amictic females to produce mictic offspring, whose haploid eggs develop into males if unfertilized and into diploid-resistant eggs when fertilized. This kind of production signals the end of the population, for the fertilized eggs will lie dormant for some time. The advantages of such a scheme whereby the population disappears while primary production is high are obscure. Apparently the males require α-tocopherol for fertility, receiving the vitamin from their mothers. Perhaps the benefits from sexuality and genetic recombination outweigh other considerations, and the population, therefore, responds to vitamin E even though it means the end of actively feeding individuals when food resources are abundant. Gilbert (1972) has written a series of articles on this subject.

EXTERNAL METABOLITES

External metabolites, or ectocrine substances, are released to the water by aquatic organisms. Some are toxic substances, such as those produced by certain bluegreens and marine dinoflagellates. Others act as growth inhibitors or as stimulators of growth for other species. Antibiotics are probably secreted more than is generally suspected.

A most remarkable case was worked out by Gilbert (1966) following the observations of Beauchamp (1952). The herbivorous rotifer *Brachionus calyciflorus* responds to some substance produced by its enemy, the carnivorous *Asplanchna,* by reproducing young with long posterolateral spines. The spines effectively hinder *Asplanchna* in attempts to engulf *Brachionus.* (*Asplanchna* has no difficulty in eating the short-spined variety.) This unusual type of embryonic induction occurs before cleavage commences and is ineffective in later stages.

14
Use and misuse of inland waters

Man has used lakes and streams for numerous purposes and for many years. Our waters satisfy domestic and industrial needs and provide transportation, hydroelectric power, a means for sewage and waste disposal, fish for food and sport, and other recreation, including esthetic appreciation. As a result of our various demands, we have created new types of lakes and streams and modified preexisting natural aquatic habitats. We have destroyed some segments of the aquatic biota while husbanding others, and we have transported species from continent to continent both inadvertently and by design.

How do the new or changed aquatic habitats differ from the old? And what is the future for limnology as a result of man's extensive modifications of inland waters? These questions lie at the very heart of modern limnology.

The areas and volumes of lentic waters on earth have increased remarkably during the twentieth century because of the impoundment of rivers to form both medium and large reservoirs (Neel 1963;

Avakian and Fortunatov 1972) and because of the construction of countless small farm ponds and stock tanks (Dendy 1963). Concomitantly, natural lotic habitats have decreased and have been altered until scarcely a major river now flows unmodified to the sea. Meanwhile, new watercourses in the form of canals and irrigation ditches have multiplied, especially in arid regions of the American West (Pennak 1958). Although artificial lakes do not appeal to many limnologists, a great deal of effort is being devoted to studying their ecology, and rightfully so. Increasing in number every year, they are now an important part of our aquatic habitats, and they differ from natural lakes in many respects.

The lakes formed by damming rivers are frequently steep sided because the most efficient place to construct a dam is where the river valley is narrow. The reservoirs on rivers, unlike natural lakes, have an asymmetrical depth distribution with a longitudinal differentiation from the upper to the lower part and with maximum depth near the dam. Often the waterflow through artifical lakes surpasses that of natural lakes, but perhaps the most striking difference is that the outflow is not always from the surface. Water may leave the reservoir from various levels, frequently from the deeper layers. Shorelines of artificial lakes commonly fluctuate, rising and falling as water is alternately stored and released. The steep-sided astatic marginal areas usually lack a flourishing flora in the littoral region, although this does not apply to many small ponds where macrophytes create problems by growing profusely, thus obliterating the open water. Although the shores of these artificial lakes in temperate regions are often barren, their counterparts in tropical zones are sometimes choked with vegetation (Little 1966). Some large tropical impoundments are covered with floating plants— the water fern *Salvinia,* the water hya-

cinth *Eichornia,* and the water lettuce *Pistia*—that are notorious nuisances.

The physical limnology of impoundments also differs from that of most natural lakes (Neel 1963). Unusual density currents flowing into river impoundments bring silt that settles out in the basin and covers areas that were once swept clean by currents. Moreover, near the perpendicular dam surface there are abnormal temperature and chemical stratifications rarely matched in natural bodies of water.

The effects that impoundment has on streams and stream-side communities are far reaching. Lacustrine plants and animals appear where once the lotic community existed. Plankton populations develop, and rheophilic invertebrates and stream fishes are replaced. Because former conditions are altered abruptly by damming, environmental instability results, and many years are required for well-balanced stable communities to develop. It is common practice to introduce plankton-feeding fishes, such as the threadfin shad *Dorosoma petenense* used in new southwestern lakes, to take advantage of increased plankton populations (Minckley 1973).

The slack waters of a river impoundment result in siltation, with disastrous effects on molluscs, sponges, and insects that require cleaner substrates. Isom (1969) estimated that the formerly rich mussel fauna of the Tennessee River system, now largely impounded, has been reduced to about one half of the original 100 or so species. He has also found that the orginal Mussel Shoals, an area unexcelled in molluscan richness, lie beneath 6 m of muck behind Wilson Dam (Stansberry 1970).

Upstream from a reservoir, the physicochemical effects of impoundment may not be marked, but other effects have been noted. Migratory fishes are eliminated from the upper reaches of the stream if there is no way to pass the barrier imposed by the dam. In some instances unionid clams, which relied on specific fishes for their parasitic glochidial stages, have disappeared because the necessary host could no longer make its way upstream. The construction of the Keokuk Dam on the Mississippi, for example, is probably indirectly responsible for the upstream absence of clam species that were once commercially important in Lake Pepin (Carlander and associates 1963).

The river and its communities below a dammed lake also change as a result of the impoundment. Because the new lake acts as a giant sediment trap, turbidity is reduced in the stream below. Temperatures may be lower than formerly if the water feeding into the stream is released from low levels in stratified reservoirs. Thus, the Colorado River flowing from the new Lake Powell is clear and cold, about 10° C for 200 km. Water rushing from the dam may offer a fast-flowing habitat where, other conditions being equal, rheophilous forms such as *Simulium* may flourish, although they were absent before. Water released from below the thermocline during summer is high in nutrients. In eutrophic waters H_2S and ammonia are often present and produce a detrimental effect for some distance downstream.

Many natural streams and lakes have been polluted by heavy metals, minerals such as asbestos, persistent biocides, fertilizers, acids, bases, oil, chlorine, and the tremendous organic loads imposed by urban sewage and waste from livestock (Hynes 1960).

Thermal pollution also has consequences—often detrimental. In the United States about two thirds of the 800 million m³ of water used each day for industry is for the purpose of cooling (Hill 1974). When this water is returned to the lakes or streams, it may be, on the average, 10° C warmer, unless treated effectively in cooling towers to dissipate heat. The warm influent may profoundly alter the metabolism and reproduction of individual plants, invertebrates, and fishes. In reviewing the subject of thermal pollution, Clark (1969) reminded us that its effect on complex aquatic ecosystems may be much greater than on any single species.

Artificial waterways have provided routes for some species to drainage systems where they had been previously absent. The most notable example in North America is the movement of the sea lamprey, *Petromyzon marinus,* and the alewife, *Alosa pseudoharengus,* into the upper Great Lakes. Presumably, they traveled via the Welland Canal, which circumvents the ancient barrier, Niagara Falls, above Lake Ontario. A southward migration of northern fauna has been noted in reservoirs on the Volga (Rzóska 1966). This has been explained by the presence of suitable cold-water habitats in the lower strata of the new lakes. Even temporary-pond fauna may be spreading via man-made stock tanks in arid regions (Pennak 1958). Two species of fairy shrimps seem to be moving northward to Arizona from Mexico because of stock ponds that serve as stepping stones (Belk 1974).

Deliberate transfers have also been made. This applies especially to fishes, although some invertebrates have been placed in lakes and streams in the hope that they will afford new food resources for fishes. The carp, *Cyprinus carpio,* which came to us from Asia via Europe, is considered a nuisance in North America; it seems incredible that it was introduced with enthusiasm during the nineteenth century as a food source. Salmonid fishes from Europe and North America have been spread through the world because of their fine flesh and recreational value.

Thus by constructing artificial waters, we have increased diversity on one hand even as we have decreased it. The overall picture, however, is probably a lessening of diversity. Although the number of fish species in Arizona was originally about 25, exotic introductions have increased the state's fish fauna to more than 100 species (Minckley 1973). Some of the original native species have disappeared or are endangered because of competition from the new arrivals and alteration of their fragile aquatic habitats.

The species we destroy are, of course, irreplaceable. For example, the inundation of Tasmanian Lake Pedder will destroy (if it has not done so already) about 18 unique endemic species of both plants and animals, including a remarkable primitive syncarid crustacean (Bayly and Williams 1973). Despite the fact that the lake is in an Australian National Park, a dam was built for hydroelectric purposes and impounds water that will eliminate this unusual biota. Although there has been little publicity, we are also in the process of gradually destroying about 1,000 species of North American freshwater molluscs through pollution and impoundment (Stansberry 1970).

Today we should realize that keeping a lake unmodified involves extended protection, which includes leaving its drainage basin untouched. Even road construction to make the lake available for study could result in loss of pristine qualities (Bormann and associates 1969). There are also problems from pollutants that arrive via the atmosphere; mercury vapor is one of these. It is normally released from mercury-containing rocks by degassing, so there is always a background amount (about 0.1 ppb) in the air; but industrial sources have augmented this greatly in recent years (Greeson 1970). Thus, there has been an increase in the conversion of mercury to dangerous organic compounds by anaerobic microbes (Wood and associates 1968). They enter the food chain and accumulate in the carnivorous fish. These are then denied to man as food when concentrations reach toxic levels.

This all paints a gloomy picture, but there are some bright spots. The recent history of Lake Washington, where pollution was abated with excellent results, shows what a concerned and informed citizenry can do (Edmondson 1972b). The science of limnology is flourishing today, and there is much to be learned from new impoundments and altered streams, as well as from natural streams and lakes, polluted though many may be. The fifteenth Congress of the International Association of Limnology met at Madison, Wisconsin, in 1962, the first time the group had assembled on the North American continent. At this meeting about 150 papers were presented by limnologists from many nations. Twelve years later the society met again in North America; the nineteenth Congress gathered at Winnipeg, Manitoba, and almost 500 papers were on the agenda. This increase, more than threefold, proclaims the study of aquatic environments alive and well!

Literature cited

Aaronson, S. 1971. The synthesis of extracellular macromolecules and membranes by a population of the phytoflagellate *Ochromonas danica*. Limnol. Oceanogr. 16:1-9.

Allen, H. L. 1971. Primary productivity, chemo-organotrophy, and nutritional interactions of epiphytic algae and bacteria on macrophytes in the littoral of a lake. Ecol. Monogr. 41:91-127.

Allen, H. L. 1972. Phytoplankton photosynthesis, micronutrient interactions, and inorganic carbon availability in a soft-water Vermont lake. Pages 63-83 *in* G. E. Likens, ed. Nutrients and eutrophication: the limiting-nutrient controversy. ASLO Special Symposia 1. American Society of Limnology and Oceanography, Lawrence, Kansas.

American Public Health Association. 1946. Standard methods for the examination of water and sewage, 9th ed. New York. 286 pp.

Anderson, D. V. 1961. A note on the morphology of the basins of the Great Lakes. J. Fish. Res. Bd. Canada 18:273-277.

Anderson, E. R. 1952. Water-loss investigations: vol. 1. Lake Hefner studies. Tech. Rept. U. S. Geol. Surv. Circ. 229:71-119.

Anderson, E. R., and D. W. Pritchard. 1951. Physical limnology of Lake Mead. U. S. Navy Electron. Lab. Rept. 258, Probl. NEL 2JI. San Diego, Cal. 152 pp.

Anderson, G. C. 1958a. Seasonal characteristics of two saline lakes in Washington. Limnol. Oceanogr. 3:51-68.

Anderson, G. C. 1958b. Some limnological features of a shallow saline meromictic lake. Limnol. Oceanogr. 3:259-270.

Anderson, R. O., and F. F. Hooper. 1956. Seasonal abundance and production of littoral bottom fauna in a southern Michigan lake. Trans. Amer. Microsc. Soc. 75:259-270.

Anderson, R. S. 1967. Diaptomid copepods from two mountain ponds in Alberta. Canadian J. Zool. 45:1043-1047.

Angino, E. E., K. B. Armitage, and J. C. Tash. 1965. A chemical and limnological study of Lake Vanda, Victoria Land, Antarctica. Univ. Kansas Sci. Bull. 45:1097-1118.

Armitage, K. B. 1958. Lagos volcánicos de El Salvador. Comun. Inst. Trop. Invest. Cient. 7:39-48; 18 figs.

Armitage, K. B., and H. B. House. 1962. A limnological reconnaissance in the area of McMurdo Sound, Antarctica. Limnol. Oceanogr. 7:36-41.

Arnold, D. E. 1971. Ingestion, assimilation, survival, and reproduction by *Daphnia pulex* fed seven species of blue-green algae. Limnol. Oceanogr. 16:906-920.

Arx, W. S. von. 1962. An introduction to physical oceanography. Addison-Wesley Publishing Co., Inc., Reading, Mass. 422 pp.

Avakian, A. B., and M. A. Fortunatov. 1972. Les lacs de barrage du monde. Verh. Internat. Verein. Limnol. 18:787-796.

Back, W., and B. B. Hanshaw. 1970. Comparison of chemical hydrogeology of the carbonate peninsulas of Florida and Yucatan. J. Hydrol. 10:330-368.

Baker, A. L., and A. J. Brook. 1971. Optical density profiles as an aid to the study of microstratified phytoplankton populations in lakes. Arch. Hydrobiol. 69:214-233.

Baldi, E. 1949. La situation actuelle de la recherche limnologique après le Congres de Zürich. Schweiz. Z. Hydrol. 11:637-649.

Bärlocher, F., and B. Kendrick. 1973. Fungi in the diet of *Gammarus pseudolimnaeus* (Amphipoda). Oikos 24:295-300.

Barnes, D. F. 1960. An investigation of a perennially frozen lake. U. S. Air Force Survey in Geophysics. (ARDC) 129. 134 pp.

Barringer, R. W. 1967. World's meteorite craters ("Astroblemes"). Version VII, Feb. 1967. Meteoritics 3:151-157.

Bartsch, A. F., and M. S. Allum. 1957. Biological factors in treatment of raw sewage in artificial ponds. Limnol. Oceanogr. 2:77-84.

Baylor, E. R., and W. H. Sutcliffe, Jr. 1963. Dissolved organic matter in seawater as a source of particulate food. Limnol. Oceanogr. 8:369-371.

Bayly, I. A. E. 1964. Chemical and biological studies on some acidic lakes of east Australian sandy coastal lowlands. Australian J. Mar. Freshwat. Res. 15:56-72.

Bayly, I. A. E. 1967. The general biological classification of aquatic environments with special reference to those of Australia. Pages 78-104 *in* A. H.

Weatherby, ed. Australian inland waters and their fauna: eleven studies. Australian National University Press, Canberra, NSW.

Bayly, I. A. E., and W. D. Williams. 1973. Inland waters and their ecology. Longmans of Australia Pty. Ltd., 316 pp.

Beamish, R. J., and H. H. Harvey. 1972. Acidification of the La Cloche Mountain Lakes, Ontario, resulting fish mortalities. J. Fish. Res. Bd. Canada 29:1131-1143.

Beauchamp, P. de. 1952. Un facteur de la variabilité chez les rotiferes du genre *Brachionus*. Compt. Rend. Acad. Sci. Paris 234:573-575.

Beauchamp. R. S. A. 1953. Sulphates in African inland waters. Nature 171:769.

Beauchamp, R. S. A. 1964. The Rift Valley lakes of Africa. Verh. Internat. Verein. Limnol. 15:91-99.

Beeton, A. M. 1962. Light penetration in the Great Lakes. Univ. Michigan, Great Lakes Res. Div., Inst. Sci. Tech. 9:68-76.

Beeton, A. M. 1969. Changes in the environment and biota of the Great Lakes. Pages 150-187 *in* Eutrophication: causes, consequences, corrections. National Academy of Sciences, Washington, D. C.

Belk, D. 1972. The biology and ecology of *Eulimnadia antlei* Mackin (Conchostraca). Southwest Nat. 16:297-305.

Belk, D. 1974. Zoogeography of the Arizona Anostraca with a key to the North American species. Ph.D. Dissertation, Arizona State University, Tempe, 90 pp.

Bell, P. R. 1959. The ability of *Sphagnum* to absorb cations differentially from dilute solutions resembling natural waters. J. Ecol. 47:351-355.

Bent, A. M. 1960. Pollen analysis of Deadman Lake, Chuska Mountains, New Mexico. M. S. Thesis, University of Minnesota, Minneapolis. 22 pp.

Berg, A. 1962. Exposé des methodes d'analyse chimique et physico-chimique des eaux humiques. Mem. Ist. Ital. Idrobiol. 15:183-206.

Berg, C. O. 1950. Biology of certain Chironomidae reared from *Potamogeton*. Ecol. Monogr. 20:83-101.

Berg, C. O. 1963. Middle Atlantic States. Pages 191-237 *in* D. G. Frey, ed. Limnology in North America. University of Wisconsin Press, Madison.

Berman, T. 1970. Alkaline phosphatases and phosphorous availability in Lake Kinneret. Limnol. Oceanogr. 15:663-674.

Beyers, R. J., and H. T. Odum. 1959. The use of carbon dioxide to construct pH curves for the measurement of productivity. Limnol. Oceanogr. 4:499-502.

Birge, E. A. 1897. Plankton studies on Lake Mendota: II. The Crustacea from the plankton from July, 1894, to December, 1896. Trans. Wisconsin Acad. Sci. Arts Lett. 11:274-448.

Birge, E. A. 1916. The work of the wind in warming

a lake. Trans. Wisconsin Acad. Sci. Arts Lett. 18:341-391.

Birge, E. A., and C. Juday. 1911. The inland lakes of Wisconsin: the dissolved gases of the water and their biological significance. Wisconsin Geol. Nat. Hist. Surv. Bull. 22. 259 pp.

Birge, E. A., and C. Juday. 1934. Particulate and dissolved organic matter in inland lakes. Ecol. Monogr. 4:440-474.

Birge, E. A., C. Juday, and H. W. March. 1928. The temperature of the bottom deposits of Lake Mendota: a chapter in the heat exchanges of the lake. Trans. Wisconsin Acad. Sci. Arts Lett. 23:187-231.

Björk, S. 1972. Swedish lake restoration program gets results. Ambio 1:153-165.

Björk, S., and others. 1972. Ecosystem studies in connection with the restoration of lakes. Verh. Internat. Verein. Limnol. 18:379-387.

Bormann, F. H., G. E. Likens, D. W. Fisher, and R. S. Pierce. 1969. Nutrient loss accelerated by clearcutting of a forest ecosystem. Science 159:882-884.

Bradbury, J. P. 1971. Limnology of Zuni Salt Lake, New Mexico. Bull. Geol. Soc. Amer. 82:379-398.

Brewer, M. C. 1958. The thermal regime of an Arctic lake. Trans. Amer. Geophysics Union 39:278-284.

Brinkhurst, R. O. 1966. The Tubificidae (Oligochaeta) of polluted waters. Verh. Internat. Verein. Limnol. 16:858-859.

Britt, N. W. 1955. Stratification in western Lake Erie in summer of 1953: effects on the *Hexagenia* (Ephemeroptera) populations. Ecology 36:239-244.

Brock, T. D. 1973. Lower pH limit for the existence of blue-green algae: evolutionary and ecological implications. Science 179:480-483.

Brönsted, J. N., and C. Wesenberg-Lund. 1911. Chemisch-physikalische Untersuchungen der dänischen Gewässer nebst Bemerkungen über ihre Bedeutung für unserere Aufassung der Temporalvariationen. Internat. Rev. Hydrobiol. 4:251-290, 437-492.

Brook, A. J. 1965. Planktonic algae as indicators of lake types, with special reference to the Desmidaceae. Limnol. Oceanogr. 10:403-411.

Brook, A. J., A. L. Baker, and A. R. Klemer. 1971. The use of turbimetry in studies of the population dynamics of phytoplankton populations with special reference to *Oscillatoria aghardii* var. *isothrix*. Mitt. Internat. Verein. Limnol. 19:244-252.

Brooks, J. L. 1959. Cladocera. Pages 587-656 *in* W. T. Edmondson, ed. Ward and Whipple's freshwater biology, 2nd ed. John Wiley & Sons, Inc., New York.

Brooks, J. L., and E. S. Deevey, Jr. 1963. New England. Pages 117-162 *in* D. G. Frey, ed. Limnology

in North America. University of Wisconsin Press, Madison.

Brooks, J. L., and S. I. Dodson. 1965. Predation, body size, and composition of plankton. Science 150:28-35.

Brown, L. A. 1929. The natural history of cladocerans in relation to temperature: II. Temperature coefficients for development. Amer. Nat. 63:346-352.

Brundin, L. 1958. The bottom faunistic lake-type system. Verh. Internat. Verein. Limnol. 13:288-297.

Brunskill, G. J. 1969. Fayetteville Green Lake, New York: II. Precipitation and sedimentation of calcite in a meromictic lake with laminated sediments. Limnol. Oceanogr. 14:830-847.

Brunskill, G. J., and D. W. Schindler. 1971. Geography and bathymetry of selected lake basins, Experimental Lakes Area, northwestern Ontario. J. Fish. Res. Bd. Canada 28:139-155.

Bryson, R. A., and V. E. Suomi. 1951. Midsummer renewal of oxygen within the hypolimnion. J. Mar. Res. 10:263-269.

Burns, C. W. 1968. The relationship between body size of filter-feeding Cladocera and the maximum size of particle injested. Limnol. Oceanogr. 13:675-678.

Burris, R. H., F. J. Eppling, H. B. Wahlin, and P. W. Wilson. 1943. Detection of nitrogen fixation with isotopic nitrogen. J. Biol. Chem. 148:349-357.

Cameron, R. E., and W. H. Fuller. 1960. Nitrogen fixation by some soil algae in Arizona soils. Proc. Amer. Soil Sci. Soc. 24:353-356.

Carlander, K. D., R. S. Campbell, and W. H. Irwin. 1963. Mid-continent states. Pages 317-348 *in* D. G. Frey, ed. Limnology in North America. University of Wisconsin Press, Madison.

Carpelan, L. H. 1957. Hydrobiology of the Alviso salt ponds. Ecology 38:375-390.

Carpelan, L. H. 1958. The Salton Sea: physical and chemical characteristics. Limnol. Oceanogr. 3:373-386.

Carpelan, L. H. 1967. Daily alkalinity changes in brackish desert pools. Internat. J. Oceanol. Limnol. 1:165-193.

Carpenter, E. J. 1973. Nitrogen fixation by *Oscillatoria (Trichodesmium) thiebautii* in the southwestern Sargasso Sea. Deep-Sea Res. 20:285-288.

Carr, J. F., and J. K. Hiltunen. 1965. Changes in the bottom fauna of western Lake Erie from 1930-1961. Limnol. Oceanogr. 10:551-569.

Carroll, D. 1962. Rainwater as a chemical agent of geologic processes—a review. U. S. Geol. Surv. Water-Supply Paper 1535-G. U. S. Government Printing Office, Washington, D. C. 23 pp.

Carter, J. C. H. 1965. The ecology of the calanoid copepod *Pseudocalanus minutus* Krøyer in Tessiarsuk, a coastal meromictic lake of northern

Labrador. Limnol. Oceanogr. 10:345-353.

Caspers, H., and L. Karbe. 1967. Vorschlage für eine saprobiologische Typisierung der Gewässer. Int. Rev. Hydrobiol. 52:145-162.

Castenholz, R. W. 1960. Seasonal changes in the attached algae of freshwater and saline lakes in the Lower Grand Coulee, Washington. Limnol. Oceanogr. 5:1-28.

Chandler, D. C. 1937. Fate of typical lake plankton in streams. Ecol. Monogr. 7:445-479.

Clark, J. R. 1969. Thermal pollution and aquatic life. Sci. Amer. 220(3): 21-27.

Clarke, F. W. 1924. The data of geochemistry, 5th ed. Bull. U. S. Geol. Surv. 770. U. S. Government Printing Office, Washington, D. C. 841 pp.

Clark, G. L. 1939. The utilization of solar energy by aquatic organisms. Pages 27-38 in E. R. Moulton, ed. Problems of lake biology. Pub. 10, A.A.A.S., Washington, D. C.

Coffin, C. C., F. R. Hayes, L. H. Jodrey, and S. G. Whiteway. 1949. Exchange of materials in a lake as studied by the addition of radioactive phosphorus. Canadian J. Res. (D) 27:207-222.

Cole, G. A. 1954. Studies on a Kentucky Knobs Lake: I. Some environmental factors. Trans. Kentucky Acad. Sci. 15:31-47.

Cole, G. A. 1955. An ecological study of the microbenthic fauna of two Minnesota lakes. Amer. Midl. Nat. 53:213-230.

Cole, G. A. 1957. Studies on a Kentucky Knobs Lake: III. Some qualitative aspects of the net plankton. Trans. Kentucky Acad. Sci. 18:88-101.

Cole, G. A. 1968. Desert limnology. Pages 423-486 in G. W. Brown, Jr., ed. Desert biology. Academic Press, Inc., New York.

Cole, G. A., and W. T. Barry. 1973. Montezuma Well, Arizona, as a habitat. J. Arizona Acad. Sci. 8:7-13.

Cole, G. A., and G. L. Batchelder. 1969. Dynamics of an Arizona travertine-forming stream. J. Arizona Acad. Sci. 5:271-283.

Cole, G. A., and R. J. Brown. 1967. The chemistry of Artemia habitats. Ecology 48:858-861.

Cole, G. A., and W. L. Minckley. 1968. "Anomalous" thermal conditions in a hypersaline inland pond. J. Arizona Acad. Sci. 5:105-107.

Cole, G. A., M. C. Whiteside, and R. J. Brown. 1967. Unusual monomixis in two saline Arizona ponds. Limnol. Oceanogr. 12:584-591.

Comita, G. W. 1964. Energy budget of Diaptomus siciloides. Verh. Internat. Verein. Limnol. 15:646-653.

Comita, G. W. 1972. The seasonal zooplankton cycles, production and transformation of energy in Severson Lake, Minnesota. Arch. Hydrobiol. 70:14-66.

Conway, E. J. 1942. Mean geochemical data in relation to oceanic evolution. Proc. Roy. Irish Acad. (B) 48:119-159.

Conway, K., and F. R. Trainor. 1972. Scenedesmus morphology and flotation. J. Phycol. 8:138-143.

Coriolis, G. G. 1835. Mémoire sur les équations du movement relatif des systèmes de corps. J. Éc. Roy. Polyt., Paris 15:142-154.

Covich, A., and M. Stuiver. 1974. Changes in oxygen 18 as a measure of long-term fluctuations in tropical lake levels and molluscan populations. Limnol. Oceanogr. 19:682-691.

Cowgill, U. M., and G. E. Hutchinson. 1970. Chemistry and mineralogy of the sediments and their source materials. Pages 37-101 in Ianula: An account of the history and development of the Lago di Monterosi, Latium, Italy. Trans. Amer. Phil. Soc. 60(4), Philadelphia.

Cowles, H. C. 1899. The ecological relations of the vegetation on the sand dunes of Lake Michigan. Bot. Gaz. 27:95-117, 167-175, 281-308, 361-391.

Cummins, K. W., and J. C. Wuycheck. 1971. Caloric equivalents for investigations in ecological energetics. Mitt. Internat. Verein. Limnol. 18:1-158.

Curl, H., Jr., J. T. Hardy, and R. Ellermeier. 1972. Spectral absorption of solar radiation in alpine snowfields. Ecology 53:1189-1194.

Darnell, R. M. 1956. Analysis of a population of the tropical freshwater shrimp, Atya scabra (Leach). Amer. Midl. Nat. 55:131-138.

Darnell, R. M. 1961. Trophic spectrum of an estuarine community, based on studies in Lake Pontchartrain, Louisiana. Ecology 42:553-568.

De, P. K. 1939. The role of blue-green algae in nitrogen fixation in rice-fields. Proc. Roy. Soc. London (B) 127:121-139.

Deevey, E. S., Jr. 1941. Limnological studies in Connecticut: VI. The quantity and composition of the bottom fauna of 36 Connecticut and New York lakes. Ecol. Monogr. 11:413-455.

Deevey, E. S., Jr. 1942a. A re-examination of Thoreau's "Walden." Quart. Rev. Biol. 17:1-11.

Deevey, E. S., Jr. 1942b. Studies on Connecticut lake sediments: III. The biostratonomy of Linsley Pond. Amer. J. Sci. 240:233-264, 313-324.

Deevey, E. S., Jr. 1951. Life in the depths of a pond. Sci. Amer. 185(4):68-72.

Deevey, E. S., Jr. 1955. The obliteration of the hypolimnion. Mem. Ist. Ital. Idrobiol. Suppl. 8:9-38.

Deevey, E. S., Jr. 1957. Limnologic studies in Middle America with a chapter on Aztec limnology. Trans. Connecticut Acad. Arts Sci. 39:213-328; 4 plates.

Deevey, E. S., Jr. 1970. In defense of mud. Bull. Ecol. Soc. Amer. 51:5-8.

Deevey, E. S., and M. Stuiver. 1964. Distribution of natural isotopes of carbon in Linsley Pond and other New England lakes. Limnol. Oceanogr. 9:1-11.

Dendy, J. S. 1963. Farm ponds. Pages 595-620 in D. G. Frey, ed. Limnology in North America. University of Wisconsin Press, Madison.

Dietz, R. S., and J. F. McHone. 1972. Laguna Quatavita: not meteoritic, probable salt collapse crater. Meteoritics 7:303-307.

Dodds, G. S. 1926. Entomostraca from the Panama Canal Zone with description of one new species. Occas. Pap. Mus. Zool. Univ. Michigan 174:1-27.

Drewes, K. 1928. Über die Assimilation des Luftstickstoffe durch Blaualgen. Zentbl. Bakt. Parasitke Abt. II, 76:88-101.

Dumont, H. J. 1972. The biological cycle of molybdenum in relation to primary production and waterbloom formation in a eutrophic pond. Verh. Internat. Verein. Limnol. 18:84-92.

Dunson, W. A., and G. W. Ehlert. 1971. Effects of temperature and salinity and surface water flow on distribution of the sea snake *Pelamis*. Limnol. Oceanogr. 16:845-853.

Dussart, B. 1966. Limnologie: L'Étude des Eaux Continentales. Gauthier-Villars, Paris. 677 pp.

Dye, J. F. 1944. The calculation of alkalinities and free carbon dioxide in water by use of nomographs. J. Amer. W. W. Assoc. 36:895-900.

Dye, J. F. 1952. Calculation of the effect of temperature on the three forms of alkalinity. J. Amer. W. W. Assoc. 44:356-372.

Eberly, W. R. 1964. Further studies on the metalimnetic oxygen maximum with special reference to its occurrence throughout the world. Invest. Indiana Lakes Streams 6:103-139.

Eddy, S. 1963. Minnesota and the Dakotas. Pages 301-315 *in* D. G. Frey, ed. Limnology in North America. University of Wisconsin Press, Madison.

Edmondson, W. T. 1956. The relation of photosynthesis by phytoplankton to light in lakes. Ecology 37:161-174.

Edmondson, W. T., ed. 1959. Ward and Whipple's fresh-water biology, 2nd ed. John Wiley & Sons, Inc., New York. 1248 pp.

Edmondson, W. T. 1960. Reproduction rates of rotifers in natural populations. Mem. Ist. Ital. Idrobiol. 12:21-77.

Edmondson, W. T. 1963. Pacific Coast and Great Basin. Pages 371-392 *in* D. G. Frey, ed. Limnology in North America. University of Wisconsin Press, Madison.

Edmondson, W. T. 1969. Eutrophication in North America. Pages 124-149 *in* Eutrophication: causes, consequences, correctives. National Academy of Sciences, Washington, D. C.

Edmondson, W. T. 1972a. Nutrients and phytoplankton in Lake Washington. Pages 172-193 *in* G. E. Likens, ed. Nutrients and eutrophication: the limiting-nutrient controversy. ASLO Special Symposia 1. American Society of Limnology and Oceanography, Lawrence, Kansas.

Edmondson, W. T. 1972b. The present condition of Lake Washington. Verh. Internat. Verein. Limnol. 18:284-291.

Edmondson, W. T., and G. C. Winberg. 1971. Secondary productivity in fresh waters. IBP Handbook 17. Blackwell Scientific Publications Ltd., Oxford, 358 pp.

Eggleton, F. E. 1931. A limnological study of the profundal bottom fauna of certain fresh-water lakes. Ecol. Monogr. 1:231-332.

Eggleton, F. E. 1956. Limnology of a meromictic interglacial plunge-basin lake. Trans. Amer. Microsc. Soc. 75:334-378.

Eichhorn, R. 1957. Zur Populationsdynamik der Calaniden Copepoden in Titisee und Feldsee. Arch. Hydrobiol. Suppl. 24:186-246.

Elster, H. I. 1954. Über die Populationsdynamik von *Eudiaptomus gracilis* Sars und *Heterocope borealis* Fischer in Bodensee-Obersee. Arch. Hydrobiol. Suppl. 20:546-614.

Elton, C. 1927. Animal ecology. Sidgwick & Jackson Ltd., London. 207 pp.

Emery, K. O., and G. T. Csanady. 1972. Surface circulation of lakes and nearly land-locked seas. Proc. Nat. Acad. Sci., Washington, D. C. 70:93-97.

Engel, R. 1962. *Eurytemora affinis,* a calanoid copepod new to Lake Erie, Ohio J. Sci. 62:252.

Eppley, R. W., and V. MaciasR. 1963. Role of the alga *Chlamydomonas mundana* in anaerobic waste stabilization lagoons. Limnol. Oceanogr. 8:411-415.

Evans, J. H. 1961. Growth of Lake Victoria phytoplankton in enriched cultures. Nature 189:417.

Ewing, M., F. Press, and W. L. Donn. 1954. An explanation of the Lake Michigan wave of 26 June 1954. Science 120:684-686.

Findenegg, I. 1935. Limnologische Untersuchungen im Kärtner Seengebiet. Internat. Rev. Hydrobiol. 32:369-423.

Findenegg, I. 1937. Holomiktische und meromiktische Seen. Internat. Rev. Hydrobiol. 35:586-610.

Findenegg, I. 1964. Types of planktonic primary production in the lakes of the Eastern Alps as found by the radioactive carbon method. Verh. Internat. Verein. Limnol. 15:352-359.

Findenegg, I. 1971. Die Produktionsleistungen einiger planktischer Algenarten in ihrem natürlischen Milieu. Arch. Hydrobiol. 69:273-293.

Fish, G. R. 1956. Chemical factors limiting growth of phytoplankton in Lake Victoria. East Afric. Agric. J. 21:152-158.

Fisher, S. G., and G. E. Likens. 1973. Energy flow in Bear Brook, New Hampshire: an integrative approach to stream ecosystem metabolism. Ecol. Monogr. 43:421-439.

Flint, R. F. 1957. Glacial and Pleistocene geology. John Wiley & Sons, Inc., New York. 553 pp.; 5 plates.

Florin, M. J., and H. E. Wright, Jr. 1969. Diatom evidence for the persistence of stagnant glacial ice in Minnesota. Bull. Geol. Soc. Amer. 80:295-704.

Fogg, G. E. 1942. Studies on nitrogen fixation by

blue-green algae: 1. Nitrogen fixation by *Anabaena cylindrica* Lemm. J. Exper. Bot. 19:78-87.

Forel, F. A. 1892, 1895, 1904. Le Léman: monographie limnologique. F. Rouge, Lausanne. 3 vols.

Foster, J. M. 1973. Limnology of two desert recharged-groundwater ponds. Ph.D. Thesis, Arizona State University, Tempe. 233 pp.

Frantz, T. C., and A. J. Cordone. 1967. Observations on deepwater plants in Lake Tahoe, California and Nevada. Ecology 48:709-714.

Fredeen, F. J. H. 1960. Bacteria as a source of food for black-fly larvae. Nature 187:963.

Frey, D. G. 1955. Längsee: a history of mermomixis. Mem. Ist. Ital. Idrobiol. Suppl. 8:141-161.

Frey, D. G. 1959. The taxonomic phylogenetic significance of the head pores of the Chydoridae (Cladocera). Internat. Rev. Hydrobiol. 44:28-50.

Frey, D. G. 1964. Remains of animals in Quaternary lake and bog sediments and their interpretation. Ergebn. Limnol. Arch. Hydrobiol., Beihefte 2:1-114.

Fryer, G. 1968. Evolution and adaptive radiation in the Chydoridae (Crustacea: Cladocera): a study in comparative morphology and ecology. Royal Soc. London Philos. Trans. (B) 254:221-385.

Gaarder, T., and H. H. Gran. 1927. Investigations of the production of plankton in the Oslo Fjord. Rapp. et Proc.-Verb., Cons. Internat. Explor. Mer. 42:1-48.

Geiling, W. T., and R. S. Campbell. 1972. The effect of temperature on the development rate of the major life stages of *Diaptomus pallidus* Herrick. Limnol. Oceanogr. 17:304-307.

Gessner, F. 1959. Hydrobotanik: II. Stoffhaushalt. Veb Deutscher Verlag Der Wissenschaften, Berlin.

Geyer, G. A. 1973. The bass is a gringo in Guatemala. Internat. Wildlife 3:18-19.

Gilbert, J. J. 1966. Rotifer ecology and embryological induction. Science 151:1234-1237.

Gilbert, J. J. 1972. α-Tocopherol in males of the rotifer *Asplanchna sieboldi:* its metabolism and its distribution in the testes and rudimentary gut. J. Exper. Zool. 181:117-128.

Goldman, C. R. 1960. Molybdenum as a factor limiting primary productivity in Castle Lake, California. Science 132:1016-1017.

Goldman, C. R. 1961. The contribution of alder trees *(Alnus tenuifolia)* to the primary productivity of Castle Lake, California. Ecology 42:282-288.

Goldman, C. R. 1970. Antarctic freshwater ecosystems. Pages 609-627 *in* M. W. Holdgate, ed. Antarctic ecology, vol. 2. Academic Press, Inc., New York.

Goldman, C. R. 1972. The role of minor nutrients in limiting the productivity of aquatic ecosystems. Pages 21-38 *in* G. E. Likens, ed. Nutrients and eutrophication: the limiting-nutrient controversy. ASLO Special Symposia 1. American Society of Limnology and Oceanography, Lawrence, Kansas.

Goldman, C. R., D. T. Mason, and J. E. Hobbie. 1967. Two Antarctic desert lakes. Limnol. Oceanogr. 12:295-310.

Goldspink, C. R., and D. B. C. Scott. 1971. Vertical migration of *Chaoborus flavicans* in a Scottish loch. Freshwat. Biol. 1:411-421.

Golterman, H. L. 1971. The determination of mineralization losses in correlatión with the estimation of net primary production with the oxygen method and chemical inhibitors. Freshwat. Biol. 1:249-256.

Golubić, S. 1969. Cyclic and noncyclic mechanisms in the formation of travertine. Verh. Internat. Verein. Limnol. 17:956-961.

Golubić, S. 1973. The relationship between blue-green algae and carbonate deposits. Pages 434-472 *in* N. G. Carr and B. A. Whitton, eds. The biology of the blue-green algae. Bot. Monogr. 9. University of California Press, Berkeley.

Gorham, E. 1957a. The chemical composition of lake waters in Halifax County, Nova Scotia. Limnol. Oceanogr. 2:12-21.

Gorham, E. 1957b. The development of peat lands. Quart. Rev. Biol. 32:145-166.

Gorham, E. 1958a. The physical limnology of Northern Britain: an epitome of the bathymetrical survey of the Scottish freshwater lochs, 1897-1909. Limnol. Oceanogr. 3:40-50.

Gorham, E. 1958b. The influence and importance of daily weather conditions in the supply of chloride, sulphate and other ions to fresh waters from atmospheric precipitation. Royal Soc. London Philos. Trans. (B) 247:147-178.

Gorham, E. 1961. Factors influencing supply of major ions to inland waters, with special reference to the atmosphere. Bull. Geol. Soc. Amer. 72:795-840.

Gorham, E. 1964. Morphometric control of annual heat budgets in temperate lakes. Limnol. Oceanogr. 9:525-529.

Gorham, P. R. 1964. Toxic algae. Pages 307-336 *in* D. F. Jackson, ed. Algae and man. Plenum Publishing Corporation, New York.

Goulden, C. E. 1968. The systematics and evolution of the Moinidae. Trans. Amer. Philos. Soc. 58(6):1-101.

Greenbank, J. T. 1945. Limnological conditions in ice-covered lakes, especially as related to winterkill of fish. Ecol. Monogr. 15:343-392.

Greeson, P. E. 1970. Biological factors in the chemistry of mercury. Pages 32-34 *in* Mercury in the environment. U. S. Geol. Surv. Prof. Paper 713. U. S. Government Printing Office, Washington, D. C.

Hadžišče, S. D. 1966. Das Mixiphänomen im Ohridsee im Laufe der Jahre 1941/42–1964/65. Verh. Internat. Verein. Limnol. 16:134-138.

Hall, C. A. S. 1972. Migration and metabolism in a temperate stream ecosystem. Ecology 53:585-604.

Hamilton, A. L. 1971. Zoobenthos of fifteen lakes in the Experimental Lakes Area, northeastern Ontario. J. Fish. Res. Bd. Canada 28:257-263.

Hamilton, R. D. 1972. The environmental acceptability of NTA: current research and areas of concern. Pages 217-228 in G. E. Likens, ed. Nutrients and eutrophication: the limiting-nutrient controversy. ASLO Special Symposia 1. American Society of Limnology and Oceanography, Lawrence, Kansas.

Hansen, K. 1959. The terms gyttja and dy. Hydrobiologia 13:309-315.

Harned, H. S., and R. Davis. 1943. The ionization constant of carbonic acid in water, and the solubility of CO_2 in water and aqueous salt solutions from 0 to 50°. J. Amer. Chem. Soc. 65:2030-2037.

Harned, H. S., and S. R. Scholes, Jr. 1941. The ionization constant of HCO_3^- from 0 to 50°. J. Amer. Chem. Soc. 63:1706-1709.

Harris, G. P., and J. N. A. Lott. 1973. Observations on Langmuir circulations in Lake Ontario. Limnol. Oceanogr. 18:584-589.

Hartland-Rowe, R. 1972. The limnology of temporary waters and the ecology of Euphyllopoda. Pages 15-31 in R. B. Clark and R. J. Wootton, eds. Essays in hydrobiology. University of Exeter Press, Exeter.

Hartman, R. T., and D. L. Brown. 1967. Changes in internal atmosphere of submersed vascular hydrophytes in relation to photosynthesis. Ecology 48:252-258.

Hasler, A. D. 1947. Eutrophication of lakes by domestic drainage. Ecology 28:383-395.

Hasler, A. D., O. M. Brynildson, and W. T. Helm. 1951. Improving conditions for fish in brown-water bog lakes by alkalization. J. Wildl. Mgt. 15:347-352.

Hayes, F. R. 1955. The effect of bacteria on the exchange of radiophosphorus at the mud-water interface. Verh. Internat. Verein. Limnol. 12:111-116.

Hayes, F. R. 1957. On the variation in bottom fauna and fish yield in relation to trophic level and lake dimensions. J. Fish. Res. Bd. Canada 14:1-32.

Hayes, F. R., and J. E. Phillips. 1958. Lake water and sediment: IV. Radiophosphorus equilibrium with mud, plants, and bacteria under oxidized and reduced conditions. Limnol. Oceanogr. 3:459-480.

Hensen, V. 1887. Über die Bestimmung des Planktons oder des im Meere treibenden Materials an Pflanzen und Thieren. Ber. Komm. Wiss, Unters. Deutschen Meere, Kiel 5:1-107.

Henson, E. B. 1966. A review of Great Lakes benthos research. Univ. Michigan, Great Lakes Res. Div., Pub. 14:37-54.

Henson, E. B., A. S. Bradshaw, and D. C. Chandler. 1961. The physical limnology of Cayuga Lake, New York. Cornell Univ. Agric. Exper. Sta. Memoir 378:1-63.

Hill, G. 1974. Cleansing our waters. Public Affairs Committee, Inc. Pamphlet 497. New York. 28 pp.

Hobbie, John E. 1964. Carbon 14 measurements of primary production in two Arctic Alaskan lakes. Verh. Internat. Verein. Limnol. 15:360-364.

Holmquist, C. 1962. The relict concept—is it a merely zoogeographical concept? Oikos 13:262-292.

Hooper, F. F. 1951. Limnological features of a Minnesota seepage lake. Amer. Midl. Nat. 46:462-481.

Hooper, F. F. 1954. Limnological features of Weber Lake, Cheboygan County, Michigan. Pap. Michigan Acad. Sci. 39:229-244.

Hooper, F. F. 1956. Some chemical and morphometric characteristics of southern Michigan lakes. Pap. Michigan Acad. Sci. 41:109-130.

Hopkins, D. M. 1949. Thaw lakes and thaw sinks in the Imuruk Lake area, Seward Peninsula, Alaska. J. Geol. 57:119-131.

Horne, A. J., and G. E. Fogg. 1970. Nitrogen fixation in some English lakes. Proc. Roy. Soc. (B) 175:351-361.

Horne, A. J., and C. R. Goldman. 1972. Nitrogen fixation in Clear Lake, California: I. Seasonal variation and the role of heterocysts. Limnol. Oceanogr. 17:678-692.

Horne, A. J., and C. R. Goldman. 1974. Suppression of nitrogen fixation by blue-green algae in a eutrophic lake with trace addition of copper. Science 183:409-411.

Hubbs, C., and W. F. Hettler. 1964. Observations on the toleration of high temperatures and low dissolved oxygen in natural waters by Crenichthys baileyi. Southwest. Nat. 9:245-248.

Hutchinson, G. E. 1937. A contribution to the limnology of arid regions primarily founded on observations made in the Lahontan Basin. Trans. Connecticut Acad. Arts Sci. 33:47-132.

Hutchinson, G. E. 1941. Limnological studies in Connecticut: IV. The mechanisms of intermediary metabolism in stratified lakes. Ecol. Monogr. 11:21-60.

Hutchinson, G. E. 1957. A treatise on limnology: vol. I. Geography, physics, and chemistry. John Wiley & Sons, Inc., New York. 1015 pp.

Hutchinson, G. E. 1967. A treatise on limnology: vol. II. Introduction to lake biology and the limnoplankton. John Wiley & Sons, Inc., New York. 1115 pp.

Hutchinson, G. E. 1969. Eutrophication, past and present. Pages 17-26 in Eutrophication: causes, consequences, corrections. National Academy of Sciences, Washington, D. C.

Hutchinson, G. E. 1970a. The chemical ecology of three species of Myriophyllum (Angiospermae, Haloragaceae). Limnol. Oceanogr. 15:1-5.

Hutchinson, G. E. 1970b. The biosphere. Sci. Amer. 223(3):44-53.

Hutchinson, G. E., and V. T. Bowen. 1947. A direct demonstration of the phosphorus cycle in a small lake. Proc. Nat. Acad. Sci., Washington, D. C. 33:148-153.

Hutchinson, G. E., and V. T. Bowen. 1950. Limnological studies in Connecticut: IX, A quantitative radiochemical study of the phosphorus cycle in Linsley Pond. Ecology 31:194-203.

Hutchinson, G. E., and H. Löffler. 1956. The thermal classification of lakes. Proc. Nat. Acad. Sci., Washington, D. C. 42:84-86.

Hutchinson, G. E., and G. E. Pickford. 1932. Limnological observations on Mountain Lake, Virginia. Internat. Rev. Hydrobiol. Hydrogr. 27:252-264.

Hutchinson, G. E., G. E. Pickford, and J. F.' M. Schuurman. 1932. A contribution to the hydrobiology of pans and other inland waters of South-Africa. Arch. Hydrobiol. 24:1-154; tables 1-6; plates 1-8.

Hynes, H. B. N. 1960. The biology of polluted waters. Liverpool University Press, Liverpool. 202 pp.

Hynes, H. B. N. 1969. The ecology of flowing water in relation to management. J. Wat. Poll. Contr. Fed. 42:418-424.

Hynes, H. B. N. 1970. The ecology of running waters. University of Toronto Press, Toronto. 555 pp.

Idso, S. B. 1973. On the concept of lake stability. Limnol. Oceanogr. 18:681-683.

Idso, S. B., and G. A. Cole. 1973. Studies on a Kentucky Knobs Lake: V. Some aspects of the vertical transport of heat in the hypolimnion. J. Ecol. 61:413-420.

Iovino, A. J., and W. H. Bradley. 1969. The role of larval Chironomidae in the production of lacustrine copropel in Mud Lake, Marion County, Florida. Limnol. Oceanogr. 14:898-905.

Isom, B. G. 1969. The mussel resource of the Tennessee River. Malacologia 7:397-425.

Jónasson, P. M., and J. Kristiansen. 1967. Primary and secondary production in Lake Esrom: growth of *Chironomus anthracinus* in relation to seasonal cycles of phytoplankton and dissolved oxygen. Internat. Rev. Hydrobiol. 52:163-217.

Jones, J. G. 1972. Studies on freshwater microorganisms: phosphatase activity in lakes of differing degrees of eutrophication. J. Ecol. 60: 777-791.

Juday, C. 1916. Limnological studies on some lakes in Central America. Trans. Wisconsin Acad. Sci. Arts Lett. 18:214-250.

Juday, C., and E. A. Birge. 1932. Dissolved oxygen and oxygen consumed in the lake waters of northeastern Wisconsin. Trans. Wisconsin Acad. Sci. Arts Lett. 27:415-486.

Judd, J. 1970. Lake stratification caused by runoff from street deicing. Water Res. 8:521-532.

Junge, C. E., and R. T. Werby. 1958. A concentration of chloride, sodium, potassium, and sulfate in rainwater over the United States. J. Meteorol. 15:417-425.

Kajak, Z., and J. I. Rybak. 1966. Production and some trophic dependencies in benthos against primary production and zooplankton production of several Masurian lakes. Verh. Internat. Verein. Limnol. 16:441-451.

Kalff, J. 1972. Net plankton and nanoplankton production and biomass in a north temperate zone lake. Limnol. Oceanogr. 17:712-720.

Kellogg, W. W., R. D. Cadle, E. R. Allen, A. L. Lazrus, and E. A. Martell. 1972. The sulfur cycle. Science 175:587-596.

Kerr, P. C., D. L. Brockway, D. F. Paris, and J. T. Barnett, Jr. 1972. The interrelation of carbon and phosphorous in regulating heterotrophic and autotrophic populations in an aquatic ecosystem, Shriner's Pond. Pages 41-62 *in* G. E. Likens, ed. Nutrients and eutrophication: the limiting-nutrient controversy. ASLO Special Symposia 1. American Society of Limnology and Oceanography, Lawrence, Kansas.

Kilham, P. 1971. A hypothesis concerning silica and the freshwater planktonic diatoms. Limnol. Oceanogr. 16:10-18.

King, D. L. 1970. The role of carbon in eutrophication. J. Water Poll. Control. Fed. 42:2035-2051.

Kleerekoper, H. 1944. Introdução ao estudo da limnologia. Minist. Agric., Rio de Janeiro. 329 pp.

Kononova, M. M. 1961. Soil organic matter (translated from the Russian). Pergamon Press Ltd., Oxford. 450 pp.

Koshinsky, G. D. 1970. The morphometry of shield lakes in Saskatchewan. Limnol. Oceanogr. 15:695-701.

Kozhov, M. 1963. Lake Baikal and its life. Dr. W. Junk N. V., Publishers, The Hague. 344 pp.

Kozlovsky, D. G. 1968. A critical evaluation of the trophic level concept: I. Ecological efficiencies. Ecology 49:48-60.

Krumholz, L. A., and G. A. Cole. 1959. Studies on a Kentucky Knobs Lake: IV. Some limnological conditions during an unusually cold winter. Limnol. Oceanogr. 4:367-385.

Lange, A. 1957. Studies on the origin of Montezuma Well and cave, Arizona. Cave Studies 1(9):31-45; 1 plate.

Langelier, W. F. 1936. The analytical control of anticorrosion water treatment. J. Amer. W. W. Assoc. 28:1500-1521.

Langmuir, I. 1938. Surface motion of water induced by wind. Science 87:119-123.

LaRow, E. J. 1969. A persistent diurnal rhythm in *Chaoborus* larvae: II. Ecological significance. Limnol. Oceanogr. 14:213-218.

Lathbury, A., R. Bryson, and B. Lettau. 1960. Some observations of currents in the hypolimnion of

Lake Mendota. Limnol. Oceanogr. 5:409-413.

Lean, D. R. S. 1973. Phosphorus dynamics in lake water. Science 179:678-679.

Leopold, L. B. 1962. Rivers. Amer. Sci. 50:511-537.

Likens, G. E. 1965. Some chemical characteristics of meromictic lakes in North America. Pages 19-62 in D. F. Jackson, ed. Symposium on meromictic lakes. Syracuse University, New York.

Likens, G. E., ed. 1972. Nutrients and eutrophication: the limiting-nutrient controversy. ASLO Special Symposia 1. American Society of Limnology and Oceanography, Lawrence, Kansas. 328 pp.

Likens, G. E., and A. D. Hasler.1962. Movements of radiosodium (Na^{24}) within an ice-covered lake. Limnol. Oceanogr. 7:48-56.

Likens, G. E., and P. L. Johnson. 1966. A chemically stratified lake in Alaska. Science 153:875-877.

Lindeman, R. L. 1941. The developmental history of Cedar Creek Bog, Minnesota. Amer. Midl. Nat. 25:101-112.

Lindeman, R. L. 1942a. Experimental simulation of winter anaerobiosis in a senescent lake. Ecology 23:1-13.

Lindeman, R. L. 1942b. The trophic-dynamic aspect of ecology. Ecology 23:399-418.

Little, E. C. S. 1966. The invasion of man-made lakes by plants. Pages 77-85 in R. H. Lowe-McConnell, ed. Man-made lakes. Academic Press, Inc., New York.

Livingstone, D. A. 1963a. Alaska, Yukon, Northwest Territories, and Greenland. Pages 559-574 in D. G. Frey, ed. Limnology in North America. University of Wisconsin Press, Madison.

Livingstone, D. A. 1963b. Chemical composition of rivers and lakes. U. S. Geol. Surv. Prof. Paper 440-G. U. S. Government Printing Office, Washington, D. C. 64 pp.

Löffler, H. 1964. The limnology of tropical high-mountain lakes. Verh. Internat. Verein. Limnol. 15:176-193.

Longstreth, D. J. 1972. Nutrient and energy flow: a comparison between a chaparral and a grass watershed in the Mazatzal Mountains, central Arizona. M.S. Thesis, Arizona State University, Tempe. 58 pp.

Lozinski, W. 1909. Über die mechanische Verwitterung der Sandsteine im germasstigen Klima. Cl. Sci., Math et Nat., Bull. Acad. Sci. Cracovie. 1-25.

Lund, J. W. G. 1964. Primary production and periodicity of phytoplankton. Verh. Internat. Verein. Limnol. 15:37-56.

Lundbeck, J. 1934. Über den primar oligotrophen Seetypus und den Wollingster See als dessen mitteleuropaischen Vertreter. Arch. Hydrobiol. 27:221-250.

Macan, T. T., and E. B. Worthington. 1951. Life in lakes and rivers (The New Naturalist Series). William Collins Sons, Co. Ltd., London. 272 pp.

MacIsaac, J. J., and R. C. Dugdall. 1969. The kinetics of nitrate and ammonia uptake by natural populations of marine phytoplankton. Deep-Sea Res. 16:45-57.

Mackereth, F. J. H. 1963. Some methods of water analysis for limnologists. Sci. Pub. Freshwat. Biol. Assoc. (England) 21:1-71.

Mackereth, F. J. H. 1966. Some chemical observations on postglacial lake sediments. Phil. Trans. Roy. Soc. London (B) 250:165-213.

Maguire, B., Jr. 1971. Phytotelmata: biota and community structure determination in plant-held waters. Pages 439-464 in R. F. Johnston, ed. Annual review ecology and systematics, vol. 2. Annual Reviews, Inc., Palo Alto, California.

Malueg, K. W., and A. D. Hasler. 1966. Echosounder studies on diel vertical movements of *Chaoborus* larvae in Wisconsin (U. S. A.) lakes. Verh. Internat. Verein. Limnol. 18:292-302.

Malueg, K. W., J. R. Tilstra, D. W. Schults, and C. F. Powers. 1972. Limnological observations on an ultra-oligotrophic lake in Oregon, U. S. A. Verh. Internat. Verein. Limnol. 18:292-302.

Mann, K. H. 1958. Annual fluctuations in sulphate and bicarbonate hardness in ponds. Limnol. Oceanogr. 3:418-422.

Mann, K. H. 1969. The dynamics of aquatic ecosystems. Pages 1-81 in J. B. Cragg, ed. Advances in ecological research, vol. 6. Academic Press Inc. Ltd., London.

Mann, K. H. 1972. Introductory remarks. Pages 13-16 in Detritus and its role in aquatic ecosystems. Mem. Ist. Ital. Idrobiol. Suppl. 29.

Martin, N. V. 1955. Limnological and biological observations in the region of the Ungava or Chubb Crater, Province of Quebec. J. Fish. Res. Bd. Canada. 12:487-496.

Martin, P. S. 1960. Effect of Pleistocene climatic change on biotic zones near the equator. Pages 265-267 in Year book of the American Philosophical Society, Philadelphia.

Mason, D. T. 1967. Limnology of Mono Lake, California. Univ. Cal. Pub. Zool. 83:1-102; 6 plates.

McConnell, W. J. 1963. Primary productivity and fish harvest in a small desert impoundment. Trans. Amer. Fish. Soc. 92:1-12.

McConnell, W. J., and W. F. Sigler. 1959. Chlorophyll and productivity in a mountain river. Limnol. Oceanogr. 4:335-351.

McEwen, G. F. 1929. A mathematical theory of the vertical distribution of temperature and salinity in water under the action of radiation, conduction, evaporation, and mixing due to the resultant convection. Bull. Scripps Oceanogr. Tech. 2:197-306.

McGaha, Y. J. 1952. The limnological relations of insects to certain aquatic flowering plants. Trans. Amer. Microsc. Soc. 71:355-381.

McIntire, C. D., and H. F. Phinney. 1965. Laboratory

studies of periphyton production and community metabolism in lotic environments. Ecol. Monogr. 35:237-258.

McLaren, I. A. 1964. Zooplankton of Lake Hazen, Ellesmere Island, and a nearby pond, with special reference to the copepod *Cyclops scutifer* Sars. Canadian J. Zool. 42:613-629.

McLaren, I. A. 1967. Physical and chemical characteristics of Ogac Lake, a landlocked fiord on Baffin Island. J. Fish. Res. Bd. Canada. 24:981-1015.

McMullen, D. B. 1941. Methods used in the control of schistosome dermatitis in Michigan. Pages 379-388 *in* J. G. Needham and others, ed. Symposium on hydrobiology. University of Wisconsin Press, Madison.

McNaught, D. C. 1971. Plasticity of cladoceran visual systems to environmental changes (abstract) Trans. Amer. Microsc. Soc. 90:113-114.

McRoy, C. P., R. J. Barsdate, and M. Nebert. 1972. Phosphorus cycling in an eelgrass (*Zostera marina* L.) ecosystem. Limnol. Oceanogr. 17:58-67.

Megard, R. O. 1964. Biostratigraphic history of Dead Man Lake, Chuska Mountains, New Mexico. Ecology 45:529-546.

Megard, R. O. 1968. Planktonic photosynthesis and the environment of calcium carbonate deposition in lakes. Univ. Minnesota, Limnol. Res. Ctr., Interim Report 2:1-47.

Megard, R. O. 1972. Phytoplankton, photosynthesis, and phosphorus in Lake Minnetonka, Minnesota. Limnol. Oceanogr. 17:68-87.

Miles, P. S. 1967. A new species of fresh water crab from northwestern Mexico (*Pseudothelphusa,* Potamonidae). J. Arizona Acad. Sci. 4:231-233.

Miller, R. R. 1946. *Gila cypha,* a remarkable new species of cyprinid fish from the Colorado River in Grand Canyon, Arizona. J. Washington Acad. Sci. 36:409-415.

Minckley, W. L. 1973. Fishes of Arizona. Pub. Ariz. Game and Fish Dept. Sims Printing Co., Phoenix. 293 pp.

Minckley, W. L., and D. R. Tindall. 1963. Ecology of *Batrachospermum* sp. (Rhodophyta) in Doe Run, Meade County, Kentucky. Bull. Torrey Bot. Club 90:391-400.

Minshall, G. W. 1967. Role of allochthonous detritus in the trophic structure of a woodland springbrook community. Ecology 48:139-149.

Montgomery, H. A. C., N. S. Thom, and A. Cockburn. 1964. Determination of dissolved oxygen by the Winkler method and the solubility of oxygen in pure water and sea water. J. Appl. Chem. 14:280-296.

Moore, E. W. 1939. Graphic determination of carbon dioxide and the three forms of alkalinity. J. Amer. Water W. Assoc. 31:51-66.

Moore, G. M. 1939. A limnological investigation of the microscopic benthic fauna of Douglas Lake, Michigan. Ecol. Monogr. 9:537-582.

Moore, W. G. 1942. Field studies on the oxygen requirements of certain fresh-water fishes. Ecology 23:319-329.

Moore, W. G. 1957. Studies on the laboratory culture of Anostraca. Trans. Amer. Microsc. Soc. 76:159-173.

Mortimer, C. H. 1941-1942. The exchange of dissolved substances between mud and water in lakes. J. An. Ecol. 29:280-329; 30:147-201.

Mortimer, C. H. 1952. Water movements in lakes during summer stratification: evidence from the distribution of temperature in Windermere. Phil. Trans. Roy. Soc. (B) 236:355-404.

Mortimer, C. H. 1955. Some effects of the earth's rotation on water movements in stratified lakes. Verh. Internat. Verein. Limnol. 12:66-77.

Mortimer, C. H. 1959. Review of G. E. Hutchinson's "A treatise on limnology." Limnol. Oceanogr. 4:108-114.

Moskalenko, B. K. 1972. Biological productive system of Lake Baikal. Verh. Internat. Verein. Limnol. 18:568-573.

Moss, B. 1972a. Studies on Gull Lake, Michigan: II. Eutrophication—evidence and prognosis. Freshwat. Biol. 2:309-320.

Moss, B. 1972b. The influence of environmental factors on the distribution of freshwater algae, an experimental study: I. Introduction and the influence of calcium concentration. J. Ecol. 60:917-932.

Moyle, J. B. 1945. Some chemical factors influencing the distribution of aquatic plants in Minnesota. Amer. Midl. Nat. 34:402-420.

Moyle, J. B. 1949. Some indices of lake productivity. Trans. Amer. Fish. Soc. 76:322-334.

Moyle, J. B. 1956. Relationships between the chemistry of Minnesota surface waters and wildlife management. J. Wildl. Mgt. 20:303-320.

Munk, W. H., and G. A. Riley. 1952. Absorption of nutrients by aquatic plants. J. Mar. Res. 11:215-240.

Naiman, R. J. 1974. Bioenergetics of a pupfish population *(Cyprinodon)* and its algal food supply in a thermal stream. Ph.D. Dissertation, Arizona State University, Tempe. 103 pp.

National Academy of Sciences. 1969. Eutrophication: causes, consequences, correctives. The Academy, Washington, D. C. 661 pp.

Naumann, E. 1932. Grundzuge der regionalen Limnologie. Die Binnengewässer 11:1-176.

Neel, J. K. 1948. A limnological investigation of the psammon in Douglas Lake, Michigan, with special reference to shoal and shoreline dynamics. Trans. Amer. Microsc. Soc. 67:1-53.

Neel, J. K. 1963. Impact of reservoirs. Pages 575-593 *in* D. G. Frey, ed. Limnology in North America. University of Wisconsin Press, Madison.

Neumann, J. 1953. Energy balance and evaporation from sweet-water lakes of the Jordan Rift. Bull. Res. Coun. Israel. 2:337-357.

Neumann, J. 1959. Maximum depth and average depth of lakes. J. Fish. Res. Bd. Canada. 16:923-927.

Newcombe, C. L., and J. V. Slater. 1950. Environmental factors of Sodon Lake—a dichothermic lake in southeastern Michigan. Ecol. Monogr. 20:207-227.

Nininger, H. H. 1972. Find a falling star. Paul S. Eriksson, Inc., New York. 254 pp.

Northcote, T. G., and W. E. Johnson. 1964. Occurrence and distribution of sea water in Sakinaw Lake, British Columbia. J. Fish. Res. Bd. Canada 2:1321-1324.

Northcote, T. G., M. S. Wilson, and D. R. Hurn. 1964. Some characteristics of Nitnat Lake, an inlet on Vancouver Island, British Columbia. J. Fish. Res. Bd. Canada 21:1069-1081.

Oana, S., and E. S. Deevey. 1960. Carbon 13 in lake waters and its possible bearing on paleolimnology. Amer. J. Sci. 258-A:253-272.

Odum, H. T. 1956. Primary production in flowing waters. Limnol. Oceanogr. 1:102-117.

Odum, H. T. 1957. Trophic structure and productivity of Silver Springs, Florida. Ecol. Monogr. 27:55-112.

Ohle, W. 1952. Die hypolimnische Kohlendioxyde-akkumulation als productionsbiologischer Indikator. Arch. Hydrobiol. 46:153-285.

Ohmori, M., and A. Hattori. 1971. Nitrogen fixation and heterocysts in the blue-green alga *Anabaena cylindrica.* Plant and Cell Physiol. 12:961-967.

Olson, F. C. W. 1960. A system of morphometry. Internat. Hydrog. Rev. 37:147-155.

Osterhaut, W. J. V., and A. R. C. Haas. 1918. On the dynamics of photosynthesis. J. Gen. Physiol. 1:1-16.

Otsuki, A., and T. Hanya. 1968. On the production of dissolved nitrogen-rich organic matter. Limnol. Oceanogr. 13:183-184.

Otsuki, A., and R. G. Wetzel. 1972. Coprecipitation of phosphate with carbonates in a marl lake. Limnol. Oceanogr. 17:763-767.

Pamatmat, M. M., and A. M. Bhagwat. 1973. Anaerobic metabolism in Lake Washington sediments. Limnol. Oceanogr. 18:611-627.

Park, K., G. H. Kennedy, and H. H. Dobson. 1964. Comparison of gas chromatographic method and pH-alkalinity method for determination of total carbon dioxide in sea water. Anal. Chem. 36:1686.

Park, P. K., G. R. Webster, and R. Yamamoto. 1969. Alkalinity budget of the Columbia River. Limnol. Oceanogr. 14:559-567.

Patten, B. C. 1959. An introduction to the cybernetics of the ecosystem: the trophic-dynamic aspect. Ecology 40:221-231.

Pearse, A. S., ed. 1936. The cenotes of Yucatan: a zoological and hydrographic survey. Carnegie Inst., Washington, Pub. 457: 28 pp.; 2 plates.

Pennak, R. W. 1940. Ecology of the microscopic Metazoa inhabiting the sandy beaches of some Wisconsin lakes. Ecol. Monogr. 10:537-615.

Pennak, R. W. 1953. Fresh-water invertebrates of the United States. The Ronald Press Co., New York. 769 pp.

Pennak, R. W. 1958. Some problems of freshwater invertebrate distribution in the western states. Pages 223-230 *in* C. L. Hubbs, ed. Zoogeography, Pub. 51, A.A.A.S., Washington, D. C.

Pennak, R. W. 1963. Ecological affinities and origins of free-living acoelomate fresh-water invertebrates. Pages 435-451 *in* E. C. Dougherty, ed. The lower Metazoa: comparative biology and phylogeny. University of California Press, Berkeley.

Pennak, R. W. 1968. Historical origins and ramifications of interstitial investigations. Trans. Amer. Microsc. Soc. 87:214-218.

Pennak, R. W. 1971. A fresh-water archiannelid from the Colorado Rocky Mountains. Trans. Amer. Microsc. Soc. 90:372-375.

Pennak, R. W., and D. J. Zinn. 1943. Mystacocarida, a new order of Crustacea from intertidal beaches in Massachusetts and Connecticut. Smithsonian Misc. Collect. 103:1-11.

Péwé, T. L. 1969. The periglacial environment. Pages 1-9 *in* T. L. Péwe, ed. The periglacial environment: past and present. McGill-Queens University Press, Montreal.

Phillips, J. 1935. Succession, development, the climax, and the complex organism; an analysis of concepts. Part III. The complex organism: conclusion. J. Ecol. 23:488-508.

Plafker, G. 1964. Oriented lakes and lineaments of northeastern Bolivia. Bull. U. S. Geol. Survey 75:503-522. U. S. Government Printing Office, Washington, D. C.

Poole, H. H., and W. R. G. Atkins. 1929. Photo-electric measurements of submarine illumination throughout the year. J. Mar. Biol. Assoc., UK. 16:297-324.

Potash, M. 1956. A biological test for determining the potential productivity of water. Ecology 37:631-639.

Povoledo, D. 1964. Some comparative physical and chemical studies on soil and lacustrine organic matter. Mem. Ist. Ital. Idrobiol. 17:21-32.

Pratt, D. M., and H. Berkson. 1959. Two sources of error in the oxygen light and dark bottle method. Limnol. Oceanogr. 4:328-334.

Proctor, V. W. 1957. Some controlling factors in the distribution of *Haematococcus pluvialis.* Ecology 38:457-462.

Provasoli, L. 1969. Algal nutrition and eutrophication. Pages 574-593 *in* Eutrophication: causes, consequences, correctives. National Academy of Sciences, Washington, D. C.

Rabinowitch, E. I. 1948. Photosynthesis. Sci. Amer. 179(2):24-35. W. H. Freeman and Co., San Francisco.

Ragotzkie, R. A., and G. E. Likens. 1964. The heat balance of two Antarctic lakes. Limnol. Oceanogr. 9:412-425.

Rainwater, F. H., and L. L. Thatcher. 1960. Methods for collection and analysis of water samples. U. S. Geol. Surv. Water-supply Paper 1454. U. S. Government Printing Office, Washington, D. C. 301 pp.

Rawson, D. S. 1939. Some physical and chemical factors in the metabolism of lakes. Pages 9-26 in E. R. Moulton, ed. Problems of lake biology. Pub. 10, A.A.A.S., Washington, D. C.

Rawson, D. S. 1951. The total mineral content of lake water. Ecology 32:669-672.

Rawson, D. S. 1953. The standing crop of net plankton in lakes. J. Fish. Res. Bd. Canada 10:224-237.

Rawson, D. S. 1955. Morphometry as a dominant factor in the productivity of large lakes. Verh. Internat. Verein. Limnol. 12:164-175.

Rawson, D. S., and J. E. Moore. 1944. The saline lakes of Saskatchewan. Canadian J. Res. (D) 22:141-201.

Redfield, A. C. 1958. The biological control of chemical factors in the environment. Amer. Sci. 46:205-221.

Reeves, C. C., Jr. 1962. Pleistocene lake basins of west Texas (abstract). Geol. Soc. Amer. Special Paper 73:122A.

Reid, G. K. 1962. Ecology of inland waters and estuaries. Van Nostrand Reinhold Publishing Co. New York. 375 pp.

Reif, C. B. 1939. The effect of stream conditions on lake plankton. Trans. Amer. Microsc. Soc. 58:398-403.

Ricker, W. E. 1937. Physical and chemical characteristics of Cultus Lake, British Columbia. J. Biol. Bd. Canada 3:363-402.

Rickert, D. A., and L. B. Leopold. 1972. Fremont Lake, Wyoming—preliminary survey of a large mountain lake. Geol. Surv. Research 1972, Chapt. D:173-188. U. S. Government Printing Office, Washington, D. C.

Rigler, F. H. 1956. A tracer study of the phosphorus cycle in lakewater. Ecology 37:550-562.

Rigler, F. H. 1964. The phosphorus fractions and the turnover time of inorganic phosphorus in different types of lakes. Limnol. Oceanogr. 9:511-518.

Riley, G. A. 1939. Limnological studies in Connecticut. Part I. General limnological survey. Part II. The copper cycle. Ecol. Monogr. 6:66-94.

Riley, G. A. 1963. Organic aggregates in seawater and the dynamics of their formation and utilization. Limnol. Oceanogr. 8:372-381.

Rodgers, G. K., and D. V. Anderson. 1961. A preliminary study of the energy budget of Lake Ontario. J. Fish. Res. Bd. Canada 18:617-636.

Rodhe, W. 1949. The ionic composition of lake waters. Verh. Internat. Verein. Limnol. 10:377-386.

Rodhe, W. 1969. Crystallization of eutrophication concepts in northern Europe. Pages 50-64 in Eutrophication: causes, consequences, correctives. National Academy of Sciences, Washington, D. C.

Rodhe, W., J. E. Hobbie, and R. T. Wright. 1966. Phototrophy and heterotrophy in high mountain lakes. Verh. Internat. Verein. Limnol. 16:302-312.

Rodina, A. G. 1963. Microbiology of detritus of lakes. Limnol. Oceanogr. 8:388-393.

Roth, J. C., and S. E. Neff. 1964. Studies of physical limnology and profundal bottom fauna, Mountain Lake, Virginia. Virginia Agric. Exper. Sta., Blacksburg. Tech. Bull. 169:1-44.

Ruttner, F. 1931. Hydrographische und hydrochemische Beobachtungen auf Java, Sumatra, und Bali. Arch. Hydrobiol. Suppl. 8:197-454.

Ruttner, F. 1952. Grundriss der Limnologie, 2nd ed. V. Gruyters et Co., Berlin. 232 pp.

Ruttner, F. 1953. Fundamentals of limnology. (Translated by D. G. Frey and F. E. J. Fry.) University of Toronto Press, Toronto. 242 pp.

Ruttner-Kolisko, A. 1972. Das Zooplankton der Binnengewässer: III. Rotatoria. Die Binnengewässer 26:99-234.

Ryther, J. H., and W. M. Dunstan. 1971. Nitrogen, phosphorus, and eutrophication in the coastal marine environment. Science 171:1008-1013.

Ryther, J. H., and C. S. Yentsch. 1957. The estimation of phytoplankton production in the ocean from chlorophyll and light data. Limnol. Oceanogr. 2:281-286.

Rzóska, J. 1961. Observations on tropical rainpools and general remarks on temporary waters. Hydrobiologia 17:265-286.

Rzóska, J. 1966. The biology of reservoirs in the U. S. S. R. Pages 149-157 in R. H. Lowe-McConnell, ed. Man-made Lakes. Academic Press, Inc., New York.

Sanders, H. L. 1955. The Cephalocarida, a new subclass of Crustacea from Long Island Sound. Proc. Nat. Acad. Sci. 41:61-66.

Saunders, G. W. 1957. Interrelations of dissolved organic matter and phytoplankton. Bot. Rev. 23:389-409.

Saunders, G. W. 1972a. Potential heterotrophy in a natural population of Oscillatoria agardhii var. isothrix Skuja. Limnol. Oceanogr. 17:704-711.

Saunders, G. W., Jr. 1972b. The kinetics of extracellular release of soluble organic matter by plankton. Verh. Internat. Verein. Limnol. 18:140-146.

Schelske, C. L., and E. F. Stoermer. 1972. Phosphorus, silica, and eutrophication of Lake Michigan. Pages 157-171 *in* G. E. Likens, ed. Nutrients and eutrophication: the limiting-nutrient controversy. ASLO Special Symposia 1. American Society of Limnology and Oceanography, Lawrence, Kansas.

Schindler, D. W. 1971a. Light, temperature, and oxygen regimes of selected lakes in the Experimental Lakes Area, northwestern Ontario. J. Fish. Res. Bd. Canada 28:157-169.

Schindler, D. W. 1971b. A hypothesis to explain differences and similarities among lakes in the Experimental Lakes Area, northwestern Ontario. J. Fish. Res. Bd. Canada 28:295-301.

Schindler, D. W. 1971c. Carbon, nitrogen and phosphorus and the eutrophication of freshwater lakes. J. Phycol. 7:321-329.

Schindler, D. W., and G. W. Comita. 1972. The dependence of primary production upon physical and chemical factors in a small, senescing lake, including the effects of complete winter oxygen depletion. Arch. Hydrobiol. 69:413-451.

Schindler, D. W., and S. K. Holmgren. 1971. Primary production and phytoplankton in the Experimental Lakes Area, northwestern Ontario, and other low-carbonate waters, and a liquid scintillation method for determining ^{14}C activity in photosynthesis. J. Fish. Res. Bd. Canada 28:189-201.

Schmalz, R. F. 1972. Calcium carbonate: geochemistry. Pages 104-118 *in* R. W. Fairbridge, ed. The encyclopedia of geochemistry and environmental sciences. Van Nostrand Reinhold Publishing Co., New York.

Schmidt, W. 1915. Über den Energie-gehalt der Seen. Mit Beispielen von Lunzer Untersee nach Messungen mit einen einfachen Temperaturlot. Internat. Rev. Hydrobiol., Suppl. 5, Leipzig.

Schmidt, W. 1928. Über Temperatur und Stabilitatsverhältnisse von Seen. Geogr. Ann. 10:145-177.

Schönborn, W. 1962. Über Planktismus und Zyklomorphose bei *Difflugia limnetica*. Limnologica 1:21-34.

Schrödinger, E. 1945. What is life? Cambridge University Press, London.

Shannon, E. E., and P. L. Brezonik. 1972. Limnological characteristics of north and central Florida lakes. Limnol. Oceanogr. 17:97-110.

Shapiro, J. 1957. Chemical and biological studies on the yellow organic acids of lake water. Limnol. Oceanogr. 2:161-179.

Shapiro, J. 1960. The cause of metalimnetic minimum of dissolved oxygen. Limnol. Oceanogr. 5:216-227.

Shapiro, J. 1966. The relation of humic color to iron in natural water. Verh. Internat. Verein. Limnol. 16:477-448.

Shapiro, J. 1973. Blue-green algae: why they become dominant. Science 179:382-384.

Sinclair, R. M. 1964. Clam pests in Tennessee water supplies. J. Amer. W. W. Assoc. 56:592-599.

Sládečková, A. 1962. Limnological investigation methods for the periphyton („Aufwuchs") community. Bot. Rev. 28:287-350.

Slobodkin, L. B. 1972. On the inconstancy of ecological efficiency and the form of ecological theories. Pages 293-305 *in* E. S. Deevey, ed. Growth by intussusception. Ecological essays in honor of G. E. Hutchinson. Trans. Connecticut Acad. Arts Sci. 44.

Small, L. F. 1972. Photosynthesis. Pages 952-955 *in* R. W. Fairbridge, ed. The encyclopedia of geochemistry and environmental sciences. Van Nostrand Reinhold Co., New York.

Smith, F. E., and E. R. Baylor. 1953. Color responses in the Cladocera and their ecological significance. Amer. Nat. 87:49-55.

Sorokin, J. I. 1965. On the trophic role of chemosynthesis and bacterial biosynthesis in water bodies. Mem. Ist. Ital. Idrobiol. Suppl. 18:187-205.

Spence, D. H. N., and J. Chrystal. 1970a. Photosynthesis and zonation of freshwater macrophytes: I. Depth distribution and shade tolerance. New Phytol. 69:205-215.

Spence, D. H. N., and J. Chrystal. 1970b. Photosynthesis and zonation of freshwater macrophytes: II. Adaptability of species of deep and shallow water. New Phytol. 69:217-227.

Stanier, R. Y. 1973. Autotrophy and heterotrophy in unicellular blue-green algae. Pages 501-518 *in* N. G. Carr and B. A. Whitton, eds. The biology of blue-green algae. Bot. Monogr. 9 University of California Press, Berkeley.

Stansberry, D. H. 1970. Eastern freshwater molluscs: I. The Mississippi and St. Lawrence River systems. Malacologia 10:9-22.

Stavn, R. H. 1971. The horizontal-vertical distribution hypothesis: Langmuir circulations and *Daphnia* distributions. Limnol. Oceanogr. 16:453-466.

Steemann Nielsen, E. 1951. Measurement of the production of organic matter in the sea by means of carbon 14. Nature 167:684-685.

Steen, H. 1958. Determinations of the solubility of oxygen in pure water. Limnol. Oceanogr. 3:423-426.

Steinböck, O. 1958. Grundsätzliches zum 'Kryoeutrophen' See. Verh. Internat. Verein. Limnol. 13:181-190.

Stevenson, F. J. 1972. Nitrogen: element and geochemistry. Pages 795-801 *in* R. W. Fairbridge, ed. The encyclopedia of geochemistry and environmental sciences. Van Nostrand Reinhold Co., New York.

Stewart, K. M. 1972. Isotherms under ice. Verh. Internat. Verein. Limnol. 18:303-311.

Stewart, W. D. P., G. P. Fitzgerald, and R. H. Burris.

1967. *In situ* studies on N_2 fixation using the acetylene reduction technique. Proc. Nat. Acad. Sci., Washington, D. C. 58:2071-2078.

Stoiber, R. E., and A. Jepsen. 1973. Sulfur dioxide contributions to the atmosphere by volcanoes. Science 182:577-578.

Stross, R. G. 1971. Photoperiodism and diapause in *Daphnia:* a strategy for all seasons (abstract). Trans. Amer. Microsc. Soc. 90:110-112.

Stuiver, M. 1970. Oxygen and carbon isotope ratios of fresh-water carbonates as climatic indicators. J. Geophys. Res. 75:5247-5257.

Stull, E. 1971. The contribution of individual species of algae to the primary production of Castle Lake. Ph.D. Thesis, University of California, Davis.

Stumm, W., and J. J. Morgan. 1970. Aquatic chemistry. John Wiley & Sons, Inc., New York. 583 pp.

Swain, F. M., A. Blumentals, and R. Millers. 1959. Stratigraphic distribution of amino acids in peats from Cedar Creek Bog, Minnesota, and Dismal Swamp, Virginia. Limnol. Oceanogr. 4:119-127.

Swain, F. M., and N. Prokopovich. 1954. Stratigraphic distribution of lipoid substances in Cedar Creek Bog, Minnesota. Bull. Geol. Soc. Amer. 65:1183-1198.

Swinyard, C. A. 1933. A limnological study of several Minnesota lakes. Ph.D. Thesis, University of Minnesota, Minneapolis.

Talling, J. F. 1965. The photosynthetic activity of phytoplankton in East African lakes. Internat. Rev. Hydrobiol. 50:1-32.

Talling, J. F., and I. B. Talling. 1965. The chemical composition of African lake waters. Internat. Rev. Hydrobiol. 50:421-463.

Talling, J. F., R. B. Wood, M. V. Prosser, and R. M. Baxter. 1973. The upper limit of photosynthetic productivity by phytoplankton: evidence from Ethiopian soda lakes. Freshwat. Biol. 3:53-76.

Tansley, A. G. 1935. The use and abuse of vegetational concepts and terms. Ecology 16:284-307.

Teal, J. M. 1957. Community metabolism in a temperate cold spring. Ecol. Monogr. 27:283-302.

Thienemann, A. 1925. Die Binnengewässer Mitteleuropas: Eine Limnologische Einfuhrung. Die Binnengewässer 1:1-255.

Thienemann, A. 1927. Der Bau des Seebeckens in seiner Bedeutung für den Ablauf des Lebens im See. Zool. Bot. Ges. Vienna, Verhandl. 77:87-91.

Thomas, E. A. 1969. The process of eutrophication in Central European lakes. Pages 29-49 *in* Eutrophication: causes, consequences, correctives. National Academy of Sciences, Washington, D. C.

Thoreau, H. D. 1854. Walden; or Life in the woods. Ticknor and Fields, Boston. 357 pp.

Tilzer, M. 1973. Zum Problem der Ausbreitungsfahigkeit von limnish-interstitiellen Grundwassertieren, am Beispiel von *Troglochaetus beranecki*

Delachaux (Polychaeta, Archiannelida). Arch. Hydrobiol. 72:263-269.

Torii, T., and J. Ossaka. 1965. Antarcticite: a new mineral, calcium chloride hexahydrate, discovered in Antarctica. Science 149:975-977.

Truesdale, G. A., A. L. Downing, and G. F. Lowden. 1955. The solubility of oxygen in pure water and sea-water. J. Appl. Chem. 5:53-63.

Trüper, H. G., and S. Genovese. 1968. Characterization of photosynthetic sulfur bacteria causing red waters in Lake Faro (Messina, Sicily). Limnol. Oceanogr. 13:225-232.

Tuunainen, P., K. Granberg, L. Hakkari, and J. Särkkä. 1972. On the effects of eutrophication of Lake Päijänne, Central Finland. Verh. Internat. Verein. Limnol. 18:388-402.

Van Gorkom, H. J., and M. Donze. 1971. Localization of nitrogen fixation in *Anabaena.* Nature 234:231-232.

Veatch, J. O., and C. R. Humphrys. 1966. Water and water use terminology. Thomas Printing and Publishing Co., Kaukauna, Wis. 375 pp.

Verduin, J. 1951. Photosynthesis in naturally reared aquatic communities. Plant Physiol. 26:45-49.

Verduin, J. 1956. Energy fixation and utilization by natural communities in western Lake Erie. Ecology 37:40-50.

Vollenweider, R. A. 1961. Photometric studies in inland waters: I. Relations existing in the spectral extinction of light in water. Mem. Ist. Ital. Idrobiol. 13:87-113.

Vollenweider, R. A. 1964. Über oligomiktishe Verhaltnisse des Lago Maggiore und einiger anderer insubrischer Seen. Mem. Ist. Ital. Idrobiol. 17:191-206.

Vollenweider, R. A. 1969. A manual on methods for measuring primary production in aquatic environments. IBP Handbook 12. Blackwell Scientific Publications Ltd., Oxford. 213 pp.

Walshe, B. M. 1947. On the function of haemoglobin in *Chironomus* after oxygen lack. J. Exper. Biol. 24:329-342.

Walshe, B. M. 1950. The function of haemoglobin in *Chironomus plumosus* under natural conditions. J. Exper. Biol. 27:73-95.

Wangersky, P. J. 1972. The control of seawater pH by ion pairing. Limnol. Oceanogr. 17:1-6.

Weber, C. A. 1907. Aufbau und Vegetation der Moore Norddeutschlands. Beibl. Bot. Jahrb. 90:19-34.

Wedderburn, E. M. 1907. The temperature of freshwater lochs of Scotland, with special reference to Loch Ness. Trans. Roy. Soc. Edinburgh 45:407-489.

Welch, P. S. 1948. Limnological methods. Blakiston Co., Philadelphia. 381 pp.

Welch, P. S. 1952. Limnology, 2d ed. McGraw-Hill Book Co., New York. 538 pp.

Westlake, D. F. 1965. Some problems in the measurement of radiation under water: a review. Photochem. Photobiol. 4:849-868.

Wetzel, R. G. 1964. A comparative study of the primary productivity of higher aquatic plants, periphyton, and phytoplankton in a large, shallow lake. Internat. Rev. Hydrobiol. 49:1-61.

Wetzel, R. G. 1969. Excretion of dissolved organic compounds by aquatic macrophytes. Bioscience 19:539-540.

Wetzel, R. G. 1972. The role of carbon in hard-water lakes. Pages 84-97 in G. E. Likens, ed. Nutrients and eutrophication: the limiting-nutrient controversy. ASLO Special Symposia 1. American Society of Limnology and Oceanography, Lawrence, Kansas.

Wetzel, R. G., P. H. Rich, M. C. Miller, and H. L. Allen. 1972. Metabolism of dissolved and particulate detrital carbon in a temperate hard-water lake. Mem. Ist. Ital. Idrobiol. Suppl. 29:185-243.

Weyl, P. 1961. The carbonate saturometer. J. Geol. 69:32-44.

Whitehead, D. R., H. Rochester, Jr., S. W. Rissing, C. B. Douglas, and M. C. Sheehan. 1973. Late glacial and postglacial productivity changes in a New England lake. Science 181:744-747.

Whiteside, M. C. 1965. Paleoecological studies of Potato Lake and its environs. Ecology 46:807-816.

Whitney, L. V. 1938. Microstratification of inland lakes. Trans. Wisconsin Acad. Sci. Arts Lett. 31:155-173.

Whitton, B. A. 1973a. Freshwater plankton. Pages 353-367 in N. G. Carr and B. A. Whitton, eds. The biology of blue-green algae. Bot. Monogr. 9. University of California Press, Berkeley.

Whitton, B. A. 1973b. Interactions with other organisms. Pages 415-433 in N. G. Carr and B. A. Whitton, eds. Biology of blue-green algae. Bot. Monogr. 9. University of California Press, Berkeley.

Wiegert, R. G., and P. C. Fraleigh. 1972. Ecology of Yellowstone thermal effluent systems: net primary production and species diversity of a successional blue-green algal mat. Limnol. Oceanogr. 17:215-228.

Williams, P. N., W. H. Mathews, and G. L. Pickard. 1961. A lake in British Columbia containing old sea-water. Nature 191:830-832.

Williams, W. D. 1964. A contribution to lake typology in Victoria, Australia. Verh. Internat. Verein. Limnol. 15:158-168.

Williams, W. D. 1966. Conductivity and the concentration of total dissolved solids in Australian lakes. Australian J. Mar. Freshwat. Res. 17:169-176.

Williams, W. D. 1969. Eutrophication of lakes. Proc. Roy. Soc. Victoria 83:17-26; 1 plate.

Williams, W. D. 1972. The uniqueness of salt lake ecosystems. Pages 349-361 in Z. Kajak and A. Hillbricht-Ilkowska, eds. Productivity problems of freshwaters. Warsaw-Krakow.

Wilson, B. W. 1972. Seiches. Pages 1-94 in Ven Te Chow, ed. Advances in Hydroscience, vol. 8. Academic Press, Inc., New York.

Winberg, G. G. 1963. The primary production of bodies of water. U. S. Atomic Energy Commission, Transl. AEC-tr-5692, Biol. Med. Office of Tech. Serv., Washington, D. C. 601 pp.

Winberg, G. G. 1971. Methods for the estimation of production of aquatic animals. Academic Press, Inc., New York. 175 pp.

Winberg, G. G. 1972. Études sur le bilan biologique energetique et la productivité des lacs en Union Soviétique. Verh. Internat. Verein. Limnol. 18:39-64.

Wolfe, P. E. 1953. Periglacial frost-thaw basins in New Jersey. J. Geol. 61:133-141.

Wood, J. M., F. S. Kennedy, and C. G. Rosen. 1968. Synthesis of methylmercury compounds by extracts of a methanogenic bacterium. Nature 220:173-174.

Wright, H. E., Jr. 1964. Origin of the lakes in the Chuska Mountains, northwestern New Mexico. Bull. Geol. Soc. Amer. 75:589-598; 4 figs.; 3 plates.

Yoshimura, S. 1936. A contribution to the knowledge of deep water temperatures of Japanese lakes. Part II. Winter temperatures. Jap. J. Astr. Geophys. 14:57-83.

Yoshimura, S. 1937. Abnormal thermal stratifications in inland lakes. Proc. Imp. Acad. Japan 13:316-319.

Zaret, T. M. 1972. Predators, invisible prey, and the nature of polymorphism in the Cladocera (Class Crustacea). Limnol. Oceanogr. 17:171-184.

Zaret, T. M., and R. T. Paine. 1973. Species introduction in a tropical lake. Science 182:449-455.

Zobell, C. E., F. D. Sisler, and C. H. Oppenheimer. 1953. Evidence of biochemical heating in Lake Mead mud. J. Sed. Petrol. 23:13-17.

Index